THE CONCISE H

ANALY
SPECTR(

Theory, Applications, an

Volume 2 **Visible Spect**

THE CONCISE HANDBOOK OF ANALYTICAL SPECTROSCOPY

Theory, Applications, and Reference Materials

Volume 2

Visible Spectroscopy

Jerry Workman

Unity Scientific, USA and National University, USA

World Scientific

NEW JERSEY • LONDON • SINGAPORE • BEIJING • SHANGHAI • HONG KONG • TAIPEI • CHENNAI • TOKYO

Published by

World Scientific Publishing Co. Pte. Ltd.
5 Toh Tuck Link, Singapore 596224
USA office: 27 Warren Street, Suite 401-402, Hackensack, NJ 07601
UK office: 57 Shelton Street, Covent Garden, London WC2H 9HE

Library of Congress Cataloging-in-Publication Data
Workman, Jerry.
The concise handbook of analytical spectroscopy : theory, applications, and reference materials / by Jerry Workman (Unity Scientific, USA & National University, USA).
volumes cm
Includes bibliographical references and index.
ISBN 978-9814508056 (Set)
ISBN 978-9814508087 (v. 1 : hardcover : alk. paper)
ISBN 978-9814508094 (v. 2 : hardcover : alk. paper)
ISBN 978-9814508100 (v. 3 : hardcover : alk. paper)
ISBN 978-9814508117 (v. 4 : hardcover : alk. paper)
ISBN 978-9814508124 (v. 5 : hardcover : alk. paper)
1. Spectrum analysis. I. Title.
QD95.W67 2015
543'.5--dc23
2014042606

British Library Cataloguing-in-Publication Data
A catalogue record for this book is available from the British Library.

Typeset by Stallion Press
Email: enquiries@stallionpress.com

Printed in Singapore

Preface

The Concise Handbook of Analytical Spectroscopy: Theory, Applications, and Reference Materials (In 5 Volumes)

Overview and Description

The concept of improving the use of electromagnetic energy to achieve a variety of qualitative and quantitative spectroscopic measurements on solid and liquid materials has been proliferating at a rapid rate. The use of such technologies to measure chemical composition and appearance; for classification; and to achieve a detailed understanding of material interactions has prompted a dramatic expansion in the use and development of spectroscopic techniques over a variety of academic and commercial fields. This multi-volume handbook is designed specifically as a reference tool for students, commercial development and quality scientists, and researchers or technologists in a variety of measurement endeavors. Each volume covers the theory, instrumentation, sampling methods, experimental design, and data analysis techniques, as well as essential reference tables, figures, and spectra for each spectroscopic region. The detailed practical aspects of applying spectroscopic tools for many of the most exciting and current applications are covered. Featured applications are included as well as common commercial analysis methods (i.e., color, appearance), spectroscopic quantitative and qualitative techniques, and advanced methods.

Outline

Each volume covers a specific region of the electromagnetic spectrum used for electronic and vibrational spectroscopic measurements. The volumes are not a series of essays, or a compilation of isolated papers on specific topics, but represent an integrated whole. The Handbook is compiled as a highly useful reference set for those directly involved in making and understanding spectroscopic measurement techniques. Each volume contains a logical progression of the material as follows.

Organization of Contents for Each Volume

Each volume commences with Front Reference Material for General Spectroscopy, preceding the following chapters.

1. General Introduction and History of Technique (includes useful basic concepts)
2. Theory of Technique (including delineation of common equations and references)
3. Types of Instrumentation (Types and design aspects)
4. Sampling Considerations (Cookbook approach to preparing samples)
5. Spectrum Data Acquisition (Experimental design and methods for data acquisition)
6. Data Analysis and Presentation Methods (The chemometrics and data analysis techniques applicable for each spectral region)
7. Applications and Spectral Examples (Cookbook approaches, results, and extensive literature reviews)
8. Reference Materials, Tables, Figures, and Spectra (The key look-up aspects for each technique)
9. Glossary of Specific Terms: Detailed Index for Reference Material and Text (Each volume includes a detailed table of contents and index that delineates the minutia of using the text and reference material in each volume.)

Each volume contains specifics for the spectral region covered, such as: common and unusual sampling devices; sampling methods (i.e., reagents, solvents, and sampling cells); and reference standard materials. Optics include: filters, etalons, prisms, and lenses; and fiber optics (principles, equipment, and connectors). In addition, reference tables and spectra, glossaries of terms, common equations and calculation methods, cookbook directions, and solved problems are included.

Reference Materials

Fundamental reference sources and early publications are referred to whenever possible as a primary source of data and information. Reference material common to each method is summarized within each volume to provide a more practical set of volumes for bench use. The intention is that each volume will stand somewhat alone for the working analyst using a specific spectroscopic method, such that required referral to other volumes is kept to a minimum and that key information is available regarding the individual spectroscopic technique within each volume.

Terminology and Symbols

Terminology use is included within the chapters and glossary sections for each volume. Note that *spectrophotometer* is the precise term used for each instrument described within the five volumes. However for brevity, the term *spectrometer* is sometimes used less precisely. Also, the symbols used are from different disciplines and thus there are some symbols used for more than one variable or parameter, depending on the common usage and the specific academic discipline where the symbology was formalized. A list of symbols used in this set of volumes may be located using the index and front material of each volume. The terms used for each equation within the volumes are defined where the equation is used.

Dedication

This book is dedicated to my fabulous wife Rebecca and to my family who have patiently sacrificed many hours of their lives for the cause of spectroscopy; and to everyone who spends many hours in laboratories analyzing samples for new knowledge, applied research, quality improvement, and the overall betterment of the lives of people … And to the One Great Designer who made all this marvelous measurement with light possible, discoverable, and such a pleasure to work with …

Author Biography

Jerome (Jerry) J. Workman, Jr. is Executive Vice President of Research & Engineering for Unity Scientific; Certified Core Adjunct Professor at National University, CA; and Principal at Biotechnology Business Associates. He was formerly Vice President of Technology Research for Masimo Corporation; Director of Research, Technology & Applications Development for Molecular Spectroscopy & Microanalysis for ThermoFisher Scientific; Senior Research Fellow at Kimberly-Clark Analytical Science & Technology; and Principal Scientist at Perkin-Elmer.

Dr. Workman has played a major role in defining and developing over twenty scientific instrument advancements and applications of novel vibrational spectroscopy technology for laboratory, process and remote monitoring of commercial synthetic and natural products and processes; and medical applications of spectroscopy. Over 55 U.S. and International Patent Applications (since 1998); 17 U.S. and International Patents issued, and multiple trade secrets. He has a total of 475 Technical Publications; and 18 reference books on a broad range of spectroscopy, chemometrics, and data processing techniques. He has received awards from the Eastern Analytical Symposium, ASTM International, and the Coblentz Society, as well as multiple fellowships, technical, and government appointments. He has taught annual courses in spectroscopy, chemometrics, and statistics for the Association of Official Analytical Chemists, the American Chemical Society, the Instrument Society of America, and the Federation of Analytical Chemists and Spectroscopy Societies; and at several universities, government agencies, and corporations.

Patented inventions include: multi-spectral monitoring (data fusion), web-based information technology in spectroscopy, scanning systems for positioning materials in manufacturing technology, invention of small molecule metabolite reporters for monitoring multiple parameters in human metabolism, advanced technology and algorithm development for instrument automation, standardization, and calibration, and for manufacturing monitoring methods for consumer products.

He is a Fellow of the American Institute of Chemists, the American Society for Testing and Materials International, and the Royal Society of Chemistry (U.K.). He is also a Chartered Chemist (CChem) of the Royal Society of Chemistry (England) and a Chartered Scientist of the Science Council (UK). He has served as Chair of the Industrial Advisory Board for the Center for Process Analytical Chemistry (CPAC) at the Univ. of Washington; and The Council for Near-Infrared Spectroscopy; and is past Chairman of ASTM Main Committee E13 on Molecular Spectroscopy and Separation Science. He has served on the U.S. National Academies NRC Panel for assessment of NIST programs.

With a B.A. in natural sciences and an M.A. in biological sciences from Saint Mary's University of Minnesota, Dr. Workman's Ph.D. is in biological chemistry from Columbia Pacific University. He is a graduate of the Columbia Senior Executive Program and also holds Columbia Business School Certificates in Executive Development (CIED) and in Business Excellence (CIBE). He also holds a Certificate in Strategy and Innovation from the M.I.T. Sloan School. He is listed in Who's Who in the World, Who's Who in America, and Who's Who in Science and Engineering.

Contents

Reference Tables: Comparison of Spectroscopic Techniques, the Electromagnetic Spectrum, Beer's Law, and Useful Spectral Ranges for Sources, Detectors and Optical Materials

0.1 Physical Constants and Conversion Factors for SI and non-SI Units

Table 0.1 Spectroscopy constants.[1]

Physical constant	Value	Standard uncertainty	Concise form
Avogadro constant. N_A, L	$6.022\,141\,29 \times 10^{23}$ mol^{-1}	$0.000\,000\,27 \times 10^{23}$ mol^{-1}	$6.022\,141\,29(27) \times 10^{23}$ mol^{-1}
Boltzmann constant, k	$1.380\,6488 \times 10^{-23}$ J K^{-1}	$0.000\,0013 \times 10^{-23}$ J K^{-1}	$1.380\,6488(13) \times 10^{-23}$ J K^{-1}
Faraday constant, F	96 485.3365 C mol^{-1}	0.0021 C mol^{-1}	96 485.3365(21) C mol^{-1}
Molar gas constant, R	8.314 4621 J mol^{-1} K^{-1}	0.000 0075 J mol^{-1} K^{-1}	8.314 4621(75) J mol^{-1} K^{-1}
Planck constant, h	$6.626\,069\,57 \times 10^{-34}$ J s	$0.000\,000\,29 \times 10^{-34}$ J s	$6.626\,069\,57(29) \times 10^{-34}$ J s
Speed of light (in vacuum), c	299 792 458 m s^{-1}	(exact)	299 792 458 m s^{-1}
Stefan-Boltzmann constant, ö	$5.670\,373 \times 10^{-8}$ W m^{-2} K^{-4}	$0.000\,021 \times 10^{-8}$ W m^{-2} K^{-4}	$5.670\,373(21) \times 10^{-8}$ W m^{-2} K^{-4}

Table 0.2 Wavelength conversions.[2]

To convert Column 1 into Column 2 multiply by	Column 1 SI Units	Column 2 non-SI Units	To convert Column 2 into Column 1 multiply by
2.54	Centimeter, cm (10^{-2} m)	Inch, in	0.394
25.4	Millimeter, mm (10^{-3} m)	Inch, in	3.94×10^{-2}
1.0	Micrometer, μm (10^{-6} m)	Micron, μ	1.0
0.1	Nanometer, nm (10^{-9} m)	Angstrom, A (10^{-10} m)	10
$1/(\text{nm} \times 10^7)$	Nanometer, nm (10^{-9} m)	Wavenumber (cm^{-1})	$1/(\text{cm}^{-1} \times 10^7)$
$1/(\text{nm} \times 2.99792458 \times 10^{17})$	Nanometer, nm (10^{-9} m)	Frequency (Hertz, Hz)	$1/(\text{Hz} \times 2.99792458 \times 10^{17})$

Example 1: To convert Nanometer, nm (10^{-9} m) in Column 1 to Angstrom, A (10^{-10} m) in Column 2 to multiply by 0.1; therefore 0.1 nm = 1 Angstrom.

Example 2: To convert Angstrom, A (10^{-10} m) in Column 2 to Nanometer, nm (10^{-9} m) in Column 1 multiply by 10; therefore 10 Angstroms = 1 nm.

Table 0.3 Length conversions.

To convert Column 1 into Column 2 multiply by	Column 1 SI Units	Column 2 non-SI Units	To convert Column 2 into Column 1 multiply by
1.609	Kilometer, km (10^3 m)	Mile, mi	0.6213
0.914	Meter, m	Yard, yd	1.094
0.304	Meter, m	Foot, ft	3.28
1.0	Micrometer, μm (10^{-6} m)	Micron, μ	1.0
1000	Micrometer, μm (10^{-6} m)	Millimeter, mm (10^{-3} m)	0.001
25.4	Millimeter, mm (10^{-3} m)	Inch, in	3.94×10^{-2}
0.1	Nanometer, nm (10^{-9} m)	Angstrom, A	10

Table 0.4 Area conversions.

To convert Column 1 into Column 2 multiply by	Column 1 SI Units	Column 2 non-SI Units	To convert Column 2 into Column 1 multiply by
0.405	Hectare, ha	Acre	2.47
4.05×10^{-3}	Square kilometer, km^2 $(10^3\ m)^2$	Acre	2.47
2.590	Square kilometer, km^2 $(10^3\ m)^2$	Square mile, mi^2	0.386
4.05×10^{3}	Square meter, m^2	Acre	2.47×10^{-4}
9.29×10^{-2}	Square meter, m^2	Square foot, ft^2	10.76
645	Square millimeter, mm^2 $(10^{-3}\ m)^2$	Square inch, in^2	1.55×10^{-3}

Table 0.5 Volume conversions

To convert Column 1 into Column 2 multiply by	Column 1 SI Units	Column 2 non-SI Units	To convert Column 2 into Column 1 multiply by
102.8	Cubic meter, m^3	Acre-inch	9.73×10^{-3}
2.83×10^{-2}	Cubic meter, m^3	Cubic foot. ft^3	35.3
1.64×10^{-5}	Cubic meter, m^3	Cubic inch, in^3	6.10×10^{4}
35.24	Liter, L $(10^{-3}\ m^3)$	Bushel, bu	2.84×10^{-2}
0.946	Liter, L $(10^{-3}\ m^3)$	Quart (liquid), qt	1.057
28.3	Liter, L $(10^{-3}\ m^3)$	Cubic foot, ft^3	3.53×10^{-2}
3.78	Liter, L $(10^{-3}\ m^3)$	Gallon	0.265
2.96×10^{-2}	Liter, L $(10^{-3}\ m^3)$	Ounce (fluid), oz	33.78
0.473	Liter, L $(10^{-3}\ m^3)$	Pint (fluid), pt	2.11

Table 0.6 Mass conversions.

To convert Column 1 into Column 2 multiply by	Column 1 SI Units	Column 2 non-SI Units	To convert Column 2 into Column 1 multiply by
453.6	Gram, g (10^{-3} kg)	Pound, lb	2.2×10^{-3}
28.4	Gram, g (10^{-3} kg)	Ounce (Avoirdupois, avdp), oz	3.52×10^{-2}
0.454	Kilogram, kg	Pound, lb	2.205
100	Kilogram, kg	Quintal (metric), q	0.01
907	Kilogram, kg	Ton (2000 lb), U.S. ton	1.10×10^{-3}
0.907	Megagram, Mg (Tonne)	Ton (U.S.), ton	1.102
0.907	Tonne, t	Ton (U.S.), ton	1.102

Table 0.7 Rate conversions.

To convert Column 1 into Column 2 multiply by	Column 1 SI Units	Column 2 non-SI Units	To convert Column 2 into Column 1 multiply by
0.447	Meter per second, m s^{-1}	Mile per hour	2.237

Table 0.8 Specific surface conversions.

To convert Column 1 into Column 2 multiply by	Column 1 SI Units	Column 2 non-SI Units	To convert Column 2 into Column 1 multiply by
0.1	Square meter per kilogram, $m^2 kg^{-1}$	Square centimeter per gram, $cm^2 g^{-1}$	10
0.001	Square meter per kilogram, $m^2 kg^{-1}$	Square millimeter per gram, $mm^2 g^{-1}$	1000

Table 0.9 Density conversions.

To convert Column 1 into Column 2 multiply by	Column 1 SI Units	Column 2 non-SI Units	To convert Column 2 into Column 1 multiply by
1.00	Megagram per cubic meter, Mg m^{-3}	Gram per cubic centimeter, g cm^{-3}	1.00

Table 0.10 Pressure conversions.

To convert Column 1 into Column 2 multiply by	Column 1 SI Units	Column 2 non-SI Units	To convert Column 2 into Column 1 multiply by
0.101	Megapascal, MPa (10^6 Pa)	Atmosphere	9.869
0.1	Megapascal, MPa (10^6 Pa)	Bar	10
47.9	Pascal, Pa	Pounds per square foot, lb ft^{-2}	2.09×10^{-2}
6.90×10^3	Pascal, Pa	Pounds per square inch, lb in^{-2}	1.45×10^{-4}

Table 0.11 Temperature conversions.

To convert Column 1 into Column 2 multiply by	Column 1 SI Units	Column 2 non-SI Units	To convert Column 2 into Column 1 multiply by
100(K-273)	Kelvin, K	Celsius, °C	1.00 (°C + 273)
(°R − 491.67) × 5/9	Rankine, °R	Celsius, °C	(°C + 273.15) × 9/5
(9/5 °C) + 32	Celsius, °C	Fahrenheit, °F	5/9 (°F − 32)
°R − 459.67	Rankine, °R	Fahrenheit, °F	°F + 459.67
[K] × 9/5 − 459.67	Kelvin, K	Fahrenheit, °F	(°F + 459.67) × 5/9
[K] × 9/5	Kelvin, K	Rankine, °R	[°R] × $^5/_9$

Table 0.12 Energy, work, quantity of heat conversions.

To convert Column 1 into Column 2 multiply by	Column 1 SI Units	Column 2 non-SI Units	To convert Column 2 into Column 1 multiply by
1.05×10^3	Joule, J	British thermal unit, Btu	9.48×10^{-4}
4.19	Joule, J	Calorie, cal	0.239
10^{-7}	Joule, J	erg	107
1.36	Joule, J	Foot-pound	0.735
4.19×10^4	Joule per square meter, $J\,m^{-2}$	Calorie per square centimeter (Langley)	2.387×10^{-5}
10^{-5}	Newton, N	Dyne	10^5
698	Watt per square meter, $W\,m^{-2}$	Calorie per square centimeter minute (irradiance), $cal\,cm^{-2}\,m^{-1}$	1.43×10^{-3}

Table 0.13 Plane angle conversions.

To convert Column 1 into Column 2 multiply by	Column 1 SI Units	Column 2 non-SI Units	To convert Column 2 into Column 1 multiply by
$1.75 \times 10^{-2} = \pi/180$	Radian, rad	Degrees (angle), °	57.3
60	Minutes (of arc), arcminute	Degrees (angle), °	$1/60 = 0.01667$
3600	Seconds (of arc), arcsecond	Degrees (angle), °	$1/3600 = 0.0002778$

Table 0.14 Electricity and magnetism conversions.

To convert Column 1 into Column 2 multiply by	Column 1 SI Units	Column 2 non-SI Units	To convert Column 2 into Column 1 multiply by
10	Siemen per meter, S m-1	Millimho per centimeter, mmho cm^{-1}	0.1
10^{-4}	Tesla, T	Gauss, G	10^4

Table 0.15 Fluid flow conversions.

To convert Column 1 into Column 2 multiply by	Column 1 SI Units	Column 2 non-SI Units	To convert Column 2 into Column 1 multiply by
102.8	Cubic meter, m^3	Acre-inch, acre-in	9.73×10^{-3}
101.9	Cubic meter per hour, $m^3\,h^{-1}$	Cubic foot per second, $ft^3\,s^{-1}$	9.81×10^{-3}
0.227	Cubic meter per hour, $m^3\,h^{-1}$	U.S. gallon per minute, gal min^{-1}	4.40
0.123	Hectare meter, ha m	Acre-foot, acre-ft	8.11
1.03×10^{-2}	Hectare meter, ha m	Acre-inch, acre-in	97.28
12.33	Hectare centimeter, ha cm	Acre-foot, acre-ft	8.1×10^{-2}

Table 0.16 Concentration conversions.

To convert Column 1 into Column 2 multiply by	Column 1 SI Units	Column 2 non-SI Units	To convert Column 2 into Column 1 multiply by
1	Centimole per kilogram, cmol kg^{-1}	Milliequivalent per 100 grams, meq 100 g^{-1}	1
0.1	Gram per kilogram, g, kg^{-1}	Percent, %	10
1	Milligrams per kilogram, mg kg^{-1}	Parts per million, ppm	1

Table 0.17 Radioactivity conversions.

To convert Column 1 into Column 2 multiply by	Column 1 SI Units	Column 2 non-SI Units	To convert Column 2 into Column 1 multiply by
3.7×10^{10}	Becquerel, Bq	Curie, Ci	2.7×10^{-11}
37	Becquerel per kilogram, Bq kg^{-1}	Picocurie per gram, pCi g^{-1}	2.7×10^{-2}
0.01	Gray, Gy (Absorbed dose)	Rad, rd	100
0.01	Sievert, Sv (equivalent dose)	Rem (Roentgen equivalent man)	100

0.2 Introduction and Comparison of Spectroscopic Methods[3]

0.2.1 *Ultraviolet (UV) Spectroscopy*

The Ultraviolet region is specified as 190 to 360 nanometers (nm) or 10^{-9} meters. The types of electrons that can be excited by UV/Vis light are few in number: nonbonding electrons, electrons in single bonds, and electrons involved in double bonds. These may be excited to several excited states. The distinction between molecules is that the ability to "jump" to higher states is affected by attached moieties — for example: double bonds, conjugations, and elements such as: oxygen, bromine, and others' with pairs of nonbonding electrons. As a consequence, most elements with UV/Vis absorbances have specific wavelengths at which their peak absorbances occur. These peaks may be used to identify a particular molecule. The UV/Vis region is not as "rich" in information as, say, the infrared spectrum, but it reveals enough detail to enable a comparison of a material with a previously identified substance. A common use of this capability is in the Pharmaceutical industry, where UV/Vis detectors are frequently used with HPLC instruments as a final check before a drug product is released for sale to consumers. The various moieties or chromophores associated with ultraviolet absorption include: Nitriles (R-C≡N), 160 nm; Acetylenes (-C≡C-), 170 nm; Alkenes (>C=C<), 175 nm; Alcohols (R-OH), 180 nm and 175–200 nm; Ethers (R-O-R), 180 nm; Ketones (R-C=O -R′), 180 nm and 280 nm; Amines, primary ($R\text{-}NH_2$), 190 nm and 200–220 nm; Aldehydes (R-C=O-H), 190 nm and 290 nm; Carboxylic acids (R-C=O-OH), 205 nm; Esters (R-C=O-OR), 205 nm; Amides, primary ($R\text{-}C{=}O\text{-}NH_2$), 210 nm; Thiols (R-SH), 210 nm; Nitrites ($R\text{-}NO_2$), 271 nm; and Azo-group (R-N=N-R′), 340 nm.

0.2.2 *Visible (Vis) Spectroscopy*

Visible light (360 to 780 nm) is the light or electromagnetic energy seen by the human eye. The actual light demonstrated by different colors is visible light and spectra in the visible region are subjected to specific mathematical algorithms to determine color coordinates or color space coordinates to enable specific colors and brightness or darkness to be precisely described in mathematical terms. The aspects of color measurement and computation are contained in the text volume on visible spectroscopy and may be located in the index for this set of volumes. The terms "color measurement" and "visible spectroscopy" are the main index topic headings to find detailed information in this set of volumes. Colors are produced by electrons in a pigment moving from one orbital transition to another around the atoms within the molecules of the colored substance. Visible reflectance or transmittance spectra demonstrate the various colors. The color appearance of the human eye to a particular visible spectrum is dependent on: the light source color temperature and emission spectrum, the observer angle of observation, and the object background brightness and color differences. The size, direction, and scattering/absorption characteristics of the object also have an effect on its color appearance. The basic seven colors first described by Isaac Newton, with their corresponding wavelength scale in nanometers, consist of: violet (360–415 nm); indigo (415–444 nm), blue (444–487 nm), green (487–540 nm), yellow (540–590 nm), orange (590–690 nm), and red (690–830 nm). A twelve color system, with corresponding wavelength information is more common in modern terminology, although technically color is defined by a series of color measurement coordinate systems. These color measurement coordinate systems include: XYZ tristimulus values, Yxy color space, L*a*b* color space, L*C*h color space, and Hunter Lab color space. These are described in detail within sections of these volumes (see index and coordinate system names for more information).

There are also molecular absorptions that occur within the visible region and these are described in various chapters within this text and include the notations for the harmonic band or overtone involved: O-H Alkyl alcohol (6ν, no hydrogen bonding), Aromatic C-H Stretch (5ν), O-H Alkyl alcohol (4ν, no hydrogen bonding), Methyl C-H Stretch (5ν), O-H Phenols (4ν, no hydrogen bonding), Methylene C-H Stretch (5ν), O-H Primary Alcohols (4ν), O-H Water (4ν), O-H Secondary Alcohols (4ν), O-H Tertiary Alcohols (4ν), and Alkenes, conjugated RC=C-C=C-R′. The visible spectra include information related to both electronic and molecular interactions of energy with atoms and molecules. Volume 2, Chapter 7 gives more details.

0.2.3 *Near-Infrared (NIR) Spectroscopy*

Near-infrared spectroscopy (780–2500 nm) is used where multicomponent molecular vibrational analysis is required in the presence of interfering substances. The near-infrared spectra consist of overtones and combination bands of the fundamental molecular absorptions found in the mid-infrared region. Near-infrared spectra consist of generally overlapping vibrational bands that are non-specific and poorly resolved. The use of chemometric mathematical data processing can be used to calibrate for qualitative or quantitative analysis despite these apparent spectroscopic limitations. Traditional near-infrared spectroscopy was used in agricultural product analysis for lignin polymers (2270 nm), paraffins and long alkane chain polymers (2310 nm), glucose based polymers such as cellulose (2336 nm), amino acid polymers as proteins (2180 nm), carbohydrates (2100 nm), and moisture (1440 and 1940 nm). The dominant near-infrared spectral features include the methyl C-H stretching vibrations, methylene C-H stretching vibrations, aromatic C-H stretching vibrations, O-H stretching vibrations, methoxy C-H stretching, and carbonyl associated C-H stretching. In addition, N-H from primary amides, secondary amides (both alkyl, and aryl group associations), N-H from primary, secondary, and tertiary amines, and N-H from amine salts predominate near-infrared spectral features of polymers and organic compounds.

0.2.4 *Infrared (IR or Mid-IR) Spectroscopy*

Mid-infrared spectroscopy (2500–25,000 nm or 4000-400 cm^{-1}) provides a measurement technique for intense, isolated and reliable absorption bands of fundamental molecular vibrations from polymers and other organic compounds. The spectrometric methodology allows for univariate calibration with higher signal strength (absorptivity) required for solid, liquids or gas phase measurements. Relatively small pathlengths of 0.1 to 1.0 mm are required for hydrocarbon liquids and solids. The technique is generally incompatible with the use of fiber optics, but specialized fiber materials exist. Instrumentation is higher cost than near-infrared spectrophotometers for the most part.

Dominant mid-infrared spectral features include the C-H (methyl, methylene, aromatic, methoxy, and carbonyl) fundamental stretching and bending molecular vibrations, O-H (hydroxyl) stretch fundamental vibrations; N-H (amine) stretching, C-F (fluorocarbon) stretching, -C≡N (nitrile) stretching, -C=O (carbonyl) stretch from esters, acetates, and amides; C-Cl stretch from chlorinated hydrocarbons, and -NO_2 from nitro- containing compounds.

0.2.5 *Raman Spectroscopy*

Raman spectroscopy (2500–25,000 nm or 4000-400 cm^{-1}) provides a variety of measurements on samples that are aqueous in nature or where glass sample holders are present. Carbon dioxide, water, and glass (silica) are weak scatterers and thus there is generally no problems in analyzing samples having these properties. There is typically no sample preparation involved in samples measured using Raman. Raman spectroscopy is complementary to mid-infrared spectroscopy in the measurement of fundamental molecular vibrations. Raman measurements are compatible with fiber optics. Raman measurements exhibit high signal-to-noise and a reasonable cost for instrumentation. The dominant Raman spectral features are acetylenic C≡C stretching, olefinic C=C stretch at 1680–1630 cm^{-1}, N=N (azo-) stretching, S-H (thio-) stretching, C=S stretching, C-S stretching, and S-S stretching bands.

Raman spectra also contain such molecular vibrational information as CH_2 twist and wagging, carbonyl C=O stretch associated with esters, acetates, and amides; C-Cl (halogenated hydrocarbons) stretching, and -NO_2 (nitro-/nitrite) stretching. In addition, Raman yields information content of phenyl- containing compounds at $1000\,cm^{-1}$.

0.3 The Electromagnetic Spectrum

The electromagnetic spectrum consists of many different types of radiation (energy): gamma, x-ray, ultraviolet (UV), visible (Vis), infrared (IR), microwave, and radio waves (Figures 0.1 through 0.3). Each type of radiation occupies its own region of the electromagnetic spectrum, and the major difference between the individual spectral regions is merely the energy involved. This energy is expressed in units of: photon energy (eV), Frequency (Hz), wavenumber (cm^{-1}), or wavelength (nm) and the manner in which these energies interact with matter.

With the possible exception of gamma radiation, most people are familiar with these types of radiation through their experiences in daily living. X-rays penetrate our bodies, allowing physicians to visualize our internal anatomy. UV light is associated with sunburn and tanning. We see colors and objects in the visible spectrum. In the kitchen, we toast our bread with IR radiation, and "zap" our meals with microwaves. We use microwave transmission for cell phone technology and we use radio waves to broadcast sound and images through AM/FM radio and television signals. The spectral region most useful in day-to-day analytical chemistry is the range of wavelengths from just below our visual perception (i.e., Ultraviolet or UV) through the colors we see (i.e., visible or Vis), known collectively as the UV/Vis spectral region. The wavelengths covered in the UV/Vis are measured in nanometers (nm), a unit of length representing one billionth of a meter. The generally accepted ranges for the UV/Vis region are ultraviolet (190–380 nm) and visible (380–750 nm). Some UV/Vis work involves longer wavelengths in the neighboring shortwave near-IR spectral region, from about 750–950 nm.

0.3.1 *Molecular and Electronic Spectroscopy Unit Conversions*

The units used to describe spectra for molecular spectroscopy vary with the academic or engineering discipline describing the spectral regions. For the most part the spectra are described in terms of an optical response specific to energy from a particular spectral region. The responses are in terms of inelastic or elastic collisions of the energy with various materials and are referred to as scattering absorption, absorbance, reflection, transmission, and so on. The various spectral energy for molecular and electronic spectroscopy is described in terms of units of wavelength (e.g., microns (μm) as 10^{-6} meters, or nanometers (nm) as 10^{-9} m, or Angstroms (Å) as 10^{-10} m). Energy is also expressed as frequency (cycles per second or sec.$^{-1}$) termed Hertz (Hz), as Wavenumbers (cm^{-1}), and as electron Volts (eV).

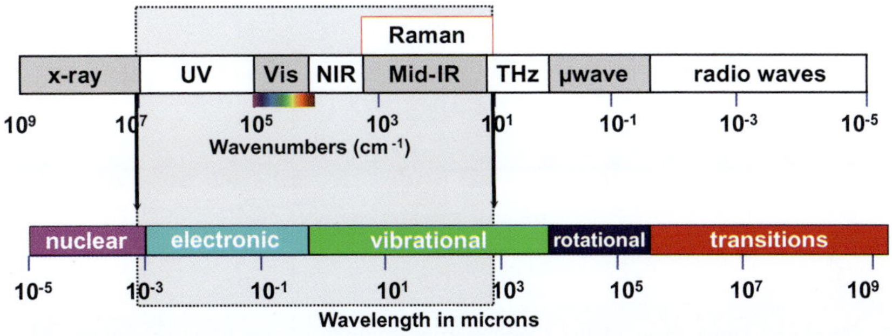

Fig. 0.1 The electromagnetic spectrum highlighting the ultraviolet to infrared/Raman spectral regions. Ultraviolet through Infrared/Raman range is shown in the rectangle. This region is from 190 nanometers to 25,000 nanometers, or 0.19 to 25 microns and represents electronic transitions through vibrational absorptions.

The various formulas used for the inter-conversion of units for spectroscopy include the following.

Molecular Electromagnetic Spectrum Regions

Region	Wavelength (nanometers)	Wavenumbers (cm^{-1})	Frequency (Hz)	Energy (eV)
Radio Waves	$1e^{9}$-$1e^{17}$	$1e^{-2}$-$1e^{-10}$	$3.0e^{8}$-3.0	$1.2e^{-6}$-$1.2e^{-14}$
Microwaves	$1e^{6}$-$1e^{9}$	10-0.01	$3.0e^{11}$-$3.0e^{8}$	$1.2e^{-3}$-$1.2e^{-6}$
Terahertz	$2.5\text{x}10^{4}$-10^{6}	400-10	$1.2e^{13}$-$3.0e^{11}$	0.05-0.001
Infrared	2500-25,000	4000-400	$1.2e^{14}$-$1.2e^{13}$	0.50-0.05
Raman	2500-25,000	4000-400	$1.2e^{14}$-$1.2e^{13}$	0.50-0.05
Near Infrared	780-2500	14,493-3,333	$3.8e^{14}$-$1.2e^{14}$	1.6-0.50
Visible	360-780	27,778-12,821	$8.3e^{14}$-$3.8e^{14}$	3.4-1.6
Ultraviolet	190-360	52,632-27,778	$1.6e^{15}$-$8.3e^{14}$	6.5-3.4
Vacuum UV	10-190	$1e^{6}$-$5.26e^{4}$	$3.0e^{16}$-$1.6e^{15}$	124-6.5
X-Rays	0.01-10	$1e^{9}$-$1e^{6}$	$3.0e^{19}$-$3.0e^{16}$	$124e^{3}$-124
Gamma Rays	<0.01	>$1e^{9}$	>$3e^{19}$	>$124e^{3}$

Fig. 0.2 Comparative Regions of the Electromagnetic Spectrum in wavelength (nanometers), wavenumbers, Frequency (Hertz), and Energy (electron Volts).

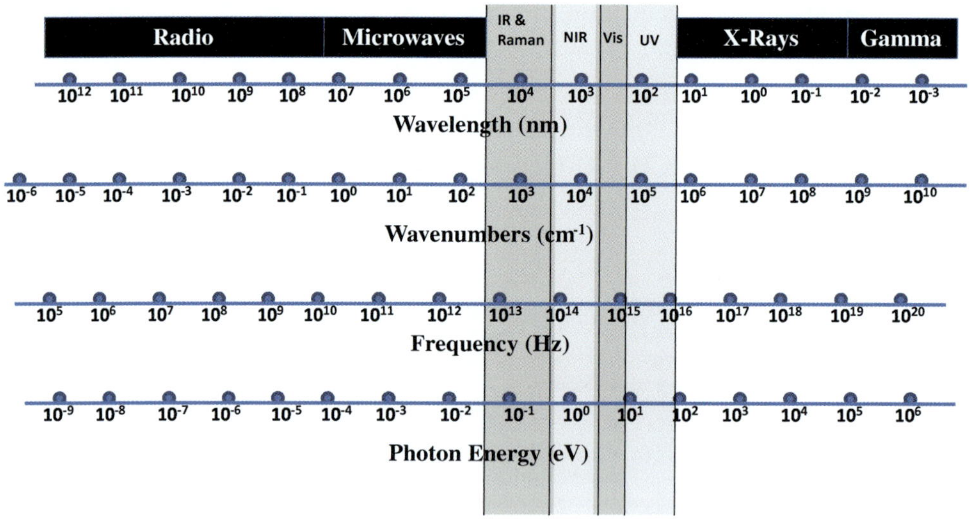

Fig. 0.3 Graphical Illustration of the Comparative Regions of the Electromagnetic Spectrum in wavelength (nanometers), wavenumbers, Frequency (Hertz), and Energy (electron Volts).

Light has both particle and wave properties, quantum theory tells us that the energy of a light "particle" or photon E_p is given by:

$$E_p = h\nu \tag{0.1}$$

$$E_p = hc\bar{\nu} \tag{0.2}$$

where: h = Planck's constant (or 6.6256×10^{-27} erg-sec.); and ν (nu) is the frequency of light, also known as Hertz (Hz) or the number of vibrations per second, in units of sec.^{-1}; $\bar{\nu}$ is the wavenumber units as cm^{-1} (i.e., the number of waves per centimeter), c is the velocity of light in a vacuum (or 2.9979×10^{10} $\text{cm}\cdot\text{sec}^{-1}$).

$$\bar{\nu} = \frac{\nu}{c \cdot n^{-1}} = \frac{1}{\lambda} \tag{0.3}$$

$$\nu = \frac{c \cdot n^{-1}}{\lambda} \tag{0.4}$$

where: $\bar{\nu}$ is the wavenumber units as cm^{-1} (i.e., the number of waves per centimeter), c is the velocity of light in a vacuum (or 2.9979×10^{10} $\text{cm}\cdot\text{sec}^{-1}$), ν (Greek: nu) is the frequency of light, also known as Hertz (Hz) or the number of vibrations per second, in units of (sec.^{-1}), and n is the refractive index of the medium the light is passing through (e.g., air = 1.0003), λ (Greek: lambda) is the wavelength in units of cm. Combining the above equations we also note:

$$\bar{\nu} = \frac{hc}{E_p} \Rightarrow \frac{1}{\lambda} = \frac{hc}{E_p} \Rightarrow \lambda = \frac{E_p}{hc} \quad (0.5)$$

0.3.2 *Direct Unit Conversions*

Wavenumbers (cm^{-1}) to wavelength (in nanometers):

$$\lambda_{nm} = \frac{10^7}{\bar{\nu}_{cm^{-1}}} \quad (0.6)$$

Wavelength (in nanometers) to wavenumbers (cm^{-1}):

$$\bar{\nu}_{cm^{-1}} = \frac{10^7}{\lambda_{nm}} \quad (0.7)$$

Wavelength (in nanometers) to frequency (in Hz):

$$\nu_{HZ} = \frac{2.9979 \times 10^{17} nm \cdot \sec^{-1}}{\lambda_{nm}} \quad (0.8)$$

Wavelength (in nanometers) convert to energy (in eV):

$$E_{p_{eV}} = \frac{1240}{\lambda_{nm}} \quad (0.9)$$

0.4 Description of Basic Quantitative Spectroscopic Measurements using Beer's Law[4]

Spectroscopic measurements depend upon the principle that light energy interacting with a material will cause absorption at a specific frequency depending upon the chemical characteristics of that material. The amplitude of the absorption at any particular frequency (or wavelength or wavenumber) is determined by the absorptivity of the molecule being measured and the number of molecules encountered by the beam path of the measuring instrument. It is assumed that a change in spectral response is related to a concentration as described by the Bouguer, Lambert, and Beer relationship, most often termed Beer's law. The Beer's law relationship is described as the absorbance (A, Au, or signal strength) of an analyte being measured using a spectrophotometer is equivalent to the product of the absorptivity (ε) of a specific type of molecular vibration at a given frequency; the concentration (c) of the molecules in the measurement beam; and the pathlength (l) of the sample holder within the measurement beam. This relationship between measured spectral signal and concentration of a molecule is most often expressed as:

$$A = \varepsilon cl \tag{0.10}$$

where ε is the molar absorptivity (referred to as molar extinction coefficient by earlier physicists) in units of Liter·Mole^{-1}·cm^{-1}; c is the concentration of molecules in the spectrometer beam in units of Mole·Liter^{-1} (Note: this is a scaled volume fraction unit); and pathlength (l) is the thickness of the sample in units of cm of the measured sample at a specific concentration. The absorptivity for any specific molecule type is calculated by careful measurements of the absorbance of a compound, generally diluted in a suitable organic solvent, and by applying the relationship:

$$\varepsilon = \frac{A}{cl} \tag{0.11}$$

Note that for transmittance (where T = 0.0 to 1.0) and percent transmittance (where %T = 0 to 100.0) spectroscopy, a more complete delineation of the relationships between the various terms is contained in an expression such as:

$$\mathrm{T} = \frac{\mathrm{I}}{\mathrm{I_0}} = 10^{-\varepsilon \mathrm{cl}} \Rightarrow \mathrm{Abs.} = \mathrm{A} = -\log_{10}\left(\frac{\mathrm{I}}{\mathrm{I_0}}\right) = -\log_{10}\mathrm{T} = \varepsilon \mathrm{cl} \tag{0.12}$$

Here the symbols I and I_0 represent the attenuated energy detected after sample interaction and the initial energy incident to the sample, respectively. For reflectance (where R = 0.0 to 1.0) and percent reflectance (Where %R = 0.0 to 100.0) spectroscopy the various relationships are expressed as:

$$R = \frac{I}{I_0} = 10^{-\varepsilon cl} \Rightarrow Abs. = A = -\log_{10}\left(\frac{I}{I_0}\right) = -\log_{10} R = \varepsilon cl \tag{0.13}$$

Noting the relationship exists where the change in intensity (I) of the transmitted or reflected light from a sample is a function of the change in pathlength (l) of the sample as expressed by the absorptivity (ε) of a specific analyte (or molecular substance) and its concentration (c) by:

$$-\frac{\partial I}{\partial l} = \varepsilon cl(\ln 10) \tag{0.14}$$

Modern spectrophotometers utilize these assumptions for making spectroscopic measurement and generally display spectroscopic data as transmission/transmittance (T), reflection/reflectance (R), and absorbance A (y-axis or ordinate axis) versus wavelength (nm, microns) or wavenumber (cm^{-1}) (as x-axis, or abscissa axis).

0.5 Spectral Ranges for Sources, Detectors and Optical Materials

Table 0.18 Source emissivity ranges (Adapted with permission from reference 3).

Source emissivity ranges (μm)	Start	End
Quartz tungsten halogen	0.22	2.7
Glass tungsten halogen	0.25	2.25
DC deuterium lamp	0.185	3.75
Pulsed xenon arc lamp	0.18	2.5
DC arc lamp	0.20	2.5
Globar (Silicon Carbide)	1.0	100
Nernst glower	0.30	35
Carbon arc	0.50	100
Mercury lamp	0.30	100
Helium-neon laser (He:Ne)	0.6327	0.6328
Neodymium yttrium aluminum garnet (Nd:YAG) laser	1.0639	1.0640

Table 0.19 Detector sensitivity ranges.[3]

Detector sensitivity ranges (μm)	Start	End
Silicon (Si)	0.30	1.1
Lead Sulfide (PbS)	1.1	3.0
Indium Arsenide (InAs)	1.7	5.7
Indium Gallium Arsenide (InGaAs), typical	0.90	1.7
Indium Gallium Arsenide (InGaAs), extended	0.65	2.4
Indium Gallium Arsenide (InGaAs), IR extended	0.65	2.70
Germanium (Ge:X)	2	40
Germanium Gold (Ge:Au)	2	9
Germanium Cadmium (Ge:Cd)	2	24
Lead Selenide (PbSe)	1.7	5.5
Germanium Zinc (Ge:Zn)	2	40
Indium Antimonide (InSb)	1.8	6.8
Lead Telluride (PbTe)	1.5	4.5
Deuterated Triglycine Sulfate (DTGS/KBr)	0.83	25
Deuterated Triglycine Sulfate (DTGS/PE)	10	120
Mercury Cadmium Telluride (MCT)	1	17
Triglycine Sulfate (TGS)	10	120
Pyroelectric Lithium Tantalate ($LiTaO_3$) (PLT)	1.5	30
Silicon Photodiode Detectors	0.19	1.1
Photomultipler Tube (PMT), S1 Type Photocathode	0.30	1.2
Photomultipler Tube, Cesium Gallium Arsenide (CsGaAs) Photocathode	0.30	0.93
Photomultipler Tube, Cesium Indium Gallium Arsenide (CsInGaAs) Photocathode	0.30	1.0
Photomultipler Tube, Cesium Antiminide CsSb Photocathode	0.25	0.75
Photomultipler Tube, Multialkali (Na-K-Sb-Cs) Photocathode	0.30	0.93
Photomultipler Tube, CsI Photocathode	0.20	0.90
Photomultipler Tube, S1 Type Photocathode	0.30	1.2
Photomultipler Tube, Cesium Gallium Arsenide (CsGaAs) Photocathode	0.30	0.93
Photomultipler Tube, Cesium Indium Gallium Arsenide (CsInGaAs) Photocathode	0.30	1.0
Silicon (Si) CCD	0.20	1.1
Indium Gallium Arsenide (InGaAs) CCD	0.80	1.7
Ultraviolet range	0.19	0.36
Visible Range	0.36	0.78
Near-Infrared Range	0.78	2.5
Infrared	2.5	25
Raman	2.5	25

Table 0.20 Optical material spectral ranges.[3]

Optical material spectral ranges	Start	End
Methacrylate, Polymer	0.25	1.1
Silica, UV Grade Fused (SiO_2)	0.20	2.5
Silica, Synthetic Fused (SiO_2)	0.23	2.6
Quartz, Crystalline (SiO_2)	0.24	2.6
Quartz, extremely low O-H	0.19	2.7
Glass, Flint (SF 10)	0.38	2.35
Glass, Flint (SF 8)	0.355	2.35
Glass (BK 7)	0.315	2.35
Glass, "Optical Crown"	0.32	2.3
Glass, "Borosilicate Crown"	0.36	2.35
Glass, Pyrex®	0.31	2.5
Glass, Zerodur®Schott	0.40	2.85
Glass, Tempax®	0.36	2.35
Sapphire (Aluminum Oxide) (Al_2O_3) 5 mm is 50 %T at 5.1 microns	0.15	5.1
Sodium Chloride (NaCl)	0.25	16.0
Suprasil 300	0.19	3.6
Diamond (C)	0.22	4.0
Silica, Fused as pure SiO_2 (IR Quality)	0.20	4.0
Quartz, Anhydrous	0.20	2.75
Zirconium Fluoride (ZrF)	0.90	4.76
Chalcogenide (NIR-IR measurements)	2.22	11.1
Cesium Iodide (CsI)	0.3	50.0
Lead Sulfide (PbS)	1.1	3.0
Potassium Bromide (KBr)	0.25	26.0
Potassium Chloride (KCl)	0.25	20.0
Thallium Bromide-Iodide (KRS-5)	0.60	40.0
Germanium (Ge)	1.1	30.0
Arsenic Sulfide (As_2S_3)	0.6	15.0
Magnesium Fluoride (MgF_2)	0.6	9.5
Zinc Selenide (ZnSe) (IRTRAN-4)	0.6	26.0
Barium Fluoride (BaF_2)	0.2	13.0
Zinc Sulfide (ZnS) (Cleartran or IRTRAN-2)	0.6	15.0
Calcium Fluoride (CaF_2) (IRTRAN-3)	0.2	9.0
Silver Bromide (AgBr)	0.5	35.0
Polyethylene, Polymer (High Density)	16	333
Glass, Silica, Fused "Water Free" (SiO_2); 10 mm is 82%T at 3.15 microns	0.15	3.15
Glass, Corning Optical Glasses as HPFS®7978 and 7979 50%T/cm	0.15	4.35

(*Continued*)

Table 0.20 (*Continued*)

Optical material spectral ranges	Start	End
Glass, Corning Optical Glasses as HPFS® 7980; 50%T/cm	0.2	2.6
Glass, Corning Optical Glasses as HPFS® 865X and 797X 50%T/cm	0.15	2.6
Glass, ESCO Optical Glasses as S1-UVA and S1-UVB Working Range (Band 1)	0.17	2.2
Glass, ESCO Optical Glasses as S1-UVA and S1-UVB Working Range (Band 2)	2.9	3.6
Glass, ESCO Optical Glasses as I2-IR Working Range	0.25	3.6
Glass, ESCO Optical Glasses as G1 and A1 Working Range	0.27	2.5
Glass, ESCO Optical Glasses as BK7 Working Range	0.35	2.0
Ultraviolet range	0.19	0.36
Visible Range	0.36	0.78
Near-Infrared Range	0.78	2.5
Infrared	2.5	25
Raman	2.5	25

Table 0.21a UV-Vis gas emission sources and peak positions (in nanometers).[5]

Position	Source	Position	Source	Position	Source
253.652	Hg	452.186	Xe	612.884	Ne
296.728	Hg	462.420	Xe	614.306	Ne
302.150	Hg	466.849	Xe	616.359	Ne
313.155	Hg	469.097	Xe	621.728	Ne
334.148	Hg	469.804	Xe	626.649	Ne
341.790	Ne	473.415	Xe	630.479	Ne
342.391	Ne	479.262	Xe	633.442	Ne
344.770	Ne	480.702	Xe	638.299	Ne
345.076	Ne	482.971	Xe	640.225	Ne
345.419	Ne	484.329	Xe	650.653	Ne
346.052	Ne	491.651	Xe	653.288	Ne
346.658	Ne	492.315	Xe	659.895	Ne
347.257	Ne	503.135	Ne	667.828	Ne
349.806	Ne	503.775	Ne	671.704	Ne
350.121	Ne	508.038	Ne	692.947	Ne
351.519	Ne	511.367	Ne	703.241	Ne
352.047	Ne	511.650	Ne	717.394	Ne
359.353	Ne	540.056	Ne	724.512	Ne
360.017	Ne	546.074	Hg	733.930	Xe
363.366	Ne	556.222	Kr	738.600	Xe
365.015	Hg	557.029	Kr	739.379	Xe
368.573	Ne	576.441	Ne	740.040	Xe
370.122	Ne	576.960	Hg	743.890	Ne
404.656	Hg	579.066	Hg	747.244	Ne
407.783	Hg	582.015	Ne	748.887	Ne
431.958	Kr	585.249	Ne	753.577	Ne
435.833	Hg	587.096	Kr	754.404	Ne
436.264	Kr	588.189	Ne	755.979	Xe
437.612	Kr	594.483	Ne	758.468	Xe
439.997	Kr	597.553	Ne	758.741	Kr
445.392	Kr	602.000	Ne	760.155	Kr
446.369	Kr	607.433	Ne	764.391	Xe
450.235	Kr	609.616	Ne	768.525	Kr
				769.454	Kr

Table 0.21b NIR gas emission sources and peak positions (in nanometers).[5]

Position	Source	Position	Source	Position	Source
780.265	Xe	1107.887	Ar	1390.748	Ar
785.482	Kr	1117.752	Ne	1409.364	Ar
788.132	Xe	1144.183	Ar	1414.244	Xe
791.343	Kr	1148.811	Ar	1442.679	Kr
796.734	Xe	1152.275	Ne	1473.281	Xe
805.726	Xe	1166.871	Ar	1473.444	Kr
805.95	Kr	1171.949	Ar	1504.65	Ar
806.134	Xe	1181.938	Kr	1517.269	Ar
810.436	Kr	1211.233	Ar	1520.31	Kr
819.006	Kr	1213.974	Ar	1532.934	Ar
823.163	Xe	1220.353	Kr	1537.204	Kr
826.324	Kr	1234.339	Ar	1541.839	Xe
826.652	Xe	1243.932	Ar	1598.949	Ar
829.811	Kr	1248.766	Ar	1605.328	Xe
837.761	Ne	1262.339	Xe	1620.872	Kr
849.536	Ne	1270.228	Ar	1647.29	Xe
866.794	Ar	1273.342	Ar	1656.023	Xe
877.675	Kr	1280.274	Ar	1672.815	Xe
878.375	Ne	1295.666	Ar	1689.676	Kr
881.941	Xe	1300.826	Ar	1694.058	Ar
892.869	Kr	1317.741	Kr	1704.288	Ar
904.545	Xe	1322.811	Ar	1755.35	Kr
912.297	Ar	1322.811	Ar	1763.882	Xe
916.265	Xe	1327.264	Ar	1785.738	Kr
922.45	Ar	1331.321	Ar	1790.45	Xe
935.422	Ar	1336.711	Ar	1800.223	Kr
965.779	Ar	1350.419	Ar	1809.09	Xe
978.45	Ar	1362.266	Ar	1816.733	Kr
979.97	Xe	1363.422	Kr	1832.53	Xe
992.319	Xe	1365.706	Xe	1959.94	Xe
1047.005	Ar	1367.855	Ar	1984.638	Xe
1067.357	Ar	1371.858	Ar	2190.851	Kr
1083.837	Xe	1382.572	Ar		

References

1. NIST: http://physics.nist.gov/cuu/Constants/index.html. (Used with Permission).
2. Adapted from Near-Infrared Spectroscopy in Agriculture xx-xxiii (Used with Permission). Tables have been changed with different values and conversion factors.
3. J. Workman, The Academic Press Handbook of Organic Compounds: NIR, IR, Raman, and UV-VIS Spectra Featuring Polymers, and Surfactants, (3 Volume Set: Vol. 1, Methods and Interpretation; Vol. 2, UV-Vis and NIR Spectra; Vol. 3, IR and Raman Spectra), Academic Press, Boston (2000).
4. J. Workman and L. Weyer, Practical Guide and Spectral Atlas to Interpretive Near-Infrared Spectroscopy, Second Edition CRC — Taylor and Francis, Boca Raton, FL (2012).
5. Ocean Optics Wavelength Calibration Sources, www.oceanoptics.com. (Used with Permission).

Chapter 1

Introduction to Visible Spectroscopy

Contents

1 Introduction

This chapter is intended to describe the basic tenets of visible spectroscopy. Included is an understanding of the electromagnetic radiation (emr) spectrum and how visible radiation interacts with matter. Methods of describing what the spectrum tells us about a sample's composition are covered. The components of visible spectrometer instruments are discussed in detail and useful information about sample preparation, sampling device selection, data analysis, and applications are provided. Finally, a glossary of basic key terms and concepts and a selective bibliography are provided to guide the reader to further discovery on the subject of visible spectroscopy.[1–12]

1.1 *Basic Theory*

1.1.1 *The Electromagnetic Spectrum*

The electromagnetic spectrum consists of many different types of radiation (energy): gamma, X-ray, ultraviolet (UV), visible (Vis), infrared (IR), microwave, and radio waves. The visible region is highlighted in Figures 1.1 and 1.2. Each type of radiation occupies its own region of the electromagnetic spectrum, and the major differences between the individual spectral regions are the energy and the frequency of the radiation. This energy is expressed in units of: photon energy or electron Volts (eV), Frequency in Hertz or cycles per second (Hz), wavenumber (cm^{-1}), or wavelength in nanometers (nm) or 10^{-9} meters; and microns (μm) or 10^{-6} meters.

The spectral region most useful in routine analytical measurements is the range of wavelengths from just below our visual perception (i.e., ultraviolet or UV) through the colors we see (i.e., visible or Vis), known collectively as the UV-Vis spectral

Molecular Electromagnetic Spectrum Regions

Region	Wavelength (nanometers)	Wavenumbers (cm^{-1})	Frequency (Hz)	Energy (eV)
Near Infrared	780-2500	14,493-3,333	3.8e^{14}-1.2e^{14}	1.6-0.50
Visible	360-780	27,778-12,821	8.3e^{14}-3.8e^{14}	3.4-1.6
Ultraviolet	190-360	52,632-27,778	1.6e^{15}-8.3e^{14}	6.5-3.4

Fig. 1.1 The electromagnetic spectrum. The visible range is from 360 through 780 nm.

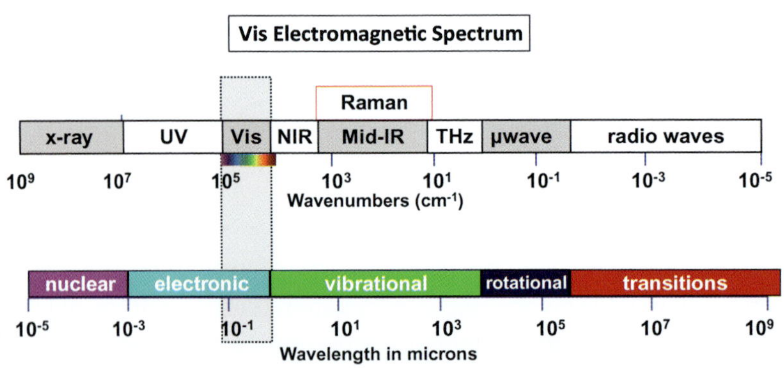

Fig. 1.2 Comparative regions of the electromagnetic spectrum (Visible region).

region. The wavelengths covered in the UV-Vis are measured in nanometers (nm), a unit of length representing one billionth of a meter. The generally accepted ranges for the UV-Vis region are ultraviolet (190–360 nm) and visible (360–780 nm). Some UV-Vis work involves longer wavelengths in the neighboring shortwave near-IR spectral region, from about 780–950 nm.

1.1.2 *The Visible Spectrum*

Visible light (360 to 780 nm) is the light or electromagnetic energy seen by the human eye. The actual light demonstrated by different colors is visible light and spectra in the visible region are subjected to specific mathematical algorithms to determine color coordinates or color space coordinates to enable specific colors and brightness or darkness to be precisely specified in mathematical terms. Color is the result of molecules absorbing or reflecting light of specific visible frequencies with the resultant color interaction based on human perception of these visible spectra. Chapter 7 of this volume contains a detailed explanation of the measurement methods and theory for color analysis.

Visible spectra are the result of electronic transitions and molecular absorptions. Electronic transitions are caused when incident radiation excites a ground-state electron to a higher energy state (higher molecular orbital). The change in the electron either makes the atom/molecule more stable (forms a bond), less stable (no bond is formed = antibonding), or has no effect on the stability (n orbital). Most notable electronic transitions occur in the higher energy ultraviolet region, see Volume 1 on ultraviolet spectra. Electronic transitions in the visible region are of the most interest and affect the color of substances.[13]

There are also molecular absorptions that occur within the visible region and these are described in various chapters within this text and include the notations for the harmonic band or overtone involved: O-H Alkyl alcohol (6ν, no hydrogen bonding), Aromatic C-H Stretch (5ν), O-H Alkyl alcohol (4ν, no hydrogen bonding), Methyl C-H Stretch (5ν), O-H Phenols (4ν, no hydrogen bonding), Methylene C-H Stretch (5ν), O-H Primary Alcohols (4ν), O-H Water (4ν), O-H Secondary Alcohols (4ν), O-H Tertiary Alcohols (4ν), and Alkenes, conjugated RC=C-C=C-R'. The visible spectra include information related to both electronic and molecular interactions of energy with atoms and molecules.

1.1.3 *Molecular and Electronic Spectroscopy Unit Conversion*

Spectra are described in terms of an optical response specific to the energy from a particular spectral region. The responses are in terms of inelastic or elastic collisions of the energy with various molecules or atoms and are referred to as: scattering, absorption, absorbance, reflectance/reflection, and transmittance/transmission. The various spectral energy for molecular and electronic spectroscopy is described in terms of units of wavelength, e.g., microns (μm) as 10^{-6} meters, or nanometers (nm) as 10^{-9} m, or Angstroms (Å) as 10^{-10} m. Energy is also expressed as frequency (cycles per second or sec^{-1}) termed Hertz (Hz), as Wavenumbers (cm^{-1}), and as electron Volts (eV).

The various formulas used for the inter-conversion of units for spectroscopy include the following. Light has both particle and wave properties, quantum theory tells us that the energy of a light "particle" or photon E_p is given by:

$$E_p = h\nu \tag{1.1}$$

$$E_p = hc\overline{\nu} \tag{1.2}$$

where: h = Planck's constant (or 6.6256×10^{-27} erg-sec; and ν (nu) is the frequency of light, also known as Hertz (Hz) or the number of vibrations per second, in units of sec^{-1}.

$$\overline{\nu} = \frac{\nu}{c \cdot n^{-1}} = \frac{1}{\lambda} \tag{1.3}$$

$$\nu = \frac{c \cdot n^{-1}}{\lambda} \tag{1.4}$$

Where: $\overline{\nu}$ is the wavenumber units as cm^{-1} (i.e., the number of waves per centimeter); c is the velocity of light in a vacuum (or $2.9979 \times 10\,\text{cm} \cdot \text{sec}^{-1}$; ν (Greek: nu) is the frequency of light, also known as Hertz (Hz) or the number of vibrations per second, in units of sec^{-1}; n is the refractive index of the medium the light is passing through (e.g., air = 1.0003); and λ (Greek: lambda) is the wavelength in units of cm. Combining the above equations we also note:

$$\overline{\nu} = \frac{hc}{E_p} \Rightarrow \frac{1}{\lambda} = \frac{hc}{E_p} \Rightarrow \lambda = \frac{E_p}{hc} \tag{1.5}$$

1.1.4 *Unit Conversions*

Wavenumbers (cm^{-1}) to wavelength (in nanometers):

$$\lambda_{nm} = \frac{10^7}{\overline{\nu}_{cm^{-1}}} \tag{1.6}$$

Wavelength (in nanometers) to wavenumbers (cm^{-1}):

$$\overline{\nu}_{\text{cm}^{-1}} = \frac{10^7}{\lambda_{nm}} \tag{1.7}$$

Wavelength (in nanometers) to frequency (in H_z):

$$\nu_{\mathrm{Hz}} = \frac{2.9979 \times 10^{17} nm \cdot \sec^{-1}}{\lambda_{nm}} \tag{1.8}$$

Wavelength (in nanometers) convert to energy (in eV):

$$E_{p_{eV}} = \frac{1240}{\lambda_{nm}} \tag{1.9}$$

1.2 *Basic Spectroscopic Measurement Instruments (Optical Configurations)*

Spectroscopy depends upon the premise that physical matter (i.e., liquids, gaseous, or solid substances) will respond in a unique manner when exposed to any type of electromagnetic radiation. The atoms and molecules that make up the matter will become "excited" and will (among other phenomena) absorb and re-emit certain amounts of the radiation as it passes through or collides with matter as atoms and molecules. Each atom or molecule will react (or interact) in precisely the same way when exposed to radiation, predictably absorbing or emitting precisely the same quantity of energy. This behavior of matter with radiation is unique — no two different types of atoms or molecules react in exactly the same way. The resulting plot of molecular or atomic behavior to radiation at various wavelengths (or frequencies) is known as a *spectrum* (plural form: spectra). The spectrum of a material is analogous to an individual "fingerprint", a substance's spectrum provides a tool for determining the identity of matter.

In the visible range, light is absorbed by matter in a selective manner. If the energy associated with a particular wavelength of light corresponds to the energy needed to boost an electron from its "resting" position to a higher energy level, an electron absorbs the photon of light and jumps to a higher energy level. It immediately returns to its resting position, but the energy used to move it is unavailable to be measured by a spectrometer, causing the detector to register a lower energy. Because light absorbance in the visible range is predictable and reproducible, these absorbances at specific wavelengths are the tools used for chemical analysis or color measurement. Visible spectroscopy is used to reveal the quantity of a particular substance in a mixture, what its identity is, and the stages of a chemical reaction. A variety of designs are possible in creating a visible spectrometer, and Figures 1.3 through 1.6 show the optical configurations for visible spectrometer systems.

1.2.1 *Components of a Visible Spectrometer*

Visible spectrometers share the same basic components, which can be configured to achieve specific optical effects (Figures 1.3 through 1.6). These components include a radiation source, a monochromator (wavelength selector), a sample holder, and a detector. The electronics include a basic power supply, computer board for processing data and low-level control, a controller board, and a detector board for amplifying and for A to D (analog to digital) conversion of basic instrument signal. Chapter 3 on instrumentation covers this subject in much greater detail.

(a) Sources: The light used in ultraviolet spectroscopy is usually produced by a deuterium lamp. Visible light is produced by incandescent lamps similar to those used in household lights. Common lamps and their working emissivity spectral ranges include: quartz tungsten-halogen filament lamp (220–2700 nm); DC deuterium lamp (185–375 nm); pulsed xenon arc lamp (180–2500 nm); and DC arc source (200–2500 nm).

(b) Wavelength Selectors: In order for the spectrometer to analyze the sample, the output of the light source must be dispersed into its individual wavelengths. Previous instruments used quartz prisms to disperse light. Today, visible light is dispersed using a holographic diffraction grating, an optical device with a series of

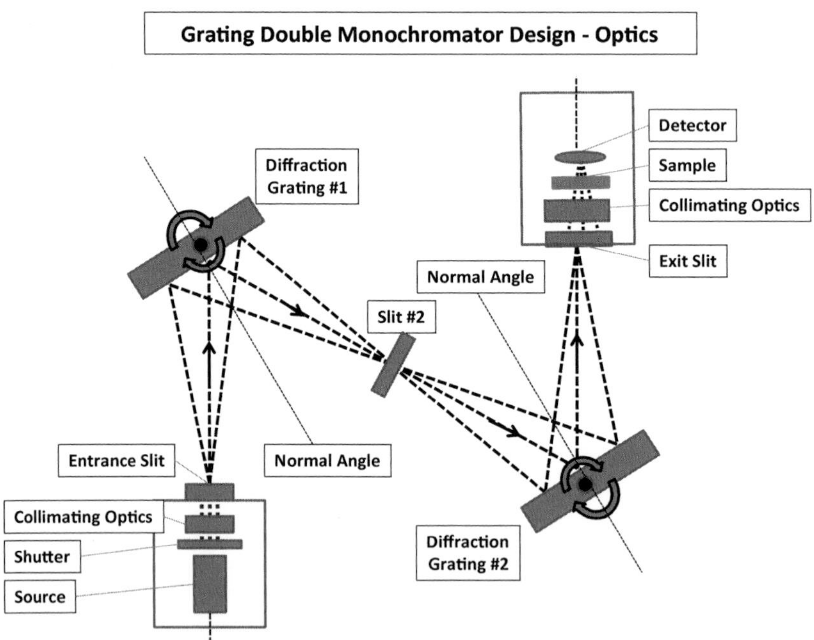

Fig. 1.3 Double monochromator visible optical system (dispersive-type).

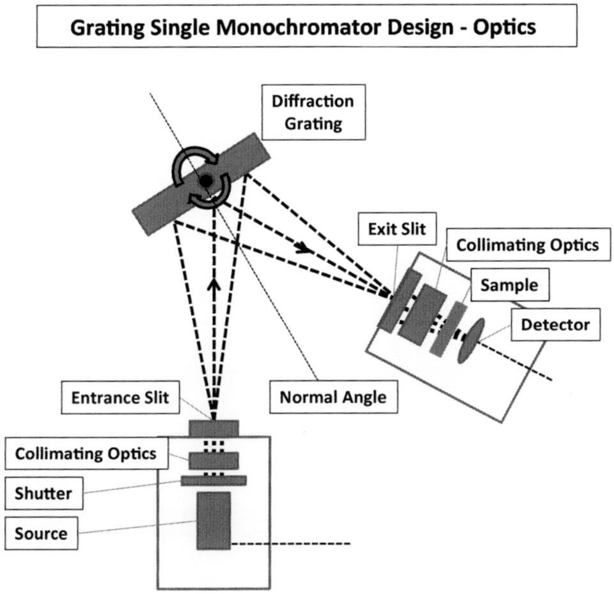

Fig. 1.4 Single monochromator visible optical system (dispersive-type).

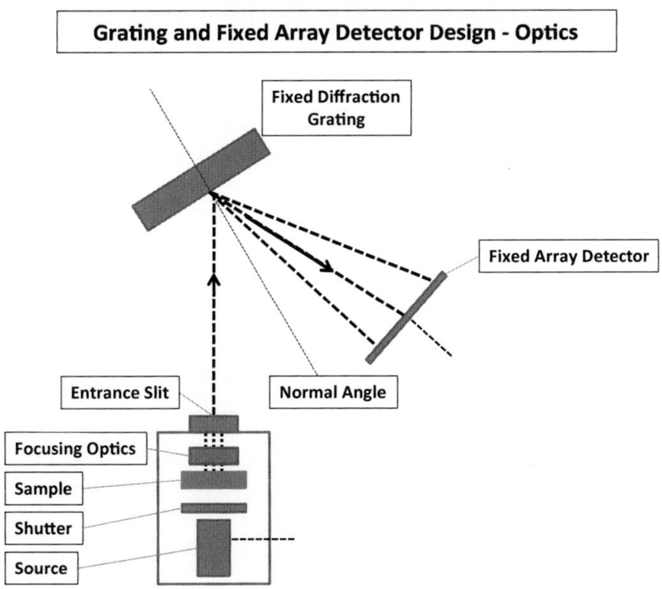

Fig. 1.5 Diode-array spectrograph visible optical system (dispersive-type).

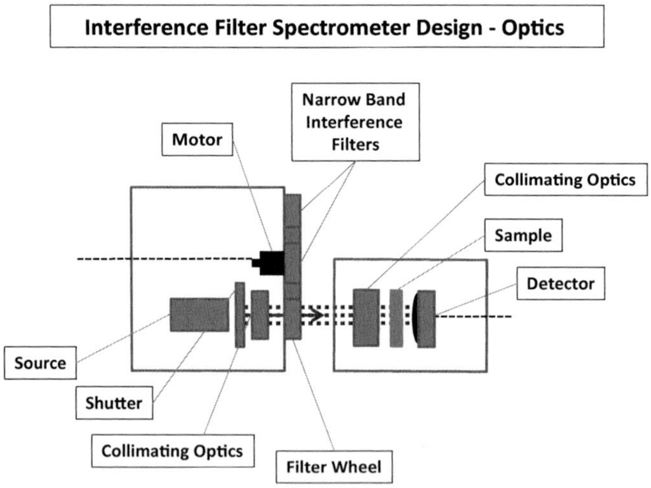

Fig. 1.6 Interference filter based photometer visible optical system (filter type).

minute physical grooves on its surface to diffract the light as it strikes the surface. The polychromatic (many-colored) light from the source is focused onto the grating. The precise grooves on the surface disperse the light according to its component wavelengths and the resulting spectrum (in the visible range) appears in the familiar "rainbow" color sequence. The grating may be rotated on its axis to "aim" the desired wavelength onto the exit slit and then onto the sample for analysis. Multiple order light is dispersed from the grating so if more than one octave is measured a cutoff filter must be incorporated to eliminate orders of light other than those of the desired wavelengths. The diffraction grating will disperse light into the zero-order (mirror reflectance), first order dispersion, second-order dispersion, and higher order dispersion (Figure 1.7).

(c) Sample Holders: The most common sample holders in visible spectroscopy analysis are cuvets (also commonly spelled as cuvettes), which are fabricated from materials that do not interfere with the light passing through the cuvette body nor do they react chemically with the sample. These include certain polymers, such as poly(methyl methacrylate) or quartz with optically flat surfaces.

(d) Detectors: UV light transmitted through a sample is almost always detected by a photomultiplier tube (PMT). The same detector can be used for visible light, but far less expensive devices such as silicon diodes or photocells are also used. In these detectors, a chip of pure silicon is "doped" with the proper element and an incoming photon causes a momentary electric impulse. The signals generated by these detectors are amplified and used to quantify the amount of light emerging

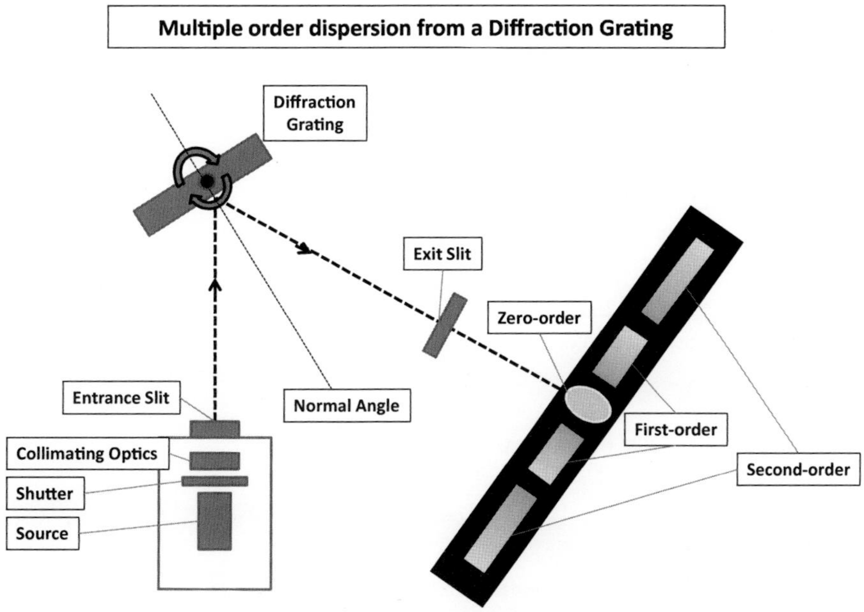

Fig. 1.7 Illustration of dispersion orders reflected/diffracted from a diffraction grating.

from a cell. A more complete list of common detectors, common abbreviations, and their useful working wavelength ranges would include: *silicon photodiodes* (350–1100 nm); *photomultiplier tubes* (PMTs, 160–1100 nm); *charge-coupled devices* (CCDs, 180–1100 nm); *silicon-based photodiode arrays* (180–1100 nm); and *indium gallium arsenide detectors or arrays* (InGaAs, most typically detects 650 nm and above).

(e) Basic Measurement Modes: The measurement modes for visible (and ultra-violet, and near-IR) spectroscopy are given in Table 1.1. A well designed general purpose spectrophotometer can make any of these measurements.

1.2.2 *The Concepts Behind Spectroscopy*

(a) Beer's Law: Beer's law is a mathematical way of expressing how light is absorbed by matter in a spectroscopic experiment. The law states that the amount of monochromatic light emerging from a sample is diminished by three physical phenomena: 1) the amount of absorbing material in its pathlength (concentration = c); 2) the distance the light must travel through the sample (pathlength = b); and 3) the probability that the photon of that particular wavelength will be absorbed by the material (absorptivity or extinction coefficient = ε).

Table 1.1 Basic UV-Vis-NIR measurement modes.

Instrument measurement mode	Description of measurement
Scan	Absorbance* vs. wavelength
Timedrive	Absorbance* vs. time at each wavelength
Individual wavelength(s)	Individual Absorbance(s)* at selected wavelength(s)
Quantitative methods	Concentration of analyte vs. absorbance
Kinetics	Kinetic rates of reaction, measurement pauses at specific wavelengths

*As $-\log_{10}$ (transmittance) or $-\log_{10}$ (reflectance).

This relationship may be expressed as:

$$A = \varepsilon bc \tag{1.10}$$

where: $A =$ absorbance; $\varepsilon =$ molar extinction coefficient (i.e., absorptivity); $b =$ pathlength (in cm); and $c =$ molar concentration. Note that ε is the molar absorptivity (referred to as molar extinction coefficient by earlier physicists) in units of $\text{Liter} \cdot \text{Mole}^{-1} \cdot \text{cm}^{-1}$; c is the concentration of molecules in the spectrometer beam in units of $\text{Mole} \cdot \text{Liter}^{-1}$ (as moles per volume, or weight percent per volume); and pathlength is the thickness in units of cm of the measured sample at a specific concentration.

In practice for dual beam instruments, the absorbance is measured by comparing the light emerging from a reference cell with the light emerging from a sample cell. The intensity of the incident radiation, I_0, is ratioed to the light emerging from a sample, I. The ratio I/I_0 is referred to as *transmittance*, or simply T. This can be plotted against the concentration, but the relationship is not linear. The negative log 10 of the transmittance, however, is more linear with concentration. Therefore, absorbance is measured as: $-\log_{10}(I/I_0) = A = \varepsilon bc$.

(b) Bandpass and Resolution: The terms *bandpass* and *resolution* are used to express the capability of a spectrometer to distinguish spectral bands or energy lines that are separated by some finite distance. For an instrument that disperses energy over a pre-specified region of the electromagnetic spectrum, the bandpass of a spectrometer is used to describe which portion of the spectrum can actually be isolated by the spectrometer in a more "pure" wavelength form. The spectrometer bandpass is dependent upon the dispersion of the grating and the entrance and exit widths (see index for detailed discussions in this set of volumes).

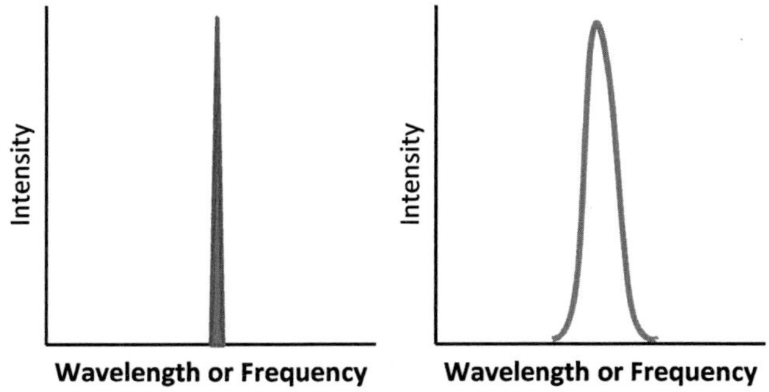

Fig. 1.8 (Left) The bright line emission spectrum at a single wavelength as it would appear in an ideal spectrophotometer. (Right) Spectrum of a bright line emission source (e.g. deuterium lamp). The characteristic broadening is an illustration of the bandpass of a spectrophotometer.

An illustration is often used to show the problem associated with measuring monochromatic light using conventional spectrometers. If the ideal spectrometer were used to measure a bright line emission spectrum at a single wavelength (λ), from an emission source (e.g., neon, argon, mercury lamps) the spectrum should appear as a single distinct line (Figure 1.8, left). What we observe when such a source is projected through a monochromator or other fixed resolution instrument is a broadening of the spectral line due to the instrument function, as shown in (Figure 1.8, right).

The spectrum assumes a Lorentzian or Gaussian-like curve. This characteristic broadening of a line spectrum through the spectrometer is an illustration of the spectral bandpass or linewidth. The bandpass for a spectrometer is assigned a value by determining the full width at half maximum (FWHM) height of the spectral lineshape. The FWHM may be empirically determined by finding the wavelength where maximum intensity occurs, and measuring the peak height at this position. This height measurement is divided in half from the baseline and the bandwidth measured at this height on the band as illustrated in Figure 1.9 (left). The actual shape of a band is the result of several instrumental characteristics including the overall quality of the optics and detector systems, as well as the width and positions of the entrance and exit slits (for dispersive instruments), or the J-Stop (for interferometric) instruments.

The measured resolution of the instrument using a graphical projection of the spectral lines is illustrated as Figure 1.9 (right), where the empirical resolution of a spectrometer is determined by measuring the FWHM in mm for two narrow bands which are fully resolved to the baseline and projected onto a hard copy display.

The spatial difference between the maximum absorbance (λ_{max}) is empirically determined between the bands (in mm); simultaneously noting the difference

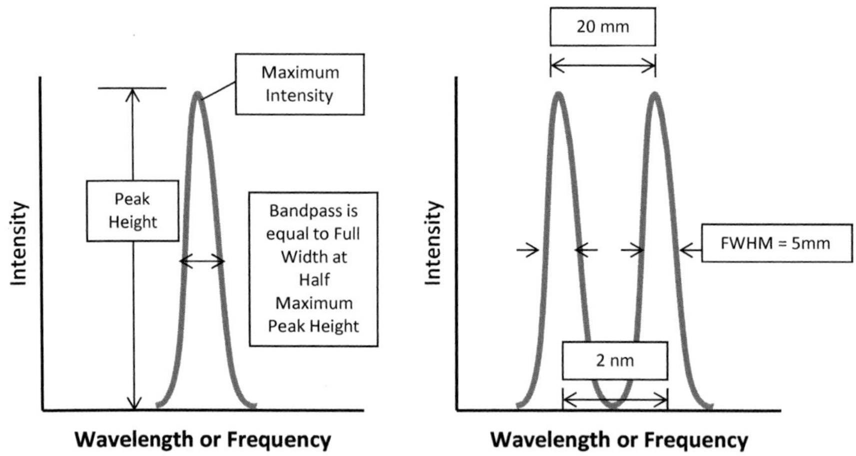

Fig. 1.9 (Left) Illustration of the determination of bandpass using the bell-shaped peak obtained by using a bright line source projected through a monochromator optical system. (Right) The method to determine maximum resolution of a spectrometer under specific measurement conditions. In the example shown Bandpass = Resolution = FWHM × Dispersion illustrated in Equations (1.11) and (1.12).

between the λ_{max} points in nm on the spectrometer measurement axis. The various measurements required for this calculation are shown in Figure 1.9 (right) and illustrated by the relationship:

$$\begin{aligned}\text{The bandpass} &= \text{resolution}\\ &= \frac{\text{band.difference.in.nm}}{\text{band.difference.in.mm}} \times \text{FWHM in mm} \qquad (1.11)\end{aligned}$$

$$\begin{aligned}\text{Measured Bandpass/Resolution} &= 2\,\text{nm}/20\,\text{mm} \times 5\,\text{mm}\\ &= 0.5\,\text{nm} \qquad (1.12)\end{aligned}$$

The theoretical resolution of a spectrometer is the minimum distance between two peaks that can be detected by the spectrometer under designated operational performance settings. Theoretical resolution is calculated by multiplying the slit width (generally expressed in mm) by the dispersion of the monochromator (in nm per mm). The actual resolution of a spectrometer must be slightly less (poorer) than the theoretical value because of practical issues such as non-ideal optics. A high performance visible spectrometer may have a theoretical resolution as follows, where the slit width (mm) × dispersion of the grating (in nm/mm) is as follows:

$$\text{Theoretical Resolution} = 1\,\text{mm} \times 0.5\,\text{nm/mm} = 0.5\,\text{nm} \qquad (1.13)$$

A basic resolution test for ultraviolet and visible spectrometers is made by measuring a standard sample and comparing the absorbance (A) of a peak height to the absorbance at a peak trough and designating a threshold ratio as the measure of adequate resolution. For example, in ultraviolet-visible spectrometers there is a resolution test used by the European Pharmacopoeia that defines adequate resolution for a spectrophotometer as determining the absorbance ratio for a solution of 0.02% w/v toluene in hexane. The peak is measured at 269 nm and the trough at 266 nm. The ratio for passing this test is > 1.5. In summary, the ratio of absorbance at 269 nm divided by the absorbance at 266 nm must exceed 1.5 for passing.[14] A basic form of resolution testing is shown in Figure 1.10. This exact resolution test is described in detail in Chapter 6 of this volume.

(c) Signal-to Noise: Simply stated, the *signal-to-noise ratio* (S/N) in a spectrometer is the numerical ratio of the amount of electrical current generated by the light from the sample striking the detector (at 100% T) relative to the amount of background

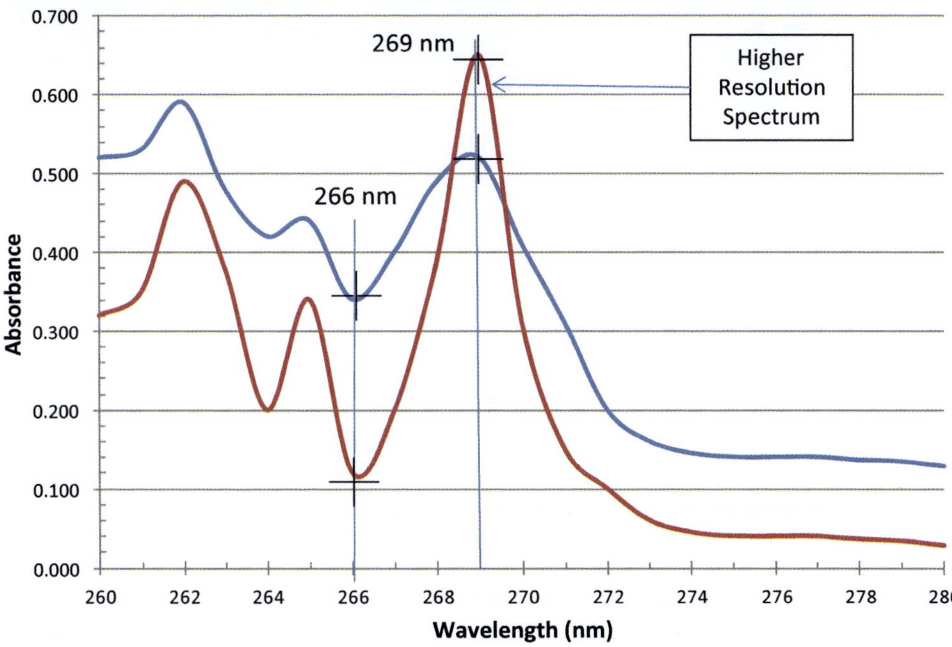

Fig. 1.10 Basic resolution test as a ratio of absorbance measurements for peak and trough of a spectral band. A higher resolution spectrum produces a larger ratio for Absorbance at 269 nm/Absorbance at 266 nm.

signal shown by the detector when no light from the sample is present (i.e., baseline noise). S/N is an important factor in determining the precision and accuracy of a visible instrument, especially when dealing with low level of analyte or highly absorbing (low transmittance) samples.

(d) Dynamic Range: The range of a specified analyte concentration over which a sensor response is directly proportional to a change in concentration is the *dynamic range* of a spectrometer. Dynamic range is stray light and noise limited. Calculating the maximum theoretical dynamic range for an instrument, the relationship of stray light, and the maximum observable absorbance value requires knowledge of Beer's law and a few simple mathematical relationships. Dynamic range is covered as a topic in Chapter 3 of this volume.

(e) Stray Radiant Energy: Any radiation reaching the detector that has not interacted with the sample at the chosen wavelength qualifies as stray light. This problem can originate from physical "light leaks" allowing outside light to enter the sample compartment, from the scattering of light from optical components within the instrument, from non-monochromatic light passing through the exit slit from a dispersive element (such as a grating), or from scattered light transmitting through, or reflecting from, the sample itself. The accompanying Table 1.2 shows the relationship between instrument stray light, the maximum dynamic range for that level of stray light, and the corresponding percent error of a measurement. Stray light measurements are made using a sharp cutoff optical filter. Examples of such filters include saturated aqueous solutions of potassium ferromanganate or lithium carbonate. Other solutions with an abrupt cutoff feature include: saturated aqueous solutions of potassium bromide, potassium chloride, potassium iodide, and sodium nitrate. Pure acetone also makes an excellent cutoff filter.

Table 1.2 Measurement error and maximum dynamic range associated with instrument stray light specification.

Stray light specification of instrument (in % T)	Absolute maximum dynamic range (in Au)	Percent measurement error for 1 Au sample
0.0001	6	0.0004
0.001	5	0.004
0.01	4	0.04
0.1	3	0.39
1	2	3.71
10	1	25.96

1.3 *Applications and Maintenance of Visible Spectrometers*

1.3.1 *Applications of UV-Vis Spectroscopy*

Visible spectroscopy is used for a variety of analytical situations in pure and applied research.

(a) Quantitative Applications: The ability of light to be absorbed in proportion to its concentration has found use in many industries, just a few of which are described here.

Pharmaceutical companies use ultraviolet and visible spectroscopy in numerous applications: measuring the strength of the component in a dosage form; monitoring dissolution (dissolving from a tablet or capsule into solution); analyzing protein and DNA; identifying polymers; and detecting species separated by thin-layer and high performance liquid chromatographic (HPLC) techniques.

Chemical companies use the ultraviolet and visible wavelengths to follow the progress of chemical reactions, determine isomeric purity of products, and in titrations (endpoint determination).

Universities, technical schools, and other teaching environments use ultraviolet and visible spectroscopy because it is the simplest and least expensive instrumental method with which to demonstrate quantitative analysis.

(b) Color and Appearance Applications: Chapter 7 describes the use of visible spectroscopy for color and appearance measurements, as well as other related measurements. Table 1.3 shows the various color designations and corresponding wavelength regions.

(c) Qualitative Applications: The types of electrons that can be excited by visible light are few in number: nonbonding electrons, electrons in single bonds, and electrons involved in double bonds. These may be excited to several excited states. The distinction between molecules is that the ability to "jump" to higher states is affected by attached moieties, for example: double bonds, conjugations, and elements such as oxygen, bromine, and others with pairs of nonbonding electrons. As a consequence, most elements with UV-Vis absorbances have specific wavelengths at which their peak absorbances occur. These peaks may be used to identify a particular molecule. The UV-Vis region is not as "rich" in information as, say, the infrared spectrum, but it reveals enough detail to enable a comparison of a material with a previously identified substance. A common use of this capability is in the Pharmaceutical industry, where UV-Vis detectors are frequently used with HPLC instruments as a final check before a drug product is released for sale to consumers.

Table 1.3 Color Designations with Corresponding Wavelength Regions (in nm).

Visible Color Designation and Band Positions (nm)	Start (nm)	End (nm)
Violet	380	440
Indigo	440	470
Sky Blue	470	480
Blue	480	490
Blue/Green	490	495
Green	495	560
Yellow/Green	560	570
Yellow	570	575
Yellow/Orange	575	590
Orange	590	600
Orange/Red	600	620
Red	620	700
Dark Red	700	780

Table 1.4 Spectral Regions and Recommended Sample Pathlengths.

Spectral Region	Wavelength Range (nm)	Pathlength (cm)
Ultraviolet	190–360 nm	0.1 to 10 cm
Visible	360–780 nm	0.1 to 10 cm
Short Wavelength NIR	780–1100 nm	5 to 10 cm
Short Wavelength NIR	780–1100 nm	10.0 cm (liquids)
Long Wavelength NIR	1050–3000 nm	0.1 to 2 cm
Long Wavelength NIR	1050–3000 nm	0.25 mm (liquids)

1.3.2 *Selection of Measurement Technique and Pathlength*

Samples are analyzed by light passing through a sample holder and separating light into individual wavelengths as it passes through. The term *pathlength* refers to the distance the light travels through the sample, as measured by the interior dimensions of the cuvette. The following pathlengths are recommended for analysis in UV-Vis-NIR spectral ranges (Table 1.4).

Spectroscopists have the choice of measuring the light just as it is transmitted through the sample, as *transmittance* or *transmission* (straight and diffuse); as it is reflected off the sample, as *reflection* or *reflectance* (specular and diffuse); or as a combination of these effects, e.g., *transflectance* or *interactance*.

The physical nature and appearance of each sample determines which measurement geometry is optimum. Samples can possess any of several different physical or optical properties that affect analysis. The following Table 1.5 gives guidelines for selecting a measurement method based upon the sample optical properties.

The accompanying Tables 1.6 and 1.7 list the characteristics of common cuvettes, including the materials they are made of, their dimensions, and other criteria for selecting the proper model for the sample and measurement technique at hand.

Table 1.5 Sample Type and Recommended Measurement Method.

Sample Type	Measurement Method
Clear solids (optical materials)	Transmittance
Translucent or opaque solids	Diffuse reflectance or diffuse transmittance (for turbid samples)
Reflecting optical surfaces	Specular reflectance
Clear liquids	Transmittance
Translucent or opaque liquids	Reflectance or diffuse transmittance
High optical density (highly absorbing)	Tiny pathlengths in transmittance

Table 1.6 Characteristics of UV-Vis window/cuvette materials.

Optical material	Transmittance Range (nm)	Refractive Index (at 600 nm)	Relative rupture strength (sapphire = 100)
Methacrylate	250–1100	—	—
UV-grade fused silica	200–2500	1.4580	10.9
Synthetic fused silica	230–2500	1.4580	10.9
Crystalline quartz (SiO_2)	240–2500	1.5437	2.3
Quartz, extremely low O-H	190–2500	1.5437	2.3
Flint glass (SF 10)	380–2350	1.7268	3.8
Flint glass (SF 8)	355–2350	1.6878	3.7
BK 7 glass	315–2350	1.5165	3.7
Optical crown glass	320–2300	1.5226	3.7
Borosilicate crown glass	360–2350	1.4736	3.7
Pyrex	360–2350	1.4736	3.8
Tempax	360–2350	1.4736	3.8
Sapphire (Al2O3)	150–5000	1.7677	100
Sodium chloride	250 nm–16 m	1.5400	0.5
Suprasil 300	190–3600	1.5400	3.8
Diamond	220–4000	2.4000	83.7
Spectrosil	170–2700	1.5400	3.8
Infrasil	220–3800	1.5400	3.8

Table 1.7 Typical sampling accessories and dimensions for UV-Vis Spectroscopy.

Cuvette type	Outer dimensions (mm)	Pathlength (mm)	Capacity (mL)
Transmittance (1 mm pathlength)	45(H) × 12.5(W) × 3.5(L)	1.0	0.3
Transmittance (5 mm pathlength)	45(H) × 12.5(W) × 7.5(L)	5.0 (0.5 cm)	1.5
Transmittance (10 mm pathlength)	45(H) × 12.5(W) × 12.5(L)	10.0 (1 cm)	3.0
Semi-micro Cell	45(H) × 12.5(W) × 12.5(L)	10.0 (1 cm)	1.0 or 1.5
Micro Cell	25(H) × 12.5(W) × 12.5(L)	10.0 (1 cm)	0.5
Cylindrical cell (10 mm pathlength)	10(L) × 22 (Diameter)	10.0 (1 cm)	3.1
Cylindrical cell (20 mm pathlength)	20(L) × 22(D)	20.0 (2 cm)	6.3
Cylindrical cell (50 mm pathlength)	50(L) × 22(D)	50.0 (5 cm)	16
Cylindrical cell (100 mm pathlength)	100(L) × 22(D)	100.0 (10 cm)	31
Micro flow cell	50(L) × 12.5(W) × 12.5(L)	10 (1 cm)	0.4 or 0.6
Test tube (round)	75(H) × 12(D)	10 (1 cm)	5.9
Test tube (round)	105(H) × 19(D)	17 (1.7 cm)	23.8
Test tube (round)	150(H) × 19(D)	17 (1.7 cm)	34.0

Note: The Z dimension for a cuvette is the distance from the bottom of the instrument cell compartment to the center of the light beam, by convention this is typically 8.5 or 15 mm.

1.3.3 *Calibration and Basic Maintenance*

A detailed description of the materials and procedures for measuring the performance of Visible instruments is shown in Chapter 6. Please see the index for specific topics.

(a) General Concepts of Calibration: Because it is difficult to predict the exact response of an instrument to a material at a given concentration, virtually all calibrations are empirical. An empirical calibration involves the preparation of multiple samples in several concentrations across the expected concentration range of samples. A calibration curve is built by graphing the response of the instrument to the concentration of the material. A wavelength is chosen at which the material has a large, distinctive maximum absorbance peak. This graph can be used to quantify unknown concentrations of later samples.

(b) Photometric Accuracy: The National Institute of Standards and Technology (NIST) provides materials designed for reference measurements to verify photometric accuracy of spectrophotometers. The materials are referred to as Standard Reference Materials (SRMs). One well-known set of standards for UV-Vis analysis is SRM 930D, consisting of a set of three individual neutral density glass filters provided in standard cuvette size, black metal holders at nominal transmittances of 10, 20, and 30%. Photometric accuracy is a term used to describe how accurately a given spectrophotometer is able to measure the total transmittance of a set of SRMs. The method of making measurements of SRMs (or other well-characterized reference standards) has been delineated by the American Society for Testing and Materials International (ASTM International).

Examples of other materials used for photometric accuracy measurements include: SRM 931 (solutions of nickel and cobalt in nitric and perchloric acids), and SRM 2031 (metal on quartz with nominal transmittances of 10, 30, and 90%). For UV, SRM 935 (potassium dichromate in perchloric acid) and SRM 84 (potassium acid phthalate in perchloric acid) are used.

(c) Linearity Checks: The linearity of the instrument may be checked by using neutral-density interference filters. These are nonspecific (i.e., they cover all wavelengths) optical filters that reduce the amount of light by specified amounts, for example, by 10% T, 20% T, and so forth. If there is a problem with the linearity, the instrument manufacturer should be contacted. These checks may be made at any time, but should be performed at least once a year.

(d) Wavelength Accuracy Checks: If an instrument is not indicating the correct wavelength during an analysis, a measurement error will be generated. Solutions of known composition and purity are used to check wavelength accuracy. Examples of materials used for wavelength accuracy checks include: potassium dichromate at pH 2.9 (maximum absorbances at 257 and 350 nm, minima at 235 and 313 nm); holmium oxide glass filter (used for calibrations at 279.3, 333.8, 385.8, 536.4, or 637.5 nm); didymium oxide glass filter (used from 250 to 2000 nm); and samarium percholorate solution (used from 225 to 520 nm).

(e) Instrument Care: The proper procedure for handling a UV-Vis spectrometer is prescribed by the manufacturer. The purchasing institution is responsible for assigning a staff member to clean and maintain the instrument. A log book is advised for any instrument to track lamp life and repair frequency.

Why and How to Clean Cuvettes: Keeping cuvettes clean and organized contributes greatly to accurate and efficient analysis. Dirty and mismatched cuvettes are a common source of error. For a light cleaning, use a detergent wash, followed by multiple pure-water rinses. For heavier cleaning, repeat the previous step followed by cleaning with chromic-sulfuric acid solution wash and multiple pure-water rinses.

When the cuvette is emptied, it is good technique to touch the inverted cuvette to a clean paper towel before righting it for the next sample. The drop or two of moisture that may run down the face of a cuvette will cause concentration or light scattering problems.

1.3.4 *Sample Preparation and Handling*

(a) Solvents and Operating Conditions: Choosing the proper solvent is important for several reasons: 1) because the solvent must interact with the analyte to dissolve it, it has an effect on the spectrum, and 2) the solvent itself might have an absorbance at the wavelength used for analysis. Good solvents have their spectral properties delineated on the label: "Spectro-Grade" or "UV-Grade", and so forth. HPLC solvents may not be sufficient for sensitive UV work. Select a solvent that dissolves the sample but does not react with it. Water is notorious for many chemical reactions. Acids and bases added (by the producer) to preserve a solvent might react with the analyte. Read the solvent specification sheet carefully. The accompanying Table 1.8 lists typical UV-Vis solvents and their appropriate cutoff wavelengths.

(b) Absorbance Bands and Chromophores: The grouping of atoms producing a characteristic absorption is called a *Chromophore*, (chromo = color and phore = carrier). A specific grouping of atoms produces a characteristic absorption band at a specific wavelength. The intensity and location of these absorption bands will change with structural changes in the group of atoms and with solvent changes. The location of bands associated with visible absorbance bands or chromophores is

Table 1.8 Typical UV-Vis solvents and approximate cutoff wavelengths.

Solvent	UV cutoff (nm)
Acetonitrile	190
Water	190
Cyclohexane	195
Isooctane	195
n−Hexane	201
Ethanol (95 vol. %)	205
Methanol	205
Trimethyl phosphate	210
Acetone	220
Chloroform	240
Xylene	280

Table 1.9 Absorptions of visible chromophores (360–780 nm).

Chromophore	Absorption band location (nm)
O-H Alkyl alcohol (6ν, no hydrogen bonding)	510
Aromatic C-H Stretch (5ν)	711
O-H Alkyl alcohol (4ν, no hydrogen bonding)	738
Methyl C-H Stretch (5ν)	744
O-H Phenols (4ν, no hydrogen bonding)	752
Methylene C-H Stretch (5ν)	759
O-H Primary Alcohols (4ν)	764
O-H Water (4ν)	767
O-H Secondary Alcohols (4ν)	770
O-H Tertiary Alcohols (4ν)	773
Alkenes, conjugated RC=C-C=C-R′	450

*Note: Peak positions are approximate.

shown in Table 1.9. Note that there is detailed information relating to band locations in Chapter 7 of this text.

(c) Troubleshooting: Because instruments are so complex, usually only limited maintenance can be performed directly by the operator. When a problem does arise, though, its cause must be isolated to determine if the source is in the instrument or the sample itself. Both should not be changed simultaneously or the cause of the problem may remain hidden.

Sample/Solvent Problem: If you suspect a problem with your sample or the solvent you are using, first try running the sample on a second instrument if available. It is always quicker to change instruments than to remake the standards and samples. If the problem persists on a different instrument, then the chemistry must be checked. Remake one or two standards or samples in a different lot of solvent, using freshly cleaned glassware. If problems such as spectral changes or nonlinearity continue, consider a different type of solvent. Because most spectrometers are quite stable, the fault is often in sample handling or unwanted chemical reactions.

Instrument Problems: If it has been determined that the samples are correctly made, then the instrument should be checked. Other than any special steps recommended by the manufacturer, the linearity and wavelength checks mentioned earlier would be good to run. If the problem is not easily solved, the best thing to do is call the instrument company for help rather than try to service the instrument yourself.

Avoiding Problems: Good laboratory techniques and reproducible sample work-up are good habits to develop. Each step of an analysis must be clearly stated and adhered to. Beyond that, routine maintenance is probably the best for avoiding problems. Keeping a log book for each instrument allows the analyst to determine whether a source lamp needs to be replaced or whether the detector may be getting old. Cleaning is also quite important. Fumes and spills in and around the instrument will eventually destroy or cloud mirrors, gratings, and lenses.

References

1. R. C. Denney and R. Sinclair, *Visible and Ultraviolet Spectroscopy* (John Wiley & Sons, New York, 1987).
2. H.-H. Perkampus, *UV-Vis Spectroscopy and Its Applications* (Springer-Verlag, New York, 1992).
3. J. W. Robinson, *Undergraduate Instrumental Analysis*, 4th ed. (Marcel Dekker, New York, 1989).
4. R. A. Sawyer, *Experimental Spectroscopy* (Dover Publications, New York, 1963).
5. J. R. Edisbury, *Practical Hints on Absorption Spectrometry: Ultraviolet and Visible* (Plenum Press, New York, 1967).
6. G. A. Vanasse, Ed., *Spectrometric Techniques — Vol. II* (Academic Press, Boston, 1981).
7. A. Knowles and C. Burgess, Eds., *Practical absorption Spectrometry Techniques in Visible and Ultraviolet Spectrometry, Vol. 3* (Chapman and Hall. London, 1984).
8. C. Burgess and D. G. Jones Eds., *Spectrophotometry, Luminescence, and Colour: Science and Compliance* (Elsevier Science B.V., Amsterdam, 1995).
9. R. M. Silverstein, G. Clayton Bassler, and Terence C. Morrill, *Spectrometric Identification of Organic Compounds*, 5th ed. (John Wiley & Sons, New York, 1991).

ASTM Practices for UV-Vis Spectroscopy:

10. ASTM Practice E169-04 (2009), Standard Practices for General Techniques of Ultraviolet-Visible Quantitative Analysis, Annual *Book* of *ASTM Standards*, Volume 03.06, 2009. ASTM International, 100 Barr Harbor Drive, PO Box C700, West Conshohocken, PA, 19428-2959 USA.
11. ASTM Practice E275-08 (2013), Standard Practice for Describing and Measuring Performance of Ultraviolet and Visible Spectrophotometers Annual *Book* of *ASTM Standards*, Volume 03.06, 2013. ASTM International, 100 Barr Harbor Drive, PO Box C700, West Conshohocken, PA, 19428-2959 USA.
12. ASTM Practice 958-13 (2013), Standard Practice for Estimation of the Spectral Bandwidth of Ultraviolet-Visible Spectrophotometers, Annual *Book* of *ASTM Standards*, Volume 03.06, 2013. ASTM International, 100 Barr Harbor Drive, PO Box C700, West Conshohocken, PA, 19428-2959 USA.
13. A. Bartecki and J. Burgess, *The Colour of Metal Compounds* (Gordon and Breach Science Publishers, Amsterdam, 2000).
14. European Pharmacopoeia, Qualification of Equipment Annex 3: Qualification of UV-Visible spectrophotometers PA/PH/OMCL (07) 11 DEF CORR, 2007.

Chapter 2

Theory of Visible Spectroscopy, Light Interaction with Matter

Contents

2.1 Theory of Spectroscopy: Light Interaction with Materials

Light energy interaction, using spectrophotometry [Greek: ($specere$ = to look at)+ ($photos$ = light) + ($metron$ = to measure), or the science of measuring light in matter is the subject of this chapter. The reader is referred to the index for detailed discussions of each of the subjects introduced within this chapter. Volume 3, Chapter 2 and the other volumes contain additional material.

2.1.1 *The Physics of Light Interaction with Solid Materials*

Matter interacts with energy in the forms of scattering, absorption, transmission (transmittance), reflectance (both regular and diffuse reflection), and diffraction. The purpose of spectroscopy is to measure these interactions by the use of a variety of special photon producing and photon detection instruments. The physics of these interaction phenomena are complex and briefly addressed in this chapter.

Solids, as black body radiators, emit light and this emitted light can be characterized by its radiated power, spectral profile, and photon flux. This chapter describes the basic mathematical concepts and relationships related to the reflectance/reflection interaction as molecular spectroscopy of solids.[1–8]

2.1.1.1 *Thermal Emission Sources as Black Body Radiators*

Planck's law describes the electromagnetic radiation emitted by a black body in thermal equilibrium at a definite temperature; the black body is an opaque and non-reflective body. When held at constant, uniform temperature, the radiation emitted from the black body radiator has a specific spectrum and intensity that depends only on the temperature of the emitting source body. The emission sources of visible spectrometers based on electric current through an illuminated filament behave as black body radiators. The spectrum of such a filament is continuous with a rapid rise in the lower wavelengths (i.e., higher frequencies), and a taper toward the higher wavelengths (lower frequencies). The intensity of the curve and the amplitude increases with temperature. In fact the maximum emission wavelength position of the filament depends upon the temperature. The relationship of this wavelength position is defined by Wien's law of displacement.

The use of Planck's radiation law describes the emissivity of a black body as follows. Several examples from multiple references are given. The classic equation for this law is often shown as:

$$B_\nu(T) = \frac{2h\nu^3}{c^2} \cdot \frac{1}{e^{h\nu/k_B T} - 1} \tag{2.1}$$

where $B_\nu(T)$ is the spectral radiant intensity per unit frequency ν and temperature T (°Kelvin),

ν = frequency (nu) in Hz (sec^{-1})
h = Planck's constant = 6.624×10^{-34} joule-second (or m^2 kg/s),
c = velocity of light = 2.9978×10^8 meters/second (m/s),
k_B = Boltzmann's constant = 1.38065×10^{-23} joule/°K, and
e = base of natural logarithms = 2.71828.

A simplified form using wavelength rather than frequency for computation is as follows: (Perkins p 493).[9]

$$I = \frac{hc^3}{\lambda^5 \cdot (e^{hc/k_B \lambda T} - 1)} \tag{2.2}$$

where I is the spectral radiant intensity per unit wavelength interval λ and temperature T (°Kelvin), λ is the wavelength of light in Angstroms or 10^{-10} m, or nanometers as 10^{-9} m. All other symbols are as the above equation.

Another common form is given by Harrison[10] as:

$$J_\lambda d\lambda = \frac{Ac_1 \lambda^{-5}}{e^{C_2/\lambda T} - 1} d\lambda \tag{2.3}$$

In this form $J_\lambda d\lambda$ is the spectral radiant intensity per unit wavelength interval λ and temperature T (°Kelvin) with respect to a change in λ,

C_1 is a radiation constant as 1.177×10^{-12} watts cm^2,
C_2 is a radiation constant equal to 1.4320 cm deg,
All other symbols are as the set of similar equations.

And simplified to Wien approximation formula of the Harrison form[9] is as:

$$J_\lambda d\lambda = Ac_1 \lambda^{-5} e^{-C_2/\lambda T} d\lambda \tag{2.4}$$

where all symbols remain as other equations in this set.

A form used by Larrabee[11] is as:

$$I_{\lambda_1} T d\lambda = \frac{8\pi ch}{\lambda^5} \frac{1}{e^{hc/KT\lambda} - 1} \tag{2.5}$$

where:

I, T = radiant intensity per unit wavelength interval at wavelength λ and temperature T (° Kelvin),
λ is the wavelength of light in Angstroms or 10^{-10} m, or nanometers as 10^{-9} m,
h = Planck's constant = 6.624×10^{-34} joule-second (or m^2 kg/s),
c = velocity of light = 2.9978×10^8 meters/second (m/s),
k = Boltzmann's constant = 1.38065×10^{-23} joule/°K, and
e = base of natural logarithms = 2.71828.

The result of the application of the above equations results in Figure 2.1, which is a plot of spectral radiant intensity per unit wavelength interval λ and temperature T (°Kelvin) with respect to a change in λ in units of watts sr^{-1} cm^{-1} λ(nm).

A useful formula for determining the wavelength position of maximum intensity is the Wien's displacement law given as:

$$\lambda_m T = W \tag{2.6}$$

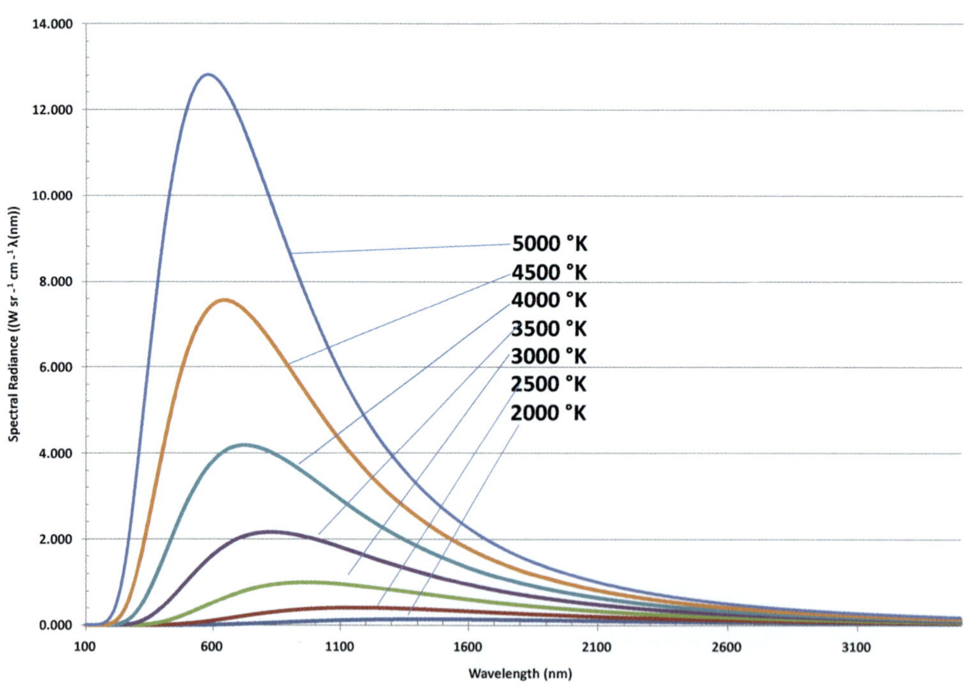

Fig. 2.1 Illustration of Planck's radiation law showing the spectral radiance as a function of temperature.

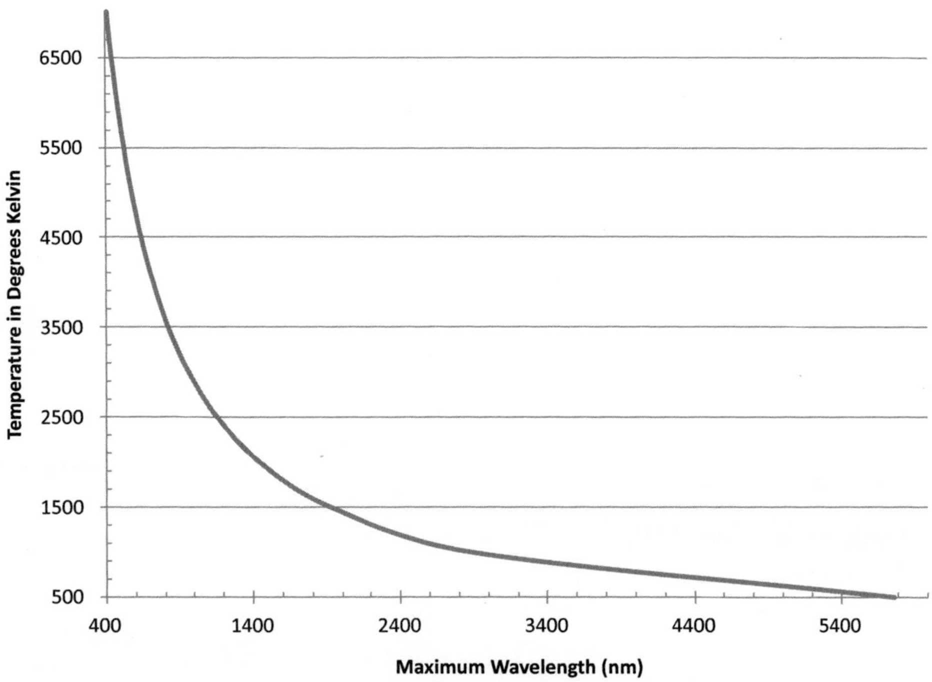

Fig. 2.2 Figure illustrating Wien's displacement law where the abscissa is the wavelength of maximum emissions and the temperature in degrees Kelvin is given on the ordinate axis.

and

$$\lambda_{\mathrm{m}} = \frac{\mathrm{W}}{\mathrm{T}} \tag{2.7}$$

where λ_{m} is the wavelength of maximum intensity,

W is a constant (2.884×10^8),
and T is the temperature in °Kelvin.

This Wien's displacement law relationship is illustrated in Figure 2.2. The higher the temperature the lower the maximum emission wavelength (i.e., the higher the frequency of the maximum emitted energy). Thus, longer wavelength maximum energy is indicative of lower temperature.

The power (p) radiated or emitted by a black body radiator in watts/cm^2 is given by the relationship:

$$p = kT^4 \tag{2.8}$$

where k is the *Stefan-Boltzmann* law proportionality constant equal to 5.67×10^{-12} watts/(cm^2 $\times$ °K^4), and T = °K = (°C + 273)[10].

The spectral profile of this emitted radiation is given by Max Planck's hypothesis as shown in the following equations:

$$E_p = h\nu \tag{2.9}$$

where E_p = the photon energy (in joules) at a given frequency (ν, in units of sec^{-1}), and where h = Planck's constant = 6.6256×10^{-3} joule-sec (equivalent to 6.6256×10^{-27} erg-sec). And since $\nu = \frac{c}{\lambda}$ it follows:

$$E_p = \frac{hc}{\lambda} \tag{2.10}$$

Thus using this equation the energy of each photon at a particular wavelength is determined.

Furthermore, since 1 Watt = $\frac{\text{joule}}{\text{sec}}$, the number of photons (N_p) per second in an emission problem is calculated as:

$$N_p = \frac{1}{E_p} \tag{2.11}$$

where N_p = the number of photons per second (as the photon flux). Thus, emission light sources are generated by heating metal filaments or metal surfaces to obtain the appropriate emission spectral characteristics in power, spectral profile, and photon flux.[5,7,12] These equations may be used to compose the requirements for an emission source based on the temperature of the source and the photon flux. The above equations may be used to calculate the spectral energy output relative to frequency or wavelength for a black body radiator. More detail is discussed for various types of emission sources, and the reader is referred to the index.

2.1.1.2 *Characteristics of Emission Sources*

The radiant power output from a filament containing lamp (such as tungsten) decreases over time due to evaporation of the metal onto the inside surface of the quartz or glass lamp. The lifetime (L) is decreased in proportion to the operating voltage (V) using the relationship:[10]

$$\frac{L_1}{L_2} = \left(\frac{V_1}{V_2}\right)^{-13} \tag{2.12}$$

where L_1 and L_2 represent the lamp life at differing voltages V_1 and V_2, respectively.

Table 2.1 Tungsten Lamp Steradiance at 2800° K and 10 nm Bandwidth.

Wavelength in nm	Watts/cm^2/steradian (10 nm bandwidth)
300	8.80×10^{-4}
400	1.46×10^{-2}
500	5.98×10^{-2}
600	1.29×10^{-1}
700	1.95×10^{-1}
800	2.44×10^{-1}
900	2.66×10^{-1}
1000	2.70×10^{-1}

Recall, the relationships defined in Ohm's Law as:

$$V = IR \quad \text{or} \quad W = A\Omega \tag{2.13}$$

Electrical Power Relationship:

$$P = IV \quad \text{or} \quad W = AV \tag{2.14}$$

Noting that V = Voltage (volts or V), I = Current (amps or amperes or A), R = Resistance (ohm's or Ω), and P = Power (watts or W).

From these equations the relationships between lamp life relative to voltage, current, resistance, and power may be calculated. Note that for tungsten the sterara-diancy has been calculated for its typical 2800 °K burn temperature (Table 2.1).

2.1.1.3 *Rayleigh Scattering*

Rayleigh light scattering is elastic (i.e., non-reactive) scattered light, and occurs when the intensity of the scattered energy (I_{RS}) is inversely proportional to the 4th power of the incident light wavelength in nanometers, microns, or meters (λ), as given by Equation (2.15).

$$I_{RS} \propto \frac{1}{\lambda^4} \tag{2.15}$$

2.1.1.4 *Absorption and Transmittance*

Light passing through an absorbing material is attenuated as a function of the absorption coefficient (normally designated as ϵ) or a of the material, and the thickness (t) of the material in cm following the relationship[13,14] as:

$$I = I_0 e^{-at} \tag{2.16}$$

2.1.1.5 *Reflectance in Media with Differing Refractive Indices*

The reflectance (R) of light at normal incidence passing through a refractive index (n_1) into a second material of refractive index (n_2) is given by the equation:

$$R = \frac{(n_2 - n_1)^2}{(n_2 + n_1)^2} \tag{2.17}$$

2.1.1.6 *Optical Density*

The Absorbance (A or Au), or optical density (O.D.) of a material is defined by the mathematical relationship:

$$A = \text{O.D.} = -\log_{10}\left(\frac{I}{I_0}\right) = \frac{1}{2.303}\ln\left(\frac{I_0}{I}\right) \tag{2.18}$$

where I_0 = the intensity of the incident light beam, and I = the intensity of the transmitted beam after sample interaction. The O.D. of the material in which the light is passing through is given by the above expression and is a term used synonymously with absorbance.

2.1.1.7 *Opacity*

Opacity is the fraction of energy that is not transmitted by a sample, and is expressed using the equation:

$$\text{O} = \frac{\text{I}_0}{\text{I}} \tag{2.19}$$

where O is Opacity, I_0 is the total initial intensity striking the sample, and I is the energy transmitted through the sample. The range for Opacity is from zero to infinity.

2.1.1.8 *Diffraction*

Diffraction can be loosely defined as the bending of light around objects.[15–17] The defining principle for diffraction is Huygens' principle, which informs us that every point of a wave front can be considered a secondary point from which waves propagate in multiple directions. A single narrow slit can demonstrate the alternating light and dark patterns shown by diffraction.

The secondary waves propagated during diffraction have an intensity ($\text{I}_\propto$) proportional to:

$$\text{I}_\propto = 1 + \cos\frac{\theta}{2} \tag{2.20}$$

where θ is the propagation angle of the secondary wave in relationship to the original (or primary) wave. This relationship defines the intensity for waves propagated in the direction of the original wave as 1, and 0 intensity for the wave propagated at 90° to the original wave. The central bright band in a diffraction pattern is approximately 20 (or more) times brighter than the next (or adjacent) bright band in a typical diffraction pattern resulting from a narrow slit. The reader is referred to the index for additional information and detailed treatment of the topic of diffraction and diffraction gratings.

2.1.2 *Spectrophotometry of Solids*

2.1.2.1 *Photometers*

Photometers are spectrophotometers (spectrometers) characterized as instruments which use interference filters to select the wavelength incident to the sample specimen. Photometers may be simple with anywhere from 1 to 3 wavelengths or more complex with multiple wavelengths and complex filter systems. Several such designs are illustrated in the section on instrumentation. The reader is referred to the index for Photometers. The optical design for a simple photometer is shown in Figure 2.3.

2.1.2.2 *Dispersive Spectrometers*

Dispersive spectrometers (or spectrophotometers) rely on the use of a monochromator (or monochromators) to disperse specific frequencies of light from a

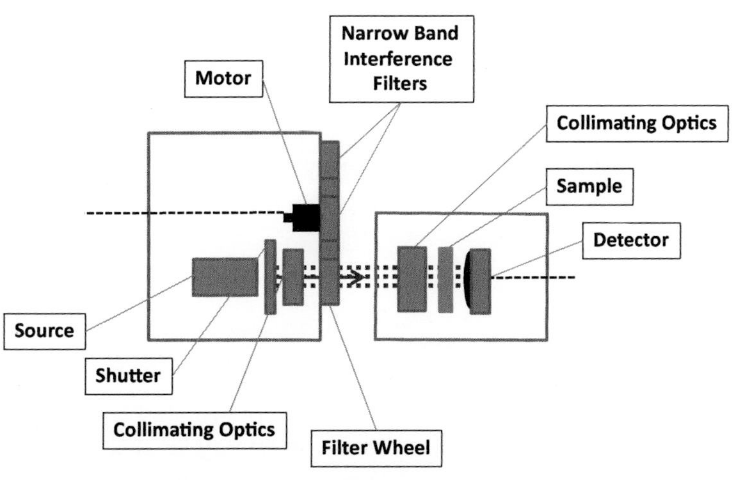

Fig. 2.3 Illustration of a simple filter photometer optical design.

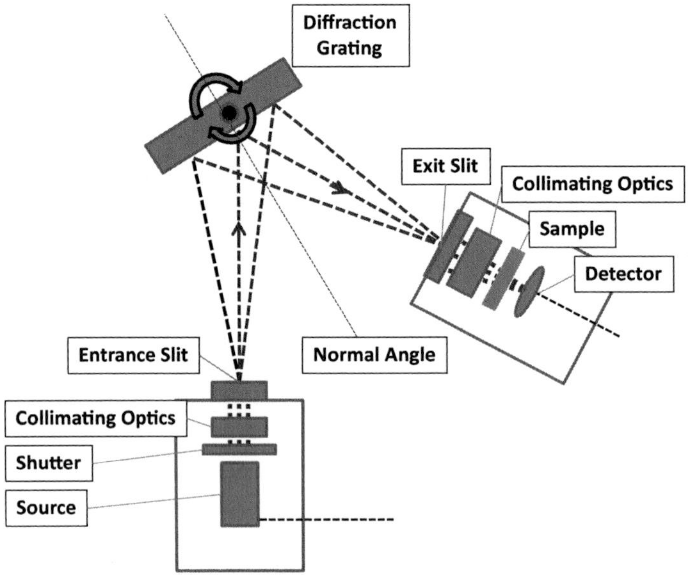

Fig. 2.4 Simple single monochromator optical design.

broadly emitting light source incident to the sample specimen. There is much more information on this type of instrument found in the index under dispersive instruments or monochromators. A simple, single monochromator optical design is shown in Figure 2.4.

2.1.2.3 *Luminometers*

A luminometer is used to measure the luminescence (light emission through luminescence) from a sample by directing light of a specific frequency onto the sample specimen and then collecting the luminescence for a specific frequency onto a detector. A simple luminometer optical configuration is shown in Figure 2.5. The luminous sample acts as the source for the instrument and the light emitted from the sample is dispersed into its various wavelengths and recorded by the detector, typically a photomultiplier tube.

2.1.2.4 *Luminescence*

The luminescence phenomenon is the emission of radiation resulting from an electron in an excited energy state falling to a lower energy state. The frequency of the emitted radiation depends upon the difference in energy levels between the excited states and lower energy state. For luminescence to occur, one or more electrons from an atom or molecule in the ground state is excited to a higher energy state.

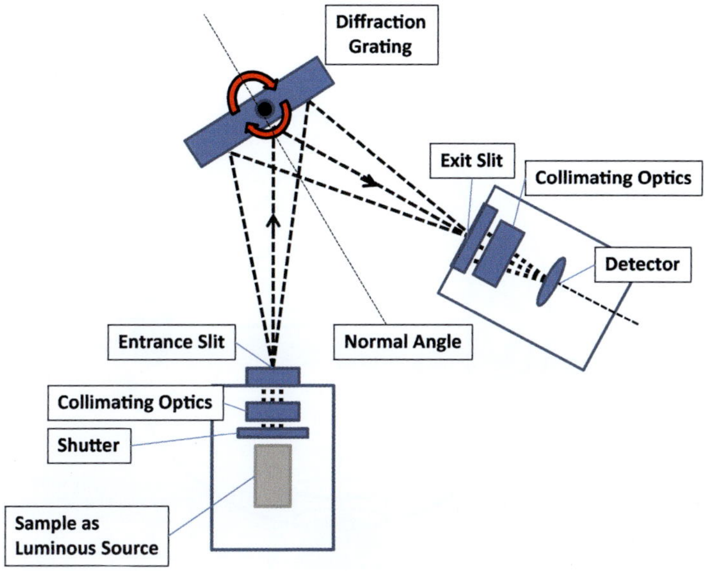

Fig. 2.5 Simple monochromator-based luminometer optical design.

The electron in the unstable excited state will return to the ground state and in the process emit energy as a photon. Luminescence is measured quantitatively on a perpendicular axis to the direction of the energy source. The intensity (I_Λ) of a luminescent material is measured using the relationship:

$$I_\Lambda = \beta \cdot I_0 c \qquad (2.21)$$

where β = a proportionality constant, I_0 = the intensity of the light source radiation, and c = the concentration of the luminescent atoms or molecules in a sample specimen. Luminescence spectra may be measured as the total emission minus the dark background.

2.1.2.5 *The Integrating Sphere*

The purpose of an integrating sphere detector system is to provide a collection device for reflected, divergent, and scattered light from a sample. Whenever it is desirable to capture the total reflected light from a sample, the integrating sphere must be used.

The integrating sphere consists of a hollow sphere or hemisphere coated with a highly Lambertian (diffusely reflecting) surface. An important characteristic of an ideal sphere is that the intensity of the reflected energy at any part of the sphere surface is proportional to the total energy entering the sphere. This relationship is

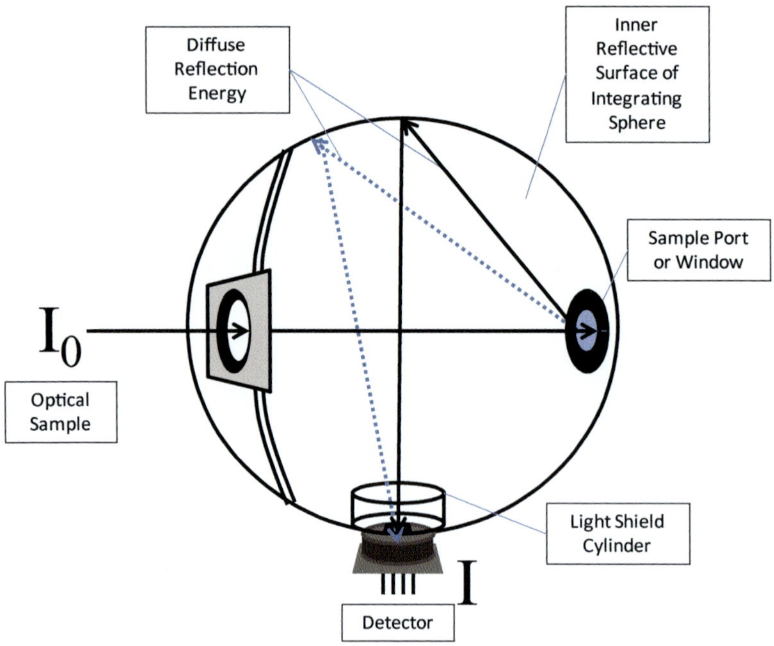

Fig. 2.6 Basic Integrating Sphere design where $A = -\log_{10}(I/I_0)$.

ideally independent of the specific point of entry to the sphere and is independent of the incident angle of the energy into the sphere. The main considerations in the use of an integrating sphere include sphere throughput, sphere efficiency, average reflectance at the sphere wall, and sphere error.

There are specific sections on the integrating sphere in this set of volumes and the reader is referred to the index for additional details. A basic design of an integrating sphere for optical measurements is shown in Figure 2.6.

2.1.3 *Total Transmittance/Absorption and Reflectance/ Absorption Spectroscopy*

The total transmittance (or transmission) of light through solids or liquids is given by the following Beer-Lambert law relationship. Note: for reflectance spectroscopy, the *R* term can be substituted for the *T* term in the following relationships:

$$I_t = I_0 e^{-ecl} \quad \text{or} \quad \ln \frac{I_0}{I_t} = ecl \quad \text{or} \quad I_t = I_0 \times 10^{-ecl} \tag{2.22}$$

where I_t = the intensity of the transmitted or reflected light at a specific wavelength, I_0 = the incident beam intensity at that wavelength, e (as exponent) is the molar extinction coefficient (absorptivity) at the wavelength of I_t and I_0, c = the concentration of the absorbing molecules, and l = the thickness of the material. Note: for the above nomenclature, ecl = the total Absorption, and e (base number) is the natural logarithm. This law is most often seen in other equation forms as:

$$\frac{1}{\mathrm{T}} = 10^{\mathrm{A}} \tag{2.23}$$

and by taking log 10 of each side of the equation we have:

$$\log \frac{1}{\mathrm{T}} = \mathrm{A} \tag{2.24}$$

Absorbance is related to the concentration of the absorbing molecules as A = ecl. And it follows that:

$$A = -\log_{10}\left(\frac{I}{I_0}\right) = \log_{10}\left(\frac{I_0}{I}\right) \tag{2.25}$$

$$-A = \log_{10}\left(\frac{I}{I_0}\right) \tag{2.26}$$

$$\frac{I}{I_0} = 10^{-A} \Rightarrow \frac{I_0}{I} = \frac{1}{10^{-A}} \tag{2.27}$$

$$\frac{I}{I_0} = T \tag{2.28}$$

$$\%\mathrm{T} = \mathrm{T} \times 100 \tag{2.29}$$

For reflectance/reflection measurements, the R term may be substituted into each occurrence of the T term.

Transmission spectroscopy is most useful with clear materials, such as thin films, crystalline plates, and clear liquids. It is not particularly useful for opaque or turbid materials, or highly scattering materials. For these materials reflectance/reflection measurements are used.[18–21]

The measurement should not be used when intermolecular interactions vary with concentration of absorbing molecules or solvent, or refractive index changes drastically with concentration. Turbidity will drastically reduce the value of transmission measurements as will significant color changes in the material. This measurement geometry is referred to as direct transmission (Figure 2.7).

2.1.3.1 *Diffuse Transmittance*

DT is defined as the total transmitted light passing through (and interacting with) a non-infinite thickness of a diffusely reflecting, or slightly scattering, medium; this medium being comprised of multiple diffusely reflective surfaces (Figure 2.8).

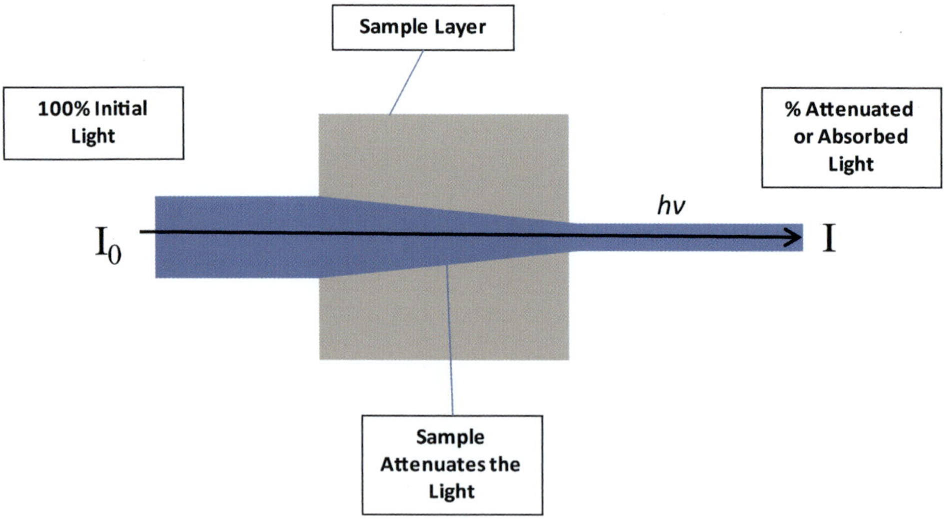

Fig. 2.7 Direct Transmittance Measurement Geometry for Solid Samples.

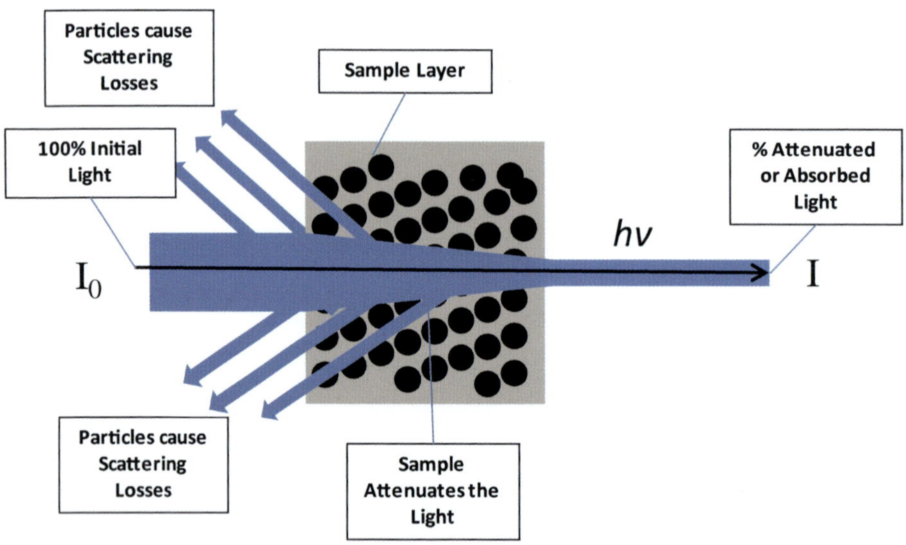

Fig. 2.8 Diffuse Transmittance Measurement Geometry for Scattering Samples.

2.1.3.2 *Illuminance and Contrast*

Contrast is defined as the ratio of the difference between the maximum illuminance (e.g. in units of lux) and the minimum illuminance of a surface exhibiting two or more distinct levels of brightness (as the numerator), and the sum of the maximum and minimum illuminance. Contrast is often specified for interference-diffraction patterns given the alternating light and dark rings created by interference at a narrow slit. Contrast then is given as:

$$\text{Contrast} = \frac{I_{Max} - I_{Min}}{I_{Max} + I_{Min}} \tag{2.30}$$

2.1.3.3 *Luminance*

Luminance is defined as the *luminous flux per unit area per solid angle*. If light is radiated equally from a light source in all directions, it is radiated at a solid angle (Ω_S) equal to 4π steradians (sr). Thus the total luminance (L) of such a source, in units of Watts $\times$ mm^{-2} $\times$ sr^{-1} is given by:

$$L = \frac{P}{A\Omega_S} \tag{2.31}$$

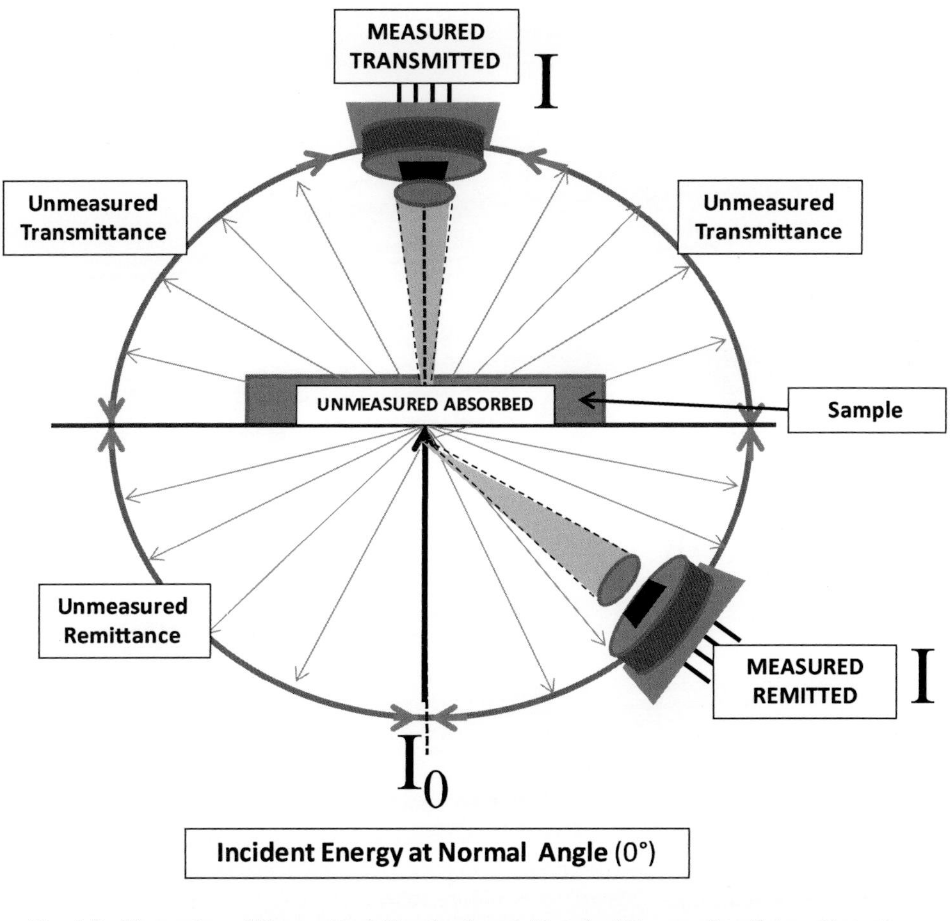

Fig. 2.9 Illustration of Transmitted, Remitted, and Absorbed Energy: Small Area Detection.

where P = the radiated power from the source (generally in units of Watts), A = the area of the radiant filament (e.g., in mm^2), and Ω_S = the solid angle of radiance. For a filament source radiating in all directions this value is 4π sr.

2.1.3.4 *Transmitted, Remitted, and Absorbed Energy: Small Area Detection*[22]

Figure 2.9 demonstrates the concept of measuring the transmitted, remitted and absorbed energy from a sample. One intuitively understands that the absorbed energy (A) is not measured directly, but is rather the difference between the incident light (1.0) and the sum of the transmitted (T) and remitted (R) light as given in Equation (2.32). Likewise this simple relationship may be used to solve for T, and R terms.

$$A = 1 - T - R \tag{2.32}$$

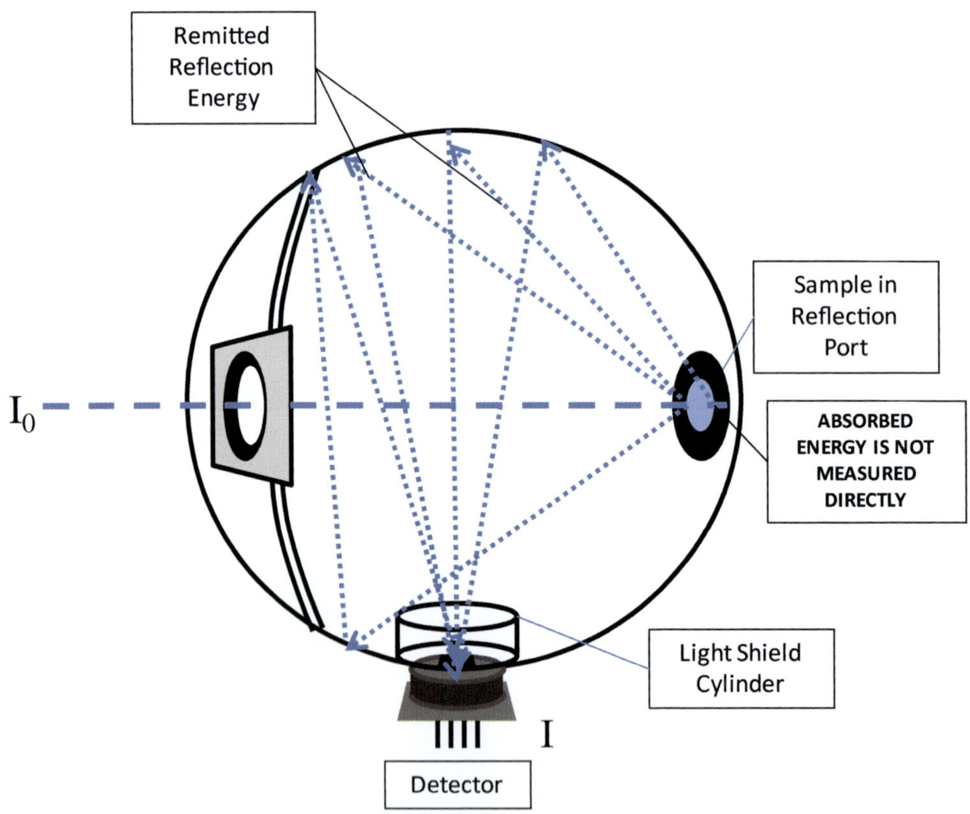

Fig. 2.10 Illustration of Remitted (Reflection) Energy Measured using Hemispherical Geometry Detection. This is sometimes referred to as diffuse reflectance/reflection measurement using an integrating sphere.

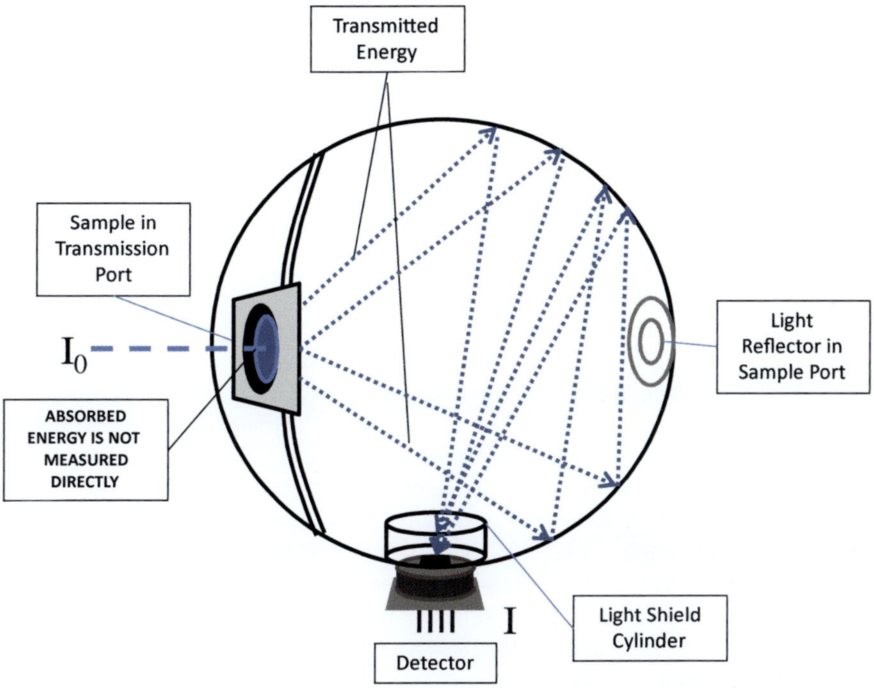

Fig. 2.11 Illustration of Transmittance (Transmission) Energy Measured using Hemispherical Geometry Detection. This is sometimes referred to as diffuse transmittance/transmission measurement using an integrating sphere.

There is a difference in the total measured energy transmitted, remitted, or absorbed based upon whether the sample has been measured using a small area detector or an integrating sphere approach. The small area detection geometry measures only a fraction of the total transmitted and remitted energy but is proportional to the total energy transmitted or remitted. The geometry for measuring the transmitted and remitted energy to infer the absorbed energy is illustrated in Figure 2.9.

2.1.3.5 *Transmitted, Remitted, and Absorbed Energy: Hemispherical Detection*

Figure 2.10 demonstrates the concept of measuring the transmitted, remitted and absorbed energy from a sample using an integrating sphere, also known as hemispherical geometry. Like small area detection, one intuitively understands that the absorbed energy (A) is inferred as the difference between the incident light (1.0) and the sum of the transmitted (T) and remitted (R) light as given in Equation (2.32).

The hemispherical measurement approach more comprehensively measures the total transmitted, remitted, or absorbed energy The geometry for measuring the transmitted and remitted energy to infer the absorbed energy using the hemispherical approaches for remission (reflection) and transmittance (transmission), are illustrated in Figures 2.10 and 2.11, respectively. See Volume 3, Chapter 2 and the index for further discussions.

References

1. J. J. Workman and A. W. Springsteen (Eds.), *Applied Spectroscopy: A Compact Reference for Practitioners* (Academic Press, Boston, 1998).
2. J. W. Blaker, *Optics II — Physical and Quantum Optics* (Barnes and Noble, New York, 1970).
3. R. W. Ditchburn, *Light*, 2nd ed. (Blackie, London, 1965).
4. M. Fogiel (Ed.), *The Optics Problem Solver* (Research & Education Association, 1981).
5. J. W. Goodman, *Statistical Optics* (Wiley, New York, 1985).
6. F. A. Jenkins and H. E. White, *Fundamentals of Optics* (McGraw-Hill, New York, 1957).
7. C. S. Johnson Jr. and L. G. Pedersen, *Problems and Solutions in Quantum Chemistry and Physics* (Dover, New York, 1986).
8. E. Mach, *The Principals of Physical Optics* (Dover, New York, 1926).
9. H. A. Perkins, *College Physics*, p. 493 (Prentice-Hall, New York, 1946).
10. G. R. Harrison, R. C. Lord, and J. R. Loofbourow, *Practical Spectroscopy*, p. 171 (Prentice-Hall, Inc. New York, 1948).
11. R. D. Larrabee, *The Spectral Emissivity and Optical Properties of Tungsten*, Doctor of Science Thesis submitted to the Department of Physics, M.I.T., May 13, 1957, Technical Report 328 May 21, 1957
12. W. R. Ware, Transient Luminescence Measurements, In Vol. 1 — *Creation and Detection of the Excited State*, A. A. Lamola (Ed.), (Marcel Dekker, New York 1971).
13. R. D. Braun, *Introduction to Instrumental Analysis* (McGraw-Hill, New York, 1987).
14. G. L. Clark (Ed.), *The Encyclopedia of Spectroscopy* (Reinhold, New York, 1960).
15. C. J. Ball, *An Introduction to the Theory of Diffraction* (Permagon, Oxford, 1971).
16. J. B. Cohen, *Diffraction Methods in Material Science* (Macmillan, New York, 1966).
17. J. Guild, *Diffraction Gratings as Measurement Scales* (Oxford University Press, London, 1960).
18. G. Kortum, *Reflectance Spectroscopy* (Springer-Verlag, New York, 1969).
19. W. W. Wendlandt and H. G. Hecht, *Reflectance Spectroscopy* (Wiley, New York, 1966).
20. G. A. Somorjai (Ed.), *The Structure and Chemistry of Solid Surfaces* (Wiley, New York, 1969).
21. D. P. Woodruff and T. A. Delchar, *Modern Techniques of Surface Science* (Cambridge University Press, Cambridge, 1986).
22. D. J. Dahm and K. D. Dahm, Representative layer theory for diffuse reflectance, *Appl. Spectrosc.* **53** (1999) 647–654.

Chapter 3

Visible Spectroscopic Instrumentation

Contents

3.1 Instrumentation for Measuring Spectra

Spectrophotometers are designed to measure the ratio, or a function of the ratio, of the radiant power of two beams as a function of spectral position (i.e., wavelength). The two beams may be separated in time, space, or both.[1] The measurement for any spectrophotometer is given by the ratio of the measurement of the sample at each wavelength divided by the measurement of a reference material at the same wavelength. If the measurements are taken with a transmittance geometry, then this ratio is equal to T the transmittance with a value of from 0 to 1.0. If the measurements are taken with a reflectance geometry, then this ratio is equal to R the reflectance with a value of from 0 to 1.0. For transmittance the (I_0) reference measurements are made with either no sample (i.e., a blank or empty cuvette) or ambient air (i.e., completely empty sample compartment). For reflectance reference measurements a highly reflective sample is used as the reference (I_0). This reflective reference is generally a ceramic, Fluorilon, or Spectralon^{TM} tile each having a surface that is 95 to 99 percent reflective for the full wavelength region measured.

A common assumption in spectrophotometric measurements is that Beer's law relationship holds (repeated as core information in different forms and contexts throughout this set of volumes). For most analytical situations Beer's law relationship does hold well enough for useful quantitative measurements.

The Beer's law relationship is described as the absorbance (A, Au, or signal strength) of an analyte being measured using a spectrophotometer is equivalent to the product of the absorptivity (ε) of a specific type of molecular vibration; the concentration (c) of the molecules in the measurement beam; and the pathlength (l) of the sample holder within the measurement beam. This relationship between measured spectral signal and concentration of a molecule is most often expressed as:

$$\mathrm{A} = \varepsilon \mathrm{cl} \tag{3.1}$$

where ε is the molar absorptivity (referred to as molar extinction coefficient by earlier physicists) in units of $\mathrm{Liter} \cdot \mathrm{Mole}^{-1} \cdot \mathrm{cm}^{-1}$; c is the concentration of molecules in the spectrometer beam in units of $\mathrm{Mole} \cdot \mathrm{Liter}^{-1}$ (as moles per volume, or weight percent per volume); and pathlength is the thickness in units of cm of the measured sample at a specific concentration. Thus the absorptivity for any specific molecule type is calculated by careful measurements of the absorbance of a compound, generally diluted in a suitable organic solvent, and by applying the relationship:

$$\varepsilon = \frac{A}{cl} \tag{3.2}$$

For transmittance (where T = 0.0 to 1.0) and percent transmittance (where % T = 0 to 100.0) spectroscopy, a more complete delineation of the relationships between the various terms is contained in an expression such as:

$$T = \frac{I}{I_0} = 10^{-\varepsilon cl} \Rightarrow Abs. = A$$
$$= -\log_{10}\left(\frac{I}{I_0}\right) = -\log_{10} T = \varepsilon cl \quad (3.3)$$

Here the symbols I and I_0 represent the attenuated energy detected after sample interaction and the initial energy incident to the sample, respectively.

For reflectance (where R = 0.0 to 1.0) and percent reflectance (where % R = 0.0 to 100.0) spectroscopy the various relationships are expressed as:

$$R = \frac{I}{I_0} = 10^{-\varepsilon cl} \Rightarrow Abs. = A = -\log_{10}\left(\frac{I}{I_0}\right)$$
$$= -\log_{10} R = \varepsilon cl \quad (3.4)$$

Modern spectrophotometers utilize these assumptions for making spectroscopic measurement and generally display spectroscopic data as transmission (T), reflection (R), and absorbance A (y-axis or ordinate axis) versus wavelength (nm, microns) or wavenumber (cm^{-1}) (as x-axis, or abscissa axis).

With a basic knowledge of Beer's law one is able to calculate the absorptivity and the other parameters of Absorbance, pathlength, and concentration. The relationship between Absorbance and Transmittance or Reflectance is given in Table 3.1.

The goal in the design of a laboratory spectrophotometer is to maximize the energy (or radiant power) from a light source through the optical components and onto the sample and then the detector. The optical throughput for a spectrometer is dependent upon multiple factors, such as the light source area, the apertures

Table 3.1 Showing thc relationships between $\%T$ and $\%R$, T and R, and A.

%Transmittance or %Reflectance	Transmittance or Reflectance	Absorbance
100.0	1.0	0.0
10.0	0.1	1.0
1.0	0.01	2.0
0.1	0.001	3.0
0.01	0.0001	4.0
0.001	0.00001	5.0
0.0001	0.000001	6.0

present within the light path, lens transmittance and mirror reflectance losses, the exit aperture, and the detector efficiency.[2,3]

Several terms are useful in any discussion of spectrometry, these include: *selectivity* or the specific sensor response to the *component of interest; sensitivity* or the *quantifiable level of response* from a sensor with respect to the concentration of a specified component of interest; and *detection limit* or the smallest concentration difference that can be detected above the background noise level of the instrument. A quick estimate of the detection limit is approximately three times the background noise signal. The concentration is estimated for the detection limit using a calibration curve.

3.1.1 *Types of Visible Spectrophotometers*

3.1.1.1 *Discrete Photometers*

Discrete photometers consist of an irradiance source, discrete interference filters, a sample compartment, and detector; along with appropriate electronics for signal amplification and stabilization of detector signals. The optical configuration for a generic discrete filter photometer is shown in Figure 3.1.

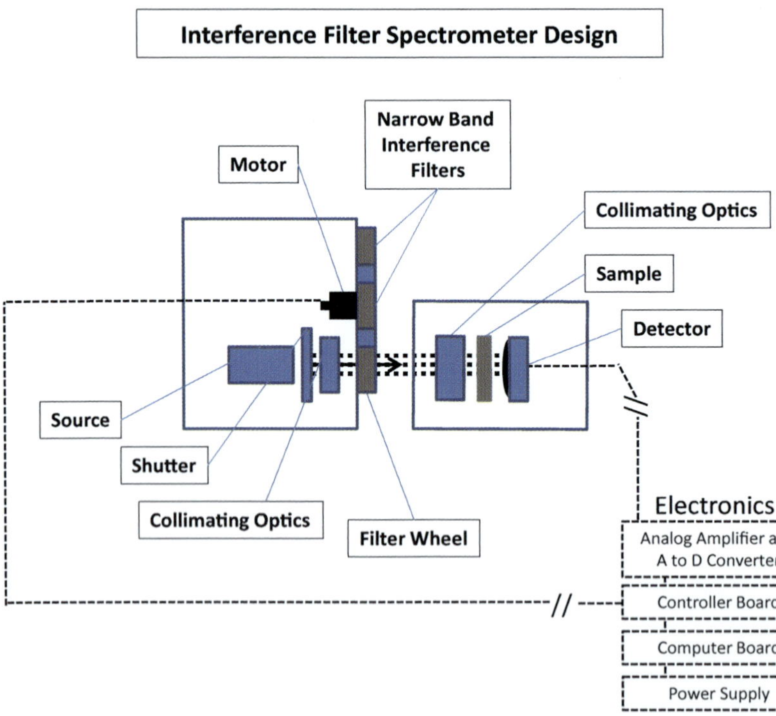

Fig. 3.1 Interference filter photometer optical configuration.

3.1.1.2 *Single-Beam*

Single-beam spectrophotometers have a single optical channel which is configured to measure either sample, or reference channel, but not both simultaneously. The resultant spectrum is the ratio of the transmission (or reflectance) spectra from sample and reference measurements, respectively. The final transmission (in T units) or reflectance (in R units) spectrum from this device is thus given as:

$$\text{Reflectance (R) or Transmittance (T)} = \left(\frac{I}{I_0}\right) \tag{3.5}$$

$$\left(\frac{I}{I_0}\right) = \left(\frac{\text{Sample} - \text{DarkSignal}}{\text{Reference} - \text{DarkSignal}}\right) \tag{3.6}$$

This ratio is reported as 0 to 1.0, or as percent from 0 to 100.0 %. If the instrument has any instabilities (either optical, mechanical, or electronic), the time delay between sample and reference measurements must be as short as possible as changes in the instrument between sample and reference measurements will not be ratioed out of the spectrum, and thus will remain as spectral artifacts or structural variation. Such variation causes loss of precision, reproducibility, and ultimately errors in analytical accuracy. Single-beam instruments must either be more inherently stable or alternate between sample and reference measurements at a frequency established to negate the rate of change of the spectrometer. Designs for single and double monochromator spectrophotometers, as well as a diode array design are shown in Figures 3.3–3.5. These designs can be configured as single- or double-beam with slight mechanical changes.

If only an internal reference is used for spectral collection, then the absorbance spectrum with respect to wavelength is computed as:

$$A = -\log_{10}\left(\frac{I}{I_0}\right) = -\log_{10}\left[\left(\frac{\mathrm{S} - \mathrm{D_S}}{\mathrm{R_I} - \mathrm{D_{R_I}}}\right)\right] \tag{3.7}$$

If an external standard material is used to calibrate the internal reference material, then the absorbance spectrum with respect to wavelength is computed as:

$$A = -\log_{10}\left(\frac{I}{I_0}\right) = -\log_{10}\left[\left(\frac{\mathrm{S} - \mathrm{D_S}}{\mathrm{R_I} + \mathrm{R_\Delta} - \mathrm{D_{RI}}}\right)\right] \tag{3.8}$$

where:

$$\mathrm{R_\Delta} = (\mathrm{R}_E - \mathrm{D_{RE}}) - (\mathrm{R_I} - \mathrm{D_{RI}}) \tag{3.9a}$$

Alternatively, Equation (3.9b) (ratio of terms) may be substituted for Equation (3.9a); note that either equation for R_Δ is acceptable.

$$R_\Delta = (R_E - D_{RE})/(R_I - D_{RI}) \tag{3.9b}$$

Where S is the sample measurement; D_S is the Dark measurement for the Sample; R_I is the internal Reference Measurement; D_{RI} is the Dark Measurement for the Internal Reference Sample; R_E is the measurement of the external standard reference material for calibration; D_{RE} is the Dark Measurement for the external standard reference material; and R_Δ is the correction factor between the dark corrected R_E and R_I. The final spectrum is simplified to the ratio of (Sample - Dark) divided by (Internal Reference corrected by External Reference minus Dark). Note that Dark is a measurement where no energy from the source is allowed to the detector (it is blocked). The Dark measurement represents the dark current changes in the instrument during a measurement that relate to electronic noise where the detection electronics, computational electronics, and control electronics perform basic measurement functions with no imputed energy reaching the detector (i.e., the source is turned off or blocked using a shutter closure during the Dark measurement).

Basic visible spectrophotometer configurations include: the laser emitting diode device (LED) spectrometer, the single monochromator, the double monochromator, and the fixed diode array spectrometer optical systems as shown in Figures 3.2 through 3.5.

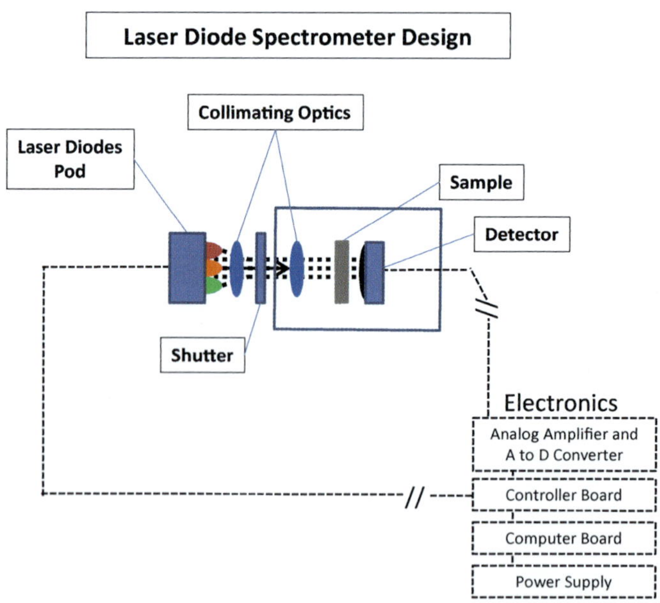

Fig. 3.2 Laser emitting diode (LED) — based spectrometer configuration.

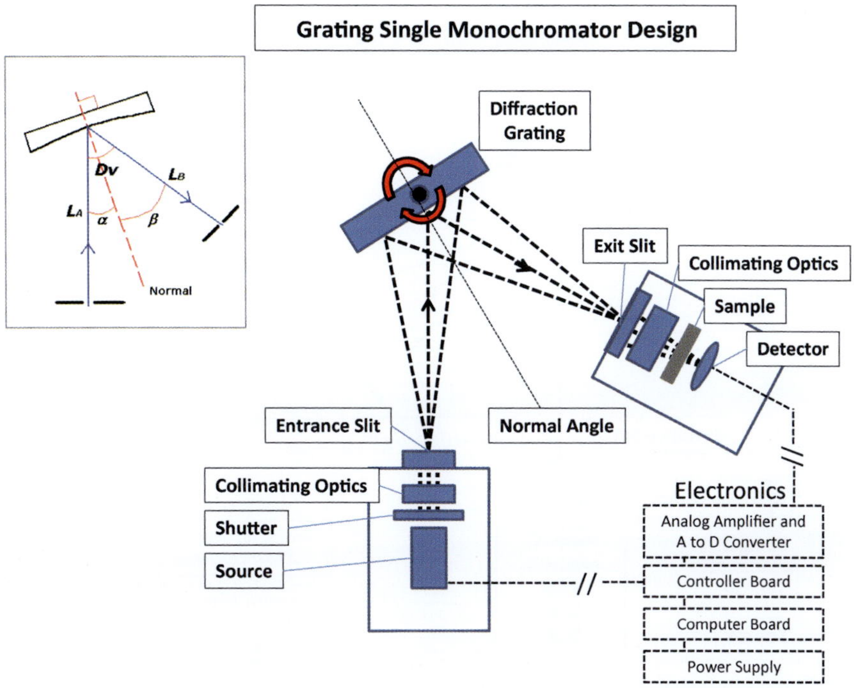

Fig. 3.3 Single monochromator system (Dispersive) optical configuration.

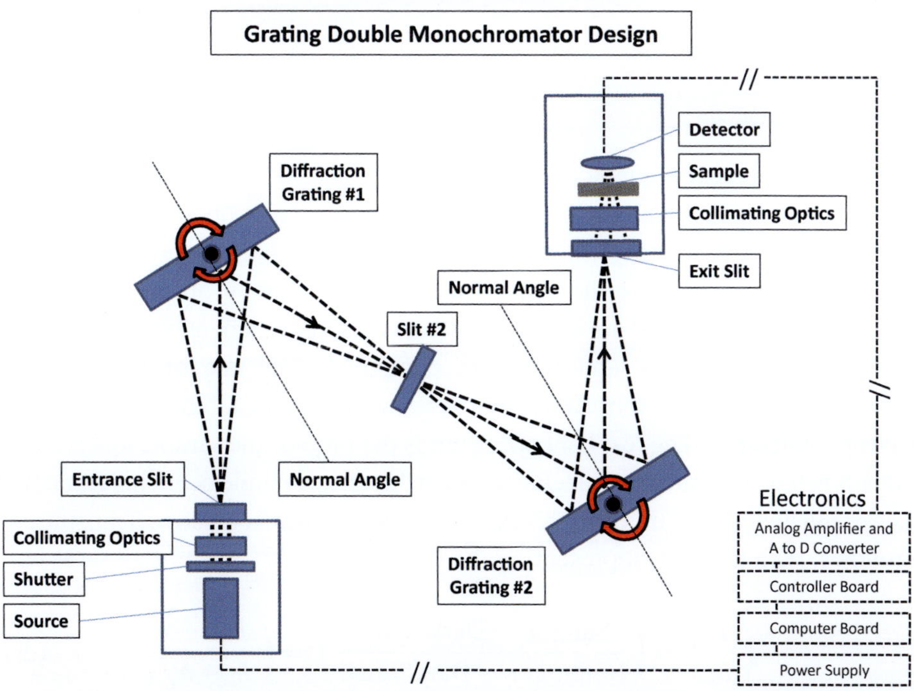

Fig. 3.4 Double monochromator system (Dispersive) optical configuration.

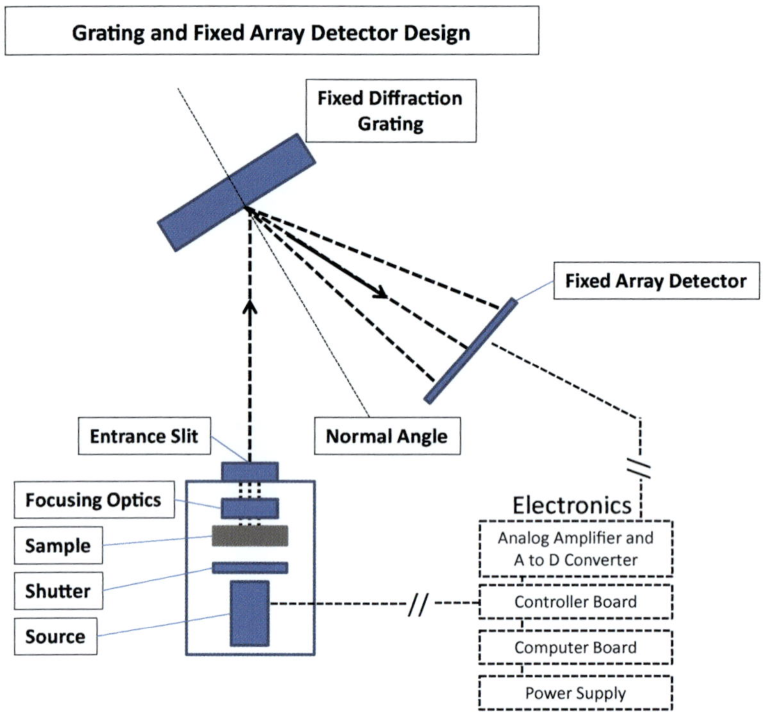

Fig. 3.5 Fixed diode array detector spectrophotometer (Dispersive) optical configuration.

3.1.1.3 *Double-Beam*

A double-beam spectrometer consists of both sample and reference channels and measures both channels simultaneously. The separation of the light beam from the source is accomplished using a fixed beam splitter or alternatively a rotating partial mirror. For the beam splitter approximately 50 % of the source emitted energy is divided to both sample and reference channels and these are measured simultaneously and the ratio computed. The use of the dual-beam concept compensates for short-term, real-time instrument instabilities inherent to all spectrophotometers. The resultant spectrum is the ratio of the sample and reference channels in transmittance or reflectance. As in the case of single beam instruments, in practice the final spectrum from this device is given as Reflectance or Transmittance as follows, with delta (δ) representing the dark signal.

$$\left(\frac{I}{I_0}\right) = \left(\frac{\text{Sample} - \text{DarkSignal}}{\text{Reference} - \text{DarkSignal}}\right) = \left(\frac{I - \delta}{I_0 - \delta}\right) \tag{3.10}$$

3.1.2 *Spectrometer Components*

3.1.2.1 *Light Sources*

A list of visible energy sources encountered with optical spectrophotometers are shown in Tables 3.2 and 3.3. Emission sources for visible spectroscopy containing a glowing filament follow the principles of a black body radiator, Wien's law, and Kirchhoff's law, stating that a black body filament also would be an ideal emitter of radiation. A discussion of these aspects for a black body radiator emission source is discussed in detail in Chapter 2 and other volumes of this set.

To express Lamp output in terms of Amps, Volts and Watts the formula used is:

$$\mathrm{A} \times \mathrm{V} = \mathrm{W} \tag{3.11}$$

$$\text{Amps} \times \text{Volts} = \text{Watts} \tag{3.12}$$

These are derived from the relationships,

Ohm's Law:

$$\mathrm{V} = \mathrm{IR} \quad \text{or} \quad \mathrm{W} = \mathrm{A}\Omega \tag{3.13}$$

Table 3.2 Various spectrometer energy sources and effective emissivity ranges.

Source Emissivity Ranges (μm)	Start (μm)	End (μm)
Quartz Tungsten-halogen	0.22	2.7
Glass Tungsten-Halogen	0.25	2.25
DC Deuterium Lamp	0.185	3.75
Pulsed Xenon Arc Lamp	0.18	2.5
DC Arc Lamp	0.2	2.5
Mercury Lamp	0.3	100
Visible Range	0.36	0.78

Table 3.3 Most common spectrometer energy sources and effective emissivity ranges.

Source	Useful Emission Range (nanometers)	Useful Emission Range (cm^{-1})
Quartz Tungsten-halogen mono-filament Lamp	220 – 2700	45,455 – 3,704
Pulsed Xenon Arc Lamp	180 – 2500	55,556 – 4,000
DC Arc Lamp	200 – 2500	50,000 – 4,000
Mercury Lamp	300 – 100000	33,333 – 100

Electrical Power Relationship:

$$P = IV \quad \text{or} \quad W = AV \tag{3.14}$$

Noting that V = Voltage (volts or V), I = Current (amps or amperes or A), R = Resistance (ohms or Ω), and P = Power (watts or W).

3.1.2.2 *Detectors (Performance and Sensitivity)*

There are two basic types of photon (photo) detectors, these being photoemissive and solid state. The photoemissive type is generally represented by the photomultiplier tube detectors; whereas the solid state type detectors are represented by photodiode detectors, pyroelectric detectors, and some photo detecting infrared detectors (e.g., photoconductive and photovoltaic), see Table 3.4.

In defining the physics of detector device performance or sensitivity, two basic terms deserve explanation. First the term specific detectivity or D-star (D*) is essential. This D* value is defined as the detectivity of a radiation detector as a function of the square root of the product of the active detector element area (A in cm^2) and the bandwidth (ω) in units of cycles per second (Hertz, Hz); divided by the noise equivalent power (NEP) in Watts of the detector element. This

Table 3.4 Most common spectrometer detectors and effective detectivity ranges.

Detector sensitivity ranges (μm)	Start (μm)	End (μm)	Difference (μm)
Silicon (Si)	0.3	1.1	0.8000
Silicon Photodiode Detectors	0.19	1.1	0.9100
Photomultipler Tube (PMT), S1 Type Photocathode	0.3	1.2	0.9000
Photomultipler Tube, Cesium Antimonide CsSb Photocathode	0.25	0.75	0.5000
Photomultipler Tube, Multialkali (Na-K-Sb-Cs) Photocathode	0.3	0.93	0.6300
Photomultipler Tube, CsI Photocathode	0.2	0.9	0.7000
Photomultipler Tube, S1 Type Photocathode	0.3	1.2	0.9000
Photomultipler Tube, Cesium Gallium Arsenide (CsGaAs) Photocathode	0.3	0.93	0.6300
Photomultipler Tube, (CsInGaAs) Photocathode	0.3	1	0.7000
Silicon (Si) CCD	0.2	1.1	0.9000
Indium Gallium Arsenide (InGaAs) CCD	0.68	1.7	1.0200
Visible Range	0.36	0.78	0.4200

is summarized by the following formula:

$$D^* = \frac{\sqrt{A \cdot \omega}}{NEP} = \mathrm{cm} \cdot \mathrm{Hz}^{1/2} \cdot W^{-1} \quad (3.15)$$

The D^* is reported in units of $\mathrm{cm} \cdot \mathrm{Hz}^{1/2}\mathrm{W}^{-1}$ units and is used to compare photodetector responsivity as a function of wavelength. These are referred to as *Jones* units, for the namesake of R. Clark Jones.

For photo-detectors, detector responsivity (R) or input-output gain, is also used to express detector response in units of Amperes per Watt (A/W) as a function of the frequency or wavelength of light incident to the detector. This is a measure of the electrical output (or detector efficiency or sensitivity) as a function of optical energy input. This relationship is expressed as follows:

$$R = Q\left(\frac{\lambda(\mu m) \cdot A}{1.23985(\mu\mathrm{m} \cdot W)}\right) = \mathrm{Amps/Watt} \quad (3.16)$$

This computational form is derived from the responsivity expression, equivalent to the quantum efficiency (Q) times the electron charge divided by Planck's constant times the frequency (or wavelength in microns) of the optical signal; the responsivity changes as a function of the wavelength of the incident energy. The physics of detectors is expressed in more detail in other volumes of this text; the reader is referred to the index for detector topics.

3.1.2.3 *Interference Filters*

Two basic types of interference filters exist, these being *Bandpass Filters*, and *Edge or Cut-on/Cut-off Filters* (also spelled as cut on and cutoff). Bandpass filters transmit light only for a defined spectral band as illustrated in Figure 3.6. The transmitted spectral bands may be from less than 1 nm FWHM (Full bandWidth at Half Maximum transmission band height) to 50 nm or more FWHM. Edge filters transmit light either above (i.e., "high-pass" as in Figure 3.7) or below ("low-pass" as in Figure 3.8) a certain wavelength region; these have been referred to as "cut-on" or "cut-off" types, respectively. These filters transmit efficiently throughout a broad region until the transmission limit of the filter substrate material is reached. Interference filters consist of a solid Fabry-Perot cavity. These filters are illustrated and described in another volume of this work.

3.1.2.4 *Diffraction Gratings*

The topic of diffraction gratings is discussed in greater detail in other volumes of this work. When incident light strikes a diffraction grating, the light is separated into its component wavelengths with each wavelength scattered at a different angle.

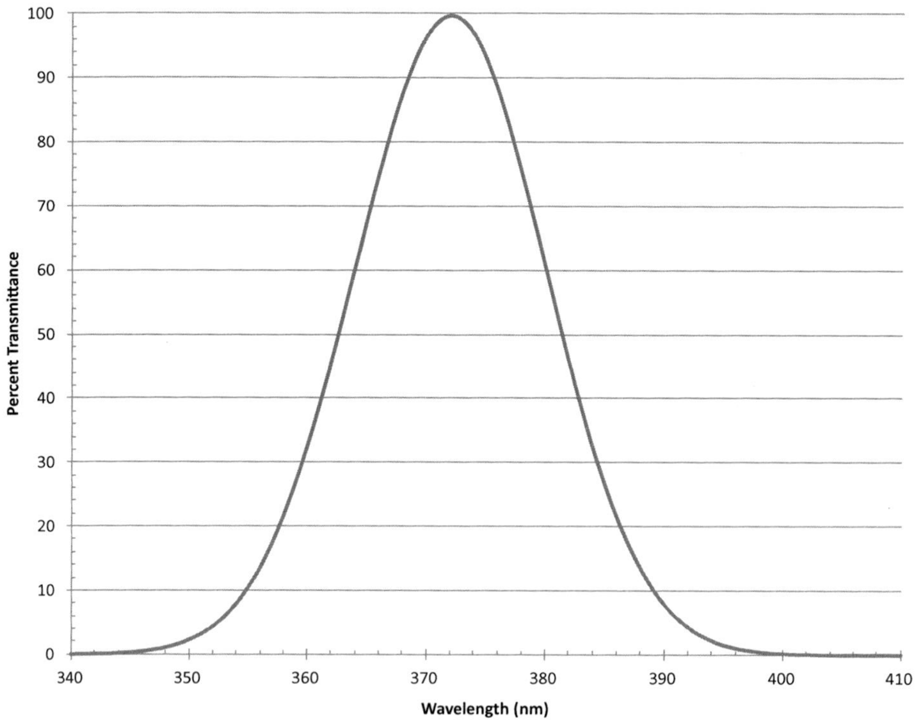

Fig. 3.6 Transmittance profile of a bandpass filter with single cavity construction (Center wavelength at 372 nm; FWHM or bandwidth of 381 nm −363 nm = 18 nm).

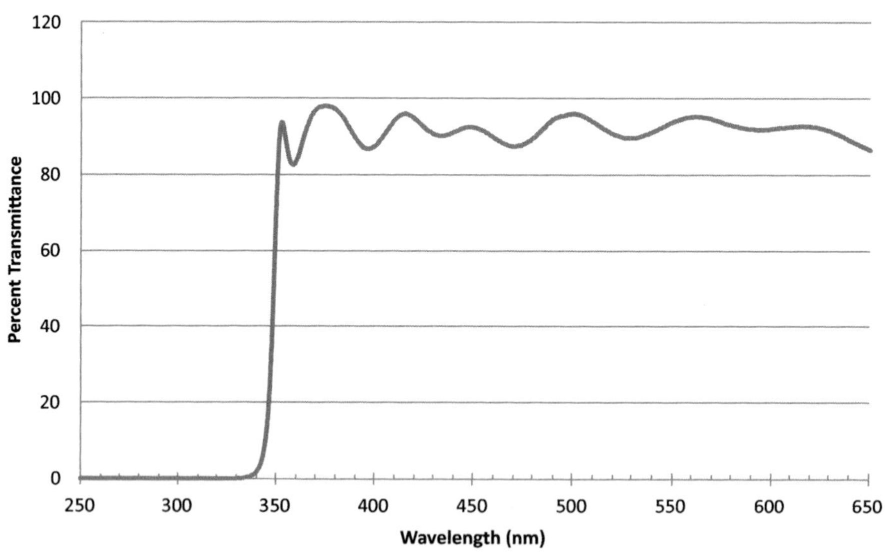

Fig. 3.7 Transmittance profile of visible high-pass filter (50% cut-on wavelength near 348 nm).

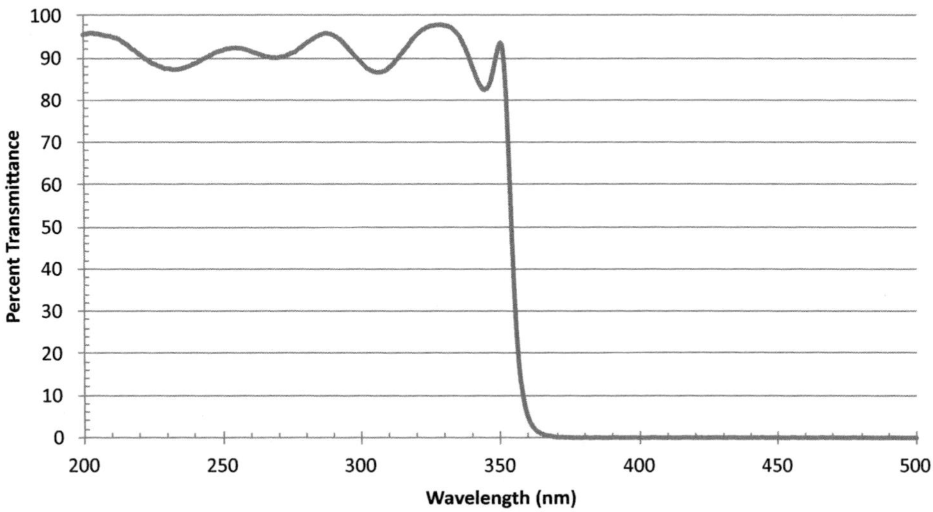

Fig. 3.8 Transmittance profile of visible low-pass filter (50% cut-off wavelength near 354 nm).

Formulas are available to calculate the angles of diffraction, grating efficiency, intensity distribution, and resolution. To calculate the particular angle (θ_d) at each wavelength of light (λ_a) which is scattered from a diffraction grating, the following expression is applied:

$$\theta_d = \sin^{-1}\left(\frac{k \cdot \lambda_a}{s}\right) \tag{3.17}$$

where θ_{d} is the angle of diffracted light from a normal angle; k is the order number (integers such as 0, 1, 2, 3, ... k); s is the spacing between the lines on the grating (in the same units as the wavelength (λ_{a}) used in the equation, e.g., microns, nanometers, etc.); and λ_{a} is the wavelength of the incident light in air (for white light it represents the wavelength of interest for a calculation of the diffraction angle following dispersion). Note that for zero-order light there is no dispersion, but only straight line reflection of the incident light (i.e., mirror reflection).

The fundamental grating equation is given by:

$$\sin\alpha + \sin\beta = 10^{-6} k \cdot n \cdot \lambda \tag{3.18}$$

In most monochromators, the location of the entrance and exit slits are fixed and the grating rotates around a plane through the center of the face. The angle, θ_{V}, is a constant determined by:

$$\theta_{\mathrm{V}} = \beta - \alpha \tag{3.19}$$

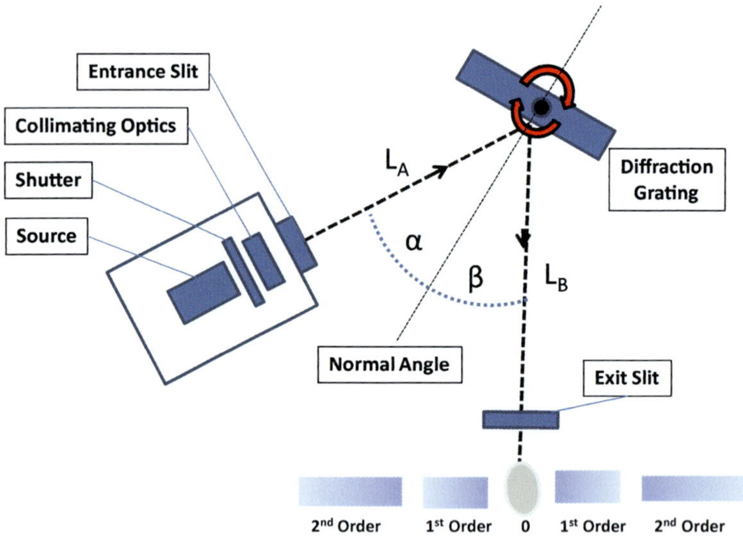

Fig. 3.9 Schematic showing multiple order dispersion from a pre-dispersive monochromator grating system.

If the value of α and β is to be determined for a given wavelength (λ), the grating equation may be expressed as:

$$kn\lambda \cdot 10^{-6} = 2\sin\left[\frac{\beta+\alpha}{2}\right]\cos\left[\frac{\beta-\alpha}{2}\right] \tag{3.20}$$

To calculate α in a Monochromator use:

$$\alpha = \sin^{-1}\left[\frac{10^{-6}kn\lambda}{2\cos\left(\frac{\theta_V}{2}\right)}\right] - \frac{\theta_V}{2} \tag{3.21}$$

The symbols for the grating equation are as follows. Please note that an illustration of multi-order diffraction is shown in Figure 3.9. For the symbols in the grating equation note that α is the angle of incidence (in degrees); β is the angle of diffraction (in degrees); k is the diffraction order number (i.e., integers of 0, 1, 2, etc.); n is the groove density (in grooves per mm); θ_V is the angle of deviation or dispersion (in degrees); and λ is the wavelength of light (in nm).

3.1.2.5 *Polarizers*

A diversity of polarizing elements have been developed for the purpose of rotating or selecting light of a specific electronic vector orientation. When the electronic direction vector of light incident to a surface is parallel to the electronic field vector of that surface, increased interaction of the incident light (as absorption) occurs. The principle is important in characterizing the surface chemistry for optical components, thin films, metal surfaces, and semiconductor interfaces. The use of a quartz plate can act as a polarizer that will rotate the plane of linearly polarized light. This rotation (P) can be described using the following relationship:

$$P = \pi \cdot t(|n_{\Lambda} - n_{P}|)\lambda^{-1} \tag{3.22}$$

where t is the thickness of a quartz plate cut perpendicularly to the optical axis; n_{Λ} is the refractive index for right circularly polarized light; n_P is refractive index for left circularly polarized light; and λ_0 is the vacuum wavelength of light entering the quartz plate. Note: for quartz $n_{\Lambda} = 1.5582$ and $n_p = 1.5581$. Please note the index section on polarization measurements for more details.

3.1.2.6 *Electronic Components Used in Spectrometry*

For references describing the electronic components of optical spectrophotometers, see modern textbooks on electronic instrumentation including references 4-6. Other volumes in this set discuss more details regarding electronic components for instrumentation, please see index for specific topics. Two special categories of electronic devices deserve mention when discussing spectrometers. The first category includes detectors and detector electronics that produce a current or voltage signal proportional to the amount of energy striking the detector. Detector stability is provided by appropriate electronic circuitry allowing the detector signal to be selectively amplified with the minimum amplification of noise, thus electronic circuitry enhances the signal-to-noise ratio of the detector signal.

Digital microcomputers comprise the second essential electronic element for modern spectrophotometers. With the addition of appropriate software, sophisticated instrument control and data processing the usefulness and user friendliness of visible instruments can be made faster, cheaper, and more accurate.

3.1.3 *Properties of Spectrophotometers*

3.1.3.1 *Aperture Diameter*

To calculate the aperture (a) required by an optical system to resolve two objects with known linear separation, the Raleigh criterion for resolution is used as:

$$\mathrm{a} = 1.22\lambda \cdot \alpha_R^{-1} \tag{3.23}$$

where α_R is the angle of separation from the measuring device exit aperture to the objects to be resolved (this is calculated as tan α = opposite/adjacent, where α_R is expressed in radians); λ is the wavelength of light observed from the objects; and a is the aperture of the optical system.

3.1.3.2 *Entrance and Exit Pupils*

The entrance pupil refers to the size and location of the entrance aperture between the light source and the remainder of an optical system. The exit pupil refers to the size and location of the exit aperture within an optical system or train just prior to the detector. Both the entrance and exit pupils affect the energy throughput and spectral resolution of a spectrophotometer.

3.1.3.3 *Band Pass (Bandpass) and Resolution*

The terms bandpass and resolution are used to express the capability of a spectrometer to separate spectral bands or lines which are separated by some finite distance on the spectral energy scale. For an instrument that disperses energy over a prespecified spectral region of the electromagnetic spectrum the bandpass of a spectrometer is used to describe which portion of the spectrum can actually be isolated by the spectrometer in a "pure" wavelength form. The spectrometer bandpass is dependent upon the dispersion of the grating and the entrance and exit slit widths. An illustration is often used to demonstrate the problem associated with measuring monochromatic light using conventional spectrophotometers. If the ideal spectrometer was used to measure a bright line emission spectrum at a single wavelength (λ_1), the spectrum would appear as a single line. What really occurs when such a spectrum is measured using a conventional spectrometer is a broad band spectrum. The spectrum assumes a Gaussian-like (or bell-shaped) curve, actually closer to Lorentzian. This characteristic broadening of a line spectrum through the spectrometer is an illustration of the spectrometer bandpass. The actual bandpass for any instruments assigned a value by determining the FullWidth at Half Maximum (FWHM) height of the bell-shaped spectrum. Thus for the band in Figure 3.10 the FWHM could be empirically determined by finding the wavelength where maximum intensity occurs, and measuring the peak height at this position. This height measurement is divided in half and the bandwidth measured at this height on the band. The combined entrance and exit slit width of the monochromator comprise the actual line width or bandpass for the spectrophotometer system.

The actual shape of a band is the result of several instrumental characteristics including the overall quality of the optics and detector systems, as well as the width and positions of the entrance and exit slits. Every dispersive spectrometer consists of a dispersive element (e.g., diffraction grating or prism) in combination with an entrance and an exit slit. The image of the entrance slit and exit slit determines

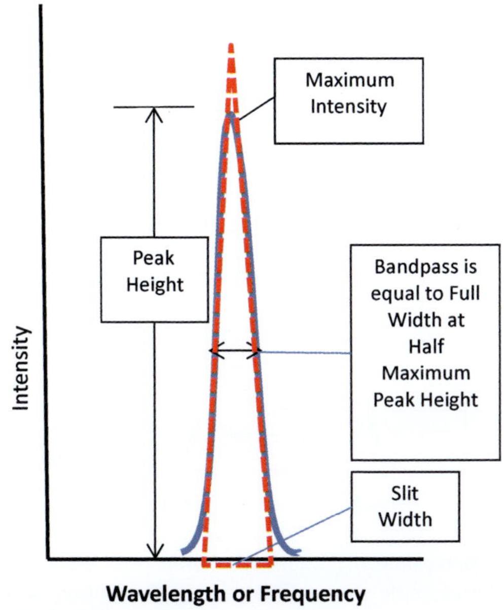

Fig. 3.10 Illustration of the determination of bandpass using the bell-shaped peak (solid line) obtained by using a bright line source projected through a monochromator optical system. The broken line indicates the actual slit width profile for the monochromator.

the spectrometer bandpass which is sometimes referred to as the slit function. Actually the slit function is the result of the combination of the images of these two slits. The bandshape of a dispersive spectrometer is as shown in Figure 3.10. Other factors associated with optical and electronic quality cause a rounded overall shape. The bandpass of a spectrometer is equal to the FWHM. Often texts dealing with instrumentation will cite that the bandpass of a spectrometer is approximated by the product of the linear dispersion of the monochromator and the entrance or exit slit width (whichever is larger).

The resolution of a spectrometer can be defined as the minimum distance between two peaks that can be detected by the spectrometer under designated operational performance settings. Resolution is calculated by multiplying the slit width (generally expressed in mm) by the dispersion of the monochromator (in nm per mm). Due to practical issues and non ideal optics, the actual resolution of a spectrometer must be slightly less (poorer) than the theoretical value.

To summarize, bandpass and resolution are identical in practice. Only the resolution specification of a spectrometer is the expression of bandpass under the specified measuring conditions of an instrument dependent upon the slit width settings.

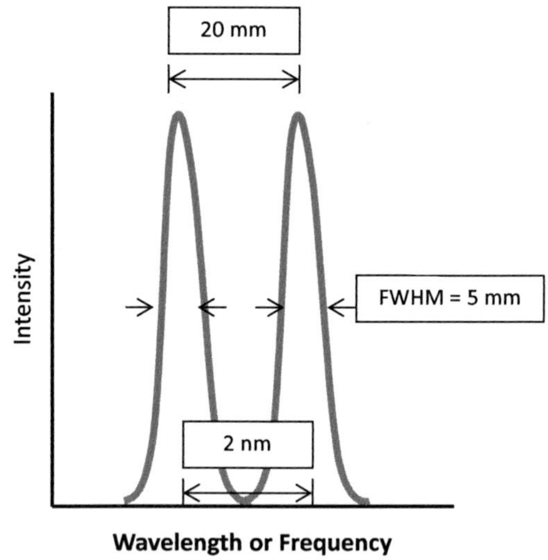

Fig. 3.11 The method to determine maximum resolution of a spectrometer under specific measurement conditions. In the example shown Bandpass = Resolution = FWHM × Dispersion = 2 nm/20 mm × 5 mm = 0.50 nm resolution. This is a hard copy depiction of the band separation.

The empirical resolution of a spectrometer is determined by measuring the FWHM in mm for two narrow bands which are completely resolved (to the baseline) using the spectrometer. The spatial difference between the maximum absorbance ($\lambda_{\max}$) is determined between the bands (in mm); simultaneously noting the difference between the $\lambda_{\max}$ points in nm. The various measurements required for this calculation are shown in Figure 3.11 and illustrated by the relationship:

$$\text{The bandpass} = \text{resolution} = \frac{\text{band.difference.in.nm}}{\text{band.difference.in.mm}} \times \text{FWHM in mm} \qquad (3.24)$$

3.1.3.4 *Numerical Aperture*

The numerical aperture, designated as NA is a measure of how much light can be collected by any optical system. The NA is expressed as the product of the refractive index of the material (n_i) where incident energy is directed ($\theta_{\max}$) times the sine of the ray angle maximum difference from normal incidence. This function is given as:

$$\text{NA} = n_i \cdot \sin\theta_{\max} \qquad (3.25)$$

Table 3.5 Etendue and relative throughput as a function of numerical aperture (NA).

NA (Numerical aperture)	Relative etendue (ε') for 1 mm diameter aperture	Relative throughput
0.20	0.10	1
0.40	0.40	4
0.60	1.00	10

3.1.3.5 *Etendue*

The etendue (or relative throughput advantage) for an optical system is the product of the potential illuminated surface area (A) times the solid angle of the optical system. Traditionally, this is represented by the following equations, where ε' represents the etendue and Ω_S represents the solid angle. Thus the etendue formula is given as:

$$\varepsilon' = \mathrm{A} \cdot \Omega_S \tag{3.26}$$

and the solid angle is given by the relationship:

$$\Omega_S = 2\pi\left(1 - \sqrt{(1 - (NA)^2)}\right) \tag{3.27}$$

Therefore, the previous equations allow us to calculate the relative improvement for an optical spectrometer. As can be seen, the NA and aperture diameter are preeminent factors for throughput in optical systems as shown in Table 3.5.

3.1.3.6 *Relative Throughput*

The relative throughput (T) of an optical system represents the overall effectiveness of an optical system to transmit light relative to the amount of energy introduced into the system (I_0) from the optical light source of the spectrophotometer. It is defined as the ratio of light energy passing into an optical system to the light energy passing out of the optical system. For dispersive spectrometers this relationship is defined as:

$$T = \frac{\pi D w_s \Sigma_g (R_1 \cdot R_2 \cdot \cdots \cdot R_k)}{4f^2} \tag{3.28}$$

where D is the dispersion constant of the diffraction grating (in nm/mm); w_s is the exit slit width in mm; f is the f/number of the optical system and is designated by (f/number $=$ 1/2(NA)); R_k is the reflectivity of mirrors or the transmittance of lenses at a particular wavelength or set of wavelengths; and Σ_g is the spectral efficiency of the grating (approximately 0.80 at the blaze wavelength), but this will vary with grating design and can be calculated or measured.

3.1.3.7 *Signal-To-Noise Ratio*

The theoretical total signal (S) from an optical system can be given by the product of a number of optical parameters as:

$$S = R_S B_\lambda \varepsilon' \tau q \tag{3.29}$$

where R_S is the light source spectral radiance; B_λ is the spectral bandwidth; ε' is the etendue of the spectrometer optical system; τ is the combined transmittance and emissivity losses; and q is the quantum efficiency.

The measured signal-to-noise (S/N) from an optical system indicates the maximum amount of signal produced by an instrument as compared to the noise of the instrument during measurement. The higher the number, the better is the quality of the instrument. The s/n ratio can be calculated from the full transmitted (or reflected) signal divided by the RMS (root means square) noise (in Transmittance or Reflectance units). Thus for a 100% line with RMS noise as 0.01 percent, the $s/n = 100/0.01 = 10,000 : 1$. This applies when RMS noise for a transmission measurement is calculated empirically as:

$$\mathrm{RMS} = \sqrt{\frac{1}{n}\sum_{i=1}^{n}(T_i - \bar{T})^2} \tag{3.30}$$

where T_i = the individual Transmission value at each data channel i, and $\bar{T}$ is the mean Transmission value for each measured data channel (i). The corresponding S/N for reflectance measurements is calculated by substituting reflectance for transmission.

3.1.3.8 *Dynamic Range and Stray Radiant Energy*

The range of a specified component concentration over which a sensor response is directly proportional to a change in concentration is a definition for the dynamic range of a spectrometer. Dynamic range is limited by both stray light and noise. A basic understanding of Beer's law allows one to calculate the maximum theoretical dynamic range for an instrument and the relationship between stray light and the maximum observable absorbance value for a spectrometer. The following relationships allows the error in a photometric measurement due to stray light to be computed.

Beer's law is given as the true absorbance measurement equal to

$$A_\tau = \log_{10}\left(\frac{I_0}{I_t}\right) \tag{3.31}$$

where A_τ is the true absorbance value for a sample; I_0 is the incident intensity measured for a true spectrometer; and I_t is the true intensity of a sample measured with the spectrometer. To follow this rationale we compare a measured absorbance value to the true absorbance value considering stray light. In this case stray light is defined as any light impinging upon the detector that is not monochromatic light. In this case the effect of stray light on the true absorbance is given by:

$$A_m = \log_{10}\left(\frac{I_0 + I_s}{I_t + I_s}\right) \tag{3.32}$$

where A_m is the measured absorbance value for a sample; I_0 is the incident intensity measured for the spectrometer; I_t is the true intensity of a sample measured with a true spectrometer; and I_s is the stray light intensity (as a fraction of the incident energy as $I_0 = 1$). The effect of stray light on a measurement is given in Table 3.6 and in Figure 3.12.

Table 3.6 True versus measured absorbance values as a function of stray light.

True absorbance	Absorbance at 0.001% stray light	Absorbance at 0.01% stray light	Absorbance at 0.10% stray light
4.0000	3.9586	3.6990	2.9590
3.0000	2.9957	2.9587	2.6994
2.0000	1.9996	1.9957	1.9590
1.3010	1.3009	1.3002	1.2929
1.0000	1.0000	0.9996	0.9961
0.8239	0.8239	0.8237	0.8215
0.6990	0.6990	0.6988	0.6972
0.6021	0.6020	0.6019	0.6008
0.5229	0.5229	0.5228	0.5219
0.4559	0.4559	0.4559	0.4551
0.3979	0.3979	0.3979	0.3973
0.3468	0.3468	0.3467	0.3463
0.3010	0.3010	0.3010	0.3006
0.2596	0.2596	0.2596	0.2593
0.2218	0.2218	0.2218	0.2216
0.1871	0.1871	0.1871	0.1869
0.1549	0.1549	0.1549	0.1547
0.1249	0.1249	0.1249	0.1248
0.0969	0.0969	0.0969	0.0968
0.0706	0.0706	0.0706	0.0705
0.0458	0.0458	0.0458	0.0457
0.0223	0.0223	0.0223	0.0223
0.0000	0.0000	0.0000	0.0000

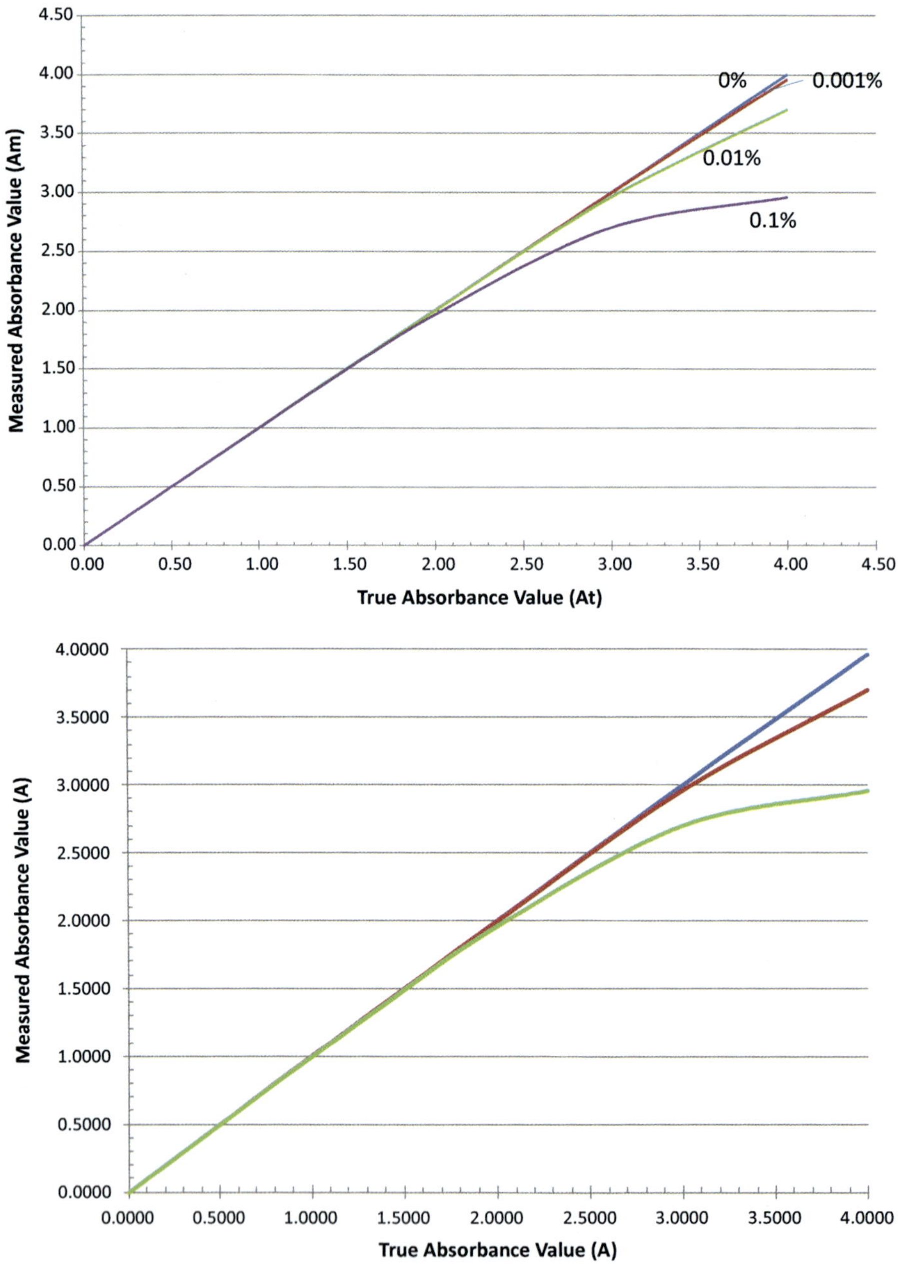

Fig. 3.12 A plot of successive true versus measured absorbance at different stray light levels. (Stray light levels are labeled on the top figure.) Bottom figure is close-up of 0% (blue), 0.01% (red), and 0.1% (green) stray light.

Table 3.7 The maximum measureable absorbance value (as dynamic range) given specific stray light levels.

Stray light level (I_S)	Stray light level (%)	Maximum measureable absorbance
0.00001	0.001	5.00
0.0001	0.01	4.00
0.001	0.1	3.00
0.01	1.0	2.00
0.02	2.0	1.71
0.03	3.0	1.54
0.04	4.0	1.41
0.05	5.0	1.32
0.06	6.0	1.25
0.07	7.0	1.18
0.08	8.0	1.13
0.09	9.0	1.08
0.10	10.0	1.04
0.11	11.0	1.00
0.12	12.0	0.97
0.13	13.0	0.94
0.14	14.0	0.91
0.15	15.0	0.88
0.15	15.0	0.88
0.17	17.0	0.84
0.18	18.0	0.82
0.19	19.0	0.80
0.20	20.0	0.78

The maximum absorbance value obtainable for a spectrometer, given any specific stray light level is equal to:

$$A_{\text{Max}} = \log_{10}\left(\frac{I_0 + I_s}{I_s}\right) = \log_{10}\left(\frac{1 + I_s}{I_s}\right) \tag{3.33}$$

This is demonstrated in Table 3.7.

Note the following equation for computing the dynamic range of an instrument having stray light. The relative dynamic range of a spectrometer in absorbance units (A_{DR}) can be written as:

$$A_{DR} = \log_{10}\left(\frac{1 + I_s}{I_s}\right) - k(RMS_A) \tag{3.34}$$

when I_s is stray light as fraction of 1; k is the multiplier for the desired confidence level using the Student's t test; and RMS_A is the Root Mean Square noise measurement (in Absorbance units). Note to simplify calculations, the $-k(RMS_A)$ term may be dropped yielding a simple estimated value for dynamic range.

Table 3.8 The relationship between absorbance (A) and transmittance (T) or reflectance (R).

Absorbance (A)	Transmittance (T)	Transmittance (%T)	Reflectance (R)	Reflectance (%R)
0.0	1.0	100.0	1.0	100.0
1.0	0.1	10.0	0.1	10.0
2.0	0.01	1.0	0.01	1.0
3.0	0.001	0.1	0.001	0.1
4.0	0.0001	0.01	0.0001	0.01
5.0	0.00001	0.001	0.00001	0.001
6.0	0.000001	0.0001	0.000001	0.0001

The relationship between transmittance (or reflectance), percent transmittance (or reflectance) and Absorbance is given as Beer's law in simplified form as:

$$A = \log_{10}\left(\frac{1}{T}\right) \tag{3.35}$$

and,

$$A = \log_{10}\left(\frac{1}{R}\right) \tag{3.36}$$

where A is the absorbance and T is transmittance, and R is Reflectance as measured. Table 3.8 illustrates this relationship.

3.1.3.9 *Percent Error in a Photometric Measurement*

The calculation of percent error (E%) in a measurement due to stray light or stray radiant energy is given by:

$$E\% = 100\left[1 - \left(\frac{\log_{10}\left(\frac{I_0+I_s}{I_t+I_s}\right)}{A_t}\right)\right] \tag{3.37}$$

where I_0 is the incident intensity measured for the spectrometer; I_t is the true intensity of a sample measured with a true spectrometer; and I_s is the stray light intensity (as a fraction of the incident energy as $I_0 = 1$). A_t is the true (or known) reference absorbance value of a sample specimen measured. More detailed descriptions of stray light are found elsewhere in this set of volumes (see index).

3.1.3.10 *Luminometers*

A luminometer is used to measure the luminescence from a sample by directing light of a specific frequency onto the sample specimen and then collecting the

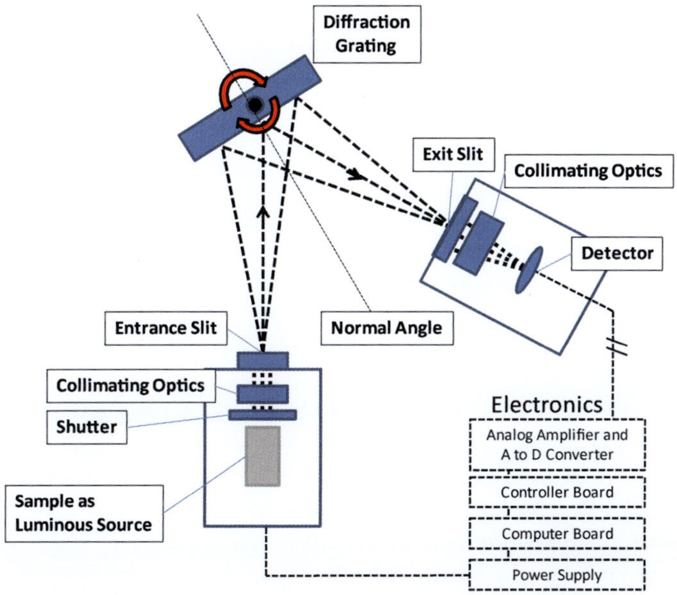

Fig. 3.13 Simple monochromator-based luminometer optical design.

luminescence for a specific frequency onto a detector. A simple luminometer optical configuration, generally measuring from 350 nm to 650 nm, is shown in Figure 3.13. The luminous sample acts as the source for the instrument and the light emitted from the sample is dispersed into its various wavelengths and recorded by the detector, typically a photomultiplier tube.

3.1.4 *Instrument Comparison and Evaluation Methods*

A number of standard measurements may be completed that allow detailed comparison of overall instrument performance. Instrument evaluation tests are described in detail throughout these volumes and may be applied to visible spectrophotometers. As a supplement, the reader is referred to the master index for descriptions of the various tests used to qualify instrument performance and for tests to determine which issues are problematic due to deficiencies in instrument design features. These tests are related to alikeness in measurement performance between instruments and to overall accuracy, and precision (as repeatability and reproducibility). Note that the terms optical density (O.D.) and absorbance units (as A, Au or AU) are synonyms. (Note that "Optical density" is found in historical documents, and is still used in physics, and biomedical and optical engineering, but not often in analytical chemistry.) The techniques used for evaluation of spectrometer performance are described in detail within Chapter 6, entitled *Data Analysis and Presentation.*

References

1. ASTM Practice E131 - 10, Standard Terminology Relating to Molecular Spectroscopy, ASTM International, 100 Barr Harbor Drive, PO Box C700, West Conshohocken, PA, 19428-2959 USA
2. P. R. Griffiths and J. A. De Haseth, *Fourier Transform Infrared Spectrometry,* 2nd edn. (Wiley-Interscience, 2007).
3. J. M. Chalmers, P. R. Griffiths, *Handbook of Vibrational Spectroscopy,* 5 Volume Set (Wiley, 2002).
4. D. M. Buchla, W. McLachlan, *Applied Electronic Instrumentation and Measurement,* 1 edn. (Prentice Hall, 1991).
5. J. Turner, M. Hill, *Instrumentation for Engineers and Scientists, Textbooks in Electrical & Electronic Engineering*, Book 8 (Oxford University Press, 1999).
6. G. S. Sawhney, *Biomedical Electronics and Instrumentation Made Easy*, 1st edn. (I. K. International Publishing House, 2011).

Chapter 4

Sampling Considerations for Visible Spectroscopy

Contents

4.1 Introduction

A quality visible spectrum depends on reproducible sample presentation and the consistency of the optical interface between the sample and the spectrophotometer. Many sampling accessories are commercially available to optimize repeatability and reproducibility of visible spectral data. The typical visible sampling techniques include transmittance of liquids or glasses, and reflectance of solid samples for color or appearance measurements.

This chapter is written as guide for sampling methods used in visible spectroscopy. The chapter is focused on the practical aspects of the subject. In sample measurements, it is an essential element to document details about each sample, its origin, sample handling techniques, and raw measurement data. One must be certain to record any abnormalities observed during sample preparation or measurements.

For many applications, the basic, unprocessed spectral measurement data is sufficient for qualitative or quantitative analysis. Spectral pre-processing may be applied, such as baseline correction, smoothing, derivatives, or normalization, and these methods are described within these text volumes. Note that when archiving spectral data, note the form of pre-processing used. Refer to Chapters 5 and 6, and the index for recommendations on instructions for spectral acquisition, data and presentation formats, and comments regarding spectral data manipulations.

4.1.1 *General Considerations*

Visible energy is a form of electromagnetic radiation nominally extending from the longer wavelength ultraviolet region (approximately 360 nm) to just before the near infrared region - practically defined as approximately 0.78 microns (i.e., 780 nm). In this chapter, it will be described as visible radiation or light, as "light" is used to describe the term visible radiation (or what we see). Chapter 7 includes a lengthy discussion of the terms and methods used for color analysis. Most visible interactions with matter are recorded as absorptions of energy, either as a direct or indirect measurement. Measurements are most often made using a transmittance/transmission geometry in the visible spectral region. However visible spectra may be measured via light reflection directly from the sample surface.

It is assumed that the reader has a basic knowledge of optical spectroscopy and the molecular theory of chemistry. Visible spectroscopy is one of the analytical techniques available for the measurement of absorption of radiation as a consequence of electronic transitions and molecular absorption due to harmonics and combination band vibrations within a molecule. For an understanding of underlying theory, the reader is directed to Chapter 1 and other references.[1]

The term visible spectroscopy can be generally applied to measurements in the spectral region of 360 to 780 nm (i.e., 0.36 to 0.78 microns). The visible region covers the frequency range of 27778–12821 cm^{-1}. This range is defined as the spectral region that is visible to the naked eye of most humans.

The lower limit is normally defined by the sampling method or matrix or by the optics of the instrument. In the latter case, the standard detector for the visible region is the silicon photodiode with a working detectivity range of 300 nm to 1100 nm (.30 to 1.1 microns). Other detectors for visible spectroscopy include: photomultiplier tubes (PMTs, 160–1100 nm); charge-coupled devices (CCDs, 180–1100 nm); silicon-based photodiode arrays (180–1100 nm); and indium gallium arsenide detectors or arrays (InGaAs, sensitive from the high end of the visible region near 650 nm into the near infrared above 2.6 microns or 2600 nm).

Table 4.1 Relative intensities of C-H stretch bands for infrared and the various NIR and visible region overtone bands.

Band	Wavelength region	Relative Intensity
Fundamental (ν)	3380–3510 nm	20,000
1st overtone (2ν)	1690–1755 nm	200
2nd overtone (3ν)	1127–1170 nm	20
3rd overtone (4ν)	845–878 nm	2
4th overtone (5ν)	690–780 nm	1

From a sampling perspective, there are differences between visible, mid-infrared, Raman, and ultraviolet spectral regions. These are due to multiple factors, including differences in absorptivity (i.e., effective pathlength), scattering, resolution and signal-to-noise requirements, selectivity, and sensitivity. Also important is the efficiency of the coupling of the radiation with the sample as a function of wavelength or light energy and the sampling device or method.

The visible spectral region is composed of combined electronic transitions and vibrational absorptions related to overtone absorptions. The absorptivity associated with the visible region is several orders of magnitude less than the overtones and combination bands found in the near infrared region, and multiple orders of magnitude less than the infrared fundamental absorptions (Table 4.1).

For example, the absorptivity of the first overtone of C-H stretching in the near infrared is 100 times less than the fundamental; the second overtone is 1000 times less; the third overtone is 10,000 times less than the infrared fundamental absorptivity; and the overtones found in the visible region are 20,000 times less than the fundamental absorptivity.

The magnitude of the absorption may be used to define the best procedure for sampling. The visible region is potentially easier for sample handling than traditional infrared spectroscopy. For this chapter, the focus will be on sampling methods as developed for the visible spectral region. For most applications sampling for visiblc analysis involves transmittance/transmission or reflectance/reflection. For a general overview of the technique and its related sampling procedures, the reader is referred to a standard text on the subject.[2]

In many cases, factors such as ease of use, throughput, precision, and reproducibility may be the main attribute in selection of a sampling method. The actual application can be an important deciding factor. Visible spectroscopy is used for biochemical analysis, clinical analysis, industrial measurements, and a myriad of color and appearance measurements. Sampling techniques may be manual or automated. For additional reading, one is referred to a comprehensive text reference.[3]

4.1.2 *Sample Type versus Sampling Method*

Visible spectroscopy is most often applied to liquid samples using transmittance/transmission spectroscopy. It is not useful for gas phase, highly turbid or dark liquids, solids, or slurries. Visible measurements often yield inconsistent/inaccurate results for scattering slurries and variable layered materials where the layers are a mixture of scattering and absorbing layers. Fine, ground material of particles less than 1 mm in diameter and well-mixed (homogeneous) material are optimized for diffuse reflectance/reflection measurements.

4.1.2.1 *Liquid Measurements*

Visible measurements are compatible with low-OH (i.e., low water) quartz, glass, silicate, and methyl methacrylate cell windows. The low water content of the window material provides minimum scattering centers and the greatest transparency. If one is able to see clearly through a sampling cuvette without cloudiness or haze, the material will be effective for visible spectroscopy. Distilled or reagent grade water is transparent in the visible region and is an excellent solvent for polar, ionic materials (i.e., hydrophilic and lipophobic) molecules. Examples of materials readily dissolved in water include ionic salts, alcohols, and surfactants. Non-polar molecules (i.e., hydrophobic and lipophilic) do not dissolve in water; these include oils and fats.

Traditionally, liquids have been considered to be relatively easy to analyze using visible spectroscopy, either in transmittance or reflectance measurement mode. Low-molecular-weight compounds may be difficult as they will evaporate quickly leaving a cuvette empty unless it is tightly sealed or measured at cooler temperatures. Low molecular weight materials often have high absorptivity requiring small pathlengths. Temperature control for most liquid samples should allow a range of from 10°C to 65°C with accurate temperature control of $\pm 0.1°$C. Pathlength variation for different cells used interchangeably for quantitative measurements should vary by less than $\pm 2\%$ relative.

Standard cuvette types for liquid measurements include rectangular, round (i.e., test tube shape) as shown in Figure 4.1; and cylindrical as depicted in Figure 4.2. Rectangular cells may be available commercially for pathlengths of 1, 2, 5, 10, 20, 40, 50, and 100 mm; having a width of 12.5 mm, height of typically 45 mm, and window thickness of 1.25 mm. Window materials with optimum spectral transmittance ranges include: Low-OH Glass, (340 to 2500 nm); Spectrosil® Quartz (180 to 2650 nm); and Infrasil® Quartz (230 to 3750 nm).[4]

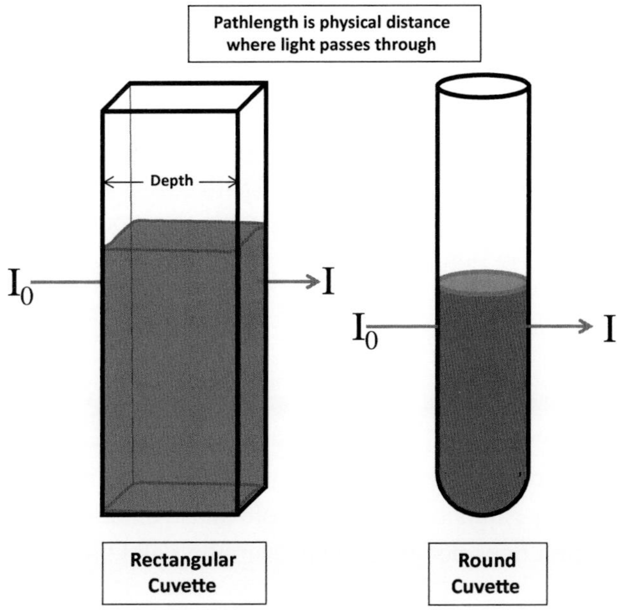

Fig. 4.1 Illustration of rectangular and round cuvette types. These cuvettes are available in varying dimensions for specific pathlengths. Height (45 mm) and width (12.5 mm) are generally the same; depth varies as required for pathlength requirements, typically from 1 to 100 mm.

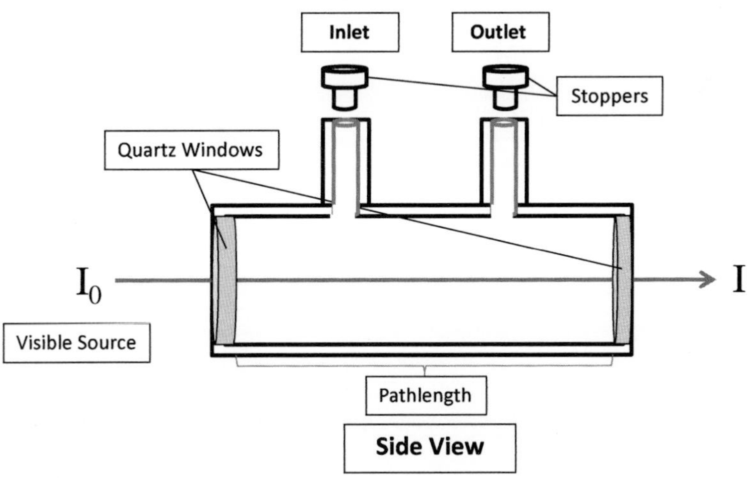

Fig. 4.2 Illustration of cylindrical cuvette type. These cuvettes are available in varying dimensions and pathlengths.

4.1.2.2 *Viscous Materials*

A simple and convenient method for measuring viscous materials using visible spectroscopy is to dilute the sample using an acceptable solvent so that it may be measured using a standard rectangular or cylindrical cuvette. If the sample cannot be diluted for some reason and the material is sufficiently viscous, one may utilize a cuvette with a well at the appropriate pathlength and a cover slide as the parallel window. This is shown in Figure 4.3.

4.1.2.3 *Pastes, Emulsions, and Slurries*

Pastes, emulsions, and slurries generally are sampled as viscous liquids, either by using dilution, special well slides, or reflectance measurements. Note that if inhomogeneity is a problem, the sample must be homogenized to provide a more uniform suspension or emulsion. With multiple phase emulsions or suspensions be certain that separation does not occur when sampling and taking measurements.

4.1.2.4 *Solids*

Finely ground solids as ground material to pass less than a 1.0 mm screen (that is, that are finer than 1.0 mm diameter particles) are preferred if using reflectance to measure special products. Often extraction techniques may be used to put specific molecules into solution for direct transmittance measurement using standard

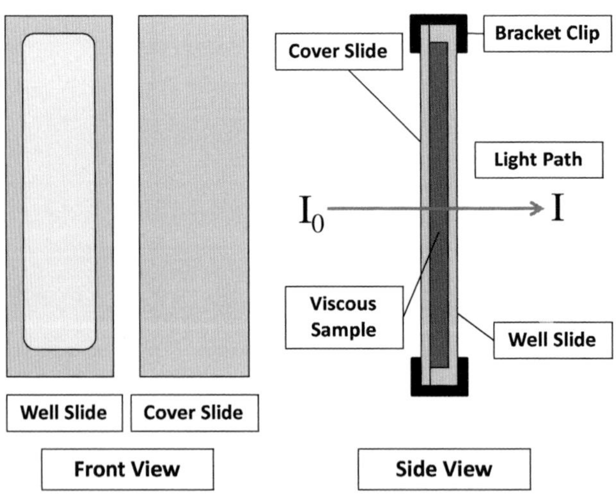

Fig. 4.3 Well slide (rectangular cuvette) for use in measuring highly viscous liquids that cannot be diluted for use in normal cuvettes. The pathlength is fixed by the well depth.

cuvettes. Solid polymer samples of sufficient thickness may also be used for direct measurement using visible reflectance. Typically visible spectroscopy may penetrate into a polymer sample and one should be aware that the visible energy is penetrating the sample and the thickness will affect both shape and intensity of spectral bands. Solids are often measured using an integrating sphere if diffuse reflectance/reflection or diffuse transmittance/transmission is required. The special aspects of sampling with an integrating sphere are discussed in Chapters 2 and 7 of this volume and in other volumes of this book set.

(a) Powders

Unlike the many methods used to prepare powders for measurement using infrared spectra, for visible measurements the samples are generally dried and milled using a cyclone mill with a 1.0 mm screen, to make particles less than 1 mm in diameter. The powdered samples are place in a sample cup and measured using an integrating sphere. Cups used for powders include the locking powder cup (Figures 4.4). Sample thickness for these cups may vary from 5 mm to 10 mm or more. The typical active window of the sample for measurement is from 20 mm up to 50 mm in diameter, depending on the sample window aperture diameter of the integrating sphere.

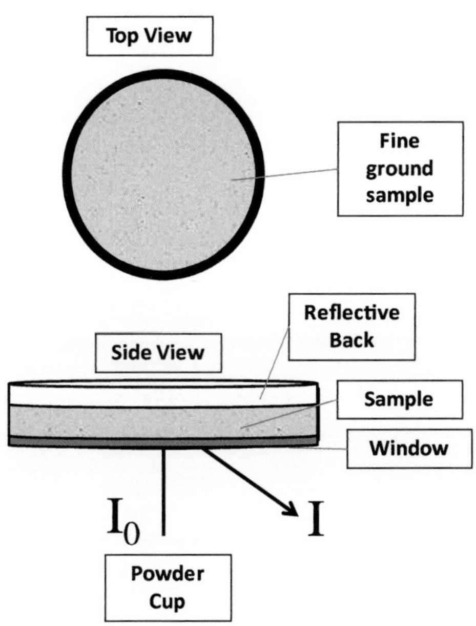

Fig. 4.4 Powder cup for reflectance spectroscopy.

(b) Amorphous Materials (Organic), Continuous Sheets, and Polymeric Films

Polymer sheets may be measured in transmittance geometry or in diffuse reflectance geometry. A film holder may be used for transmittance (Figure 4.5). For diffuse reflectance a standard reflectance cup with a diffuse back reflector may be used. For this application a piece of the sheet or film is cut to the size of the sample cup and a diffuse reflectance measurement is made. It is important to remember that for a sample with limited thickness the effective pathlength of a measurement is more than twice the physical pathlength of the sample (Figure 4.6). If the film sample has

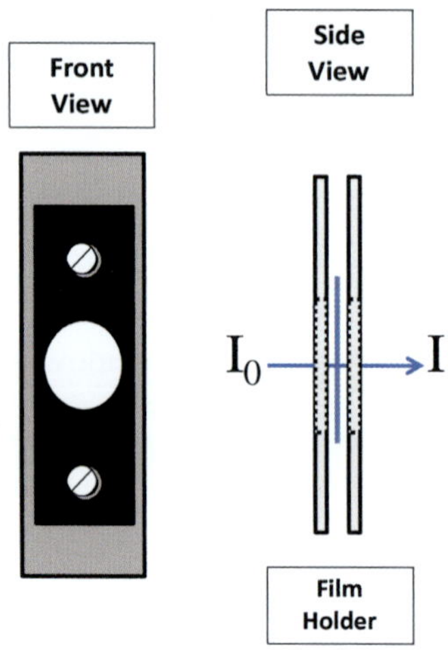

Fig. 4.5 Film holder for transmittance measurements of films.

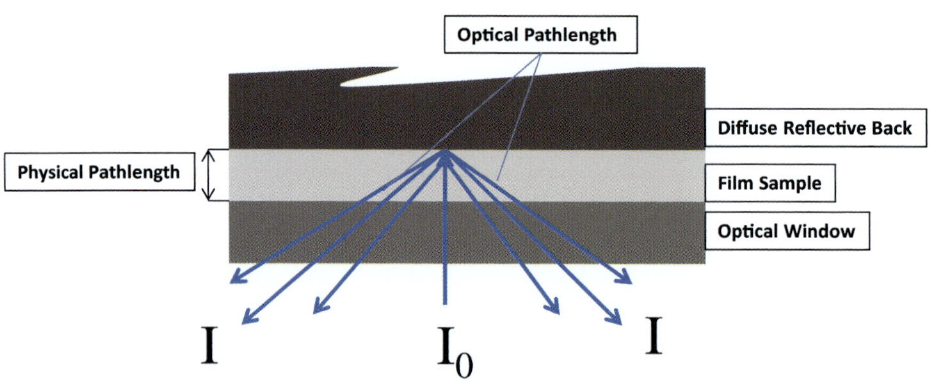

Fig. 4.6 Illustration of multiple photon pass of diffuse reflectance measurement of films.

a metalized coating it will act as an etalon and give interference fringes in addition to the molecular spectrum. These fringes are due to multiple reflections in the film and have a periodicity proportional to the film thickness. See film thickness measurement in the index of this set of volumes. Other methods for handling polymers and films may be used from infrared sampling techniques. The reader is referred to the index on thin films and polymer sampling as well as the chapter within the infrared text volume on the subject of sample preparation.

(c) Lumps, Granules, or Pellets

These solid materials may be used in various diffuse reflectance cups in bulk form or ground and mixed for sample presentation using a powder cup.

(d) Intractable Materials

Sample with high absorbance (or less than 1% reflectance) may not provide enough signal for many commercial visible spectrometers. A specialized measuring instrument may be required as discussed in Chapter 4 of Volume 3.

4.1.2.5 *Sampling Method versus Sample Type*

This section provides similar information and cross-referenced information to that of the previous section, but in this case it is more procedure oriented. Hints and tips are provided for the actual method rather than focusing on the sample and its properties.

(a) Transmittance Windows

The most basic sampling device for visible spectroscopy includes a sampling system with a visible transmissive window; see Table 4.2 for a summary of common visible transmitting window materials.

(b) Transmittance Cells (Liquid Handling)

Liquids are generally measured using a fixed transmittance/transmission geometry with many commercial visible instruments. Some instruments enable configuring either reflectance or transmittance geometry and so transmittance measurements are permitted.

(c) Specular Reflectance Measurements

Specular reflectance (or mirror reflectance) represents an elastic photon reflection where only the direction of the incoming photon is changed, therefore the original energy (i.e., frequency or wavelength) is identical after the reflection interaction. The most common applications of specular reflectance using visible spectroscopy are for direct measurement of surfaces for contaminants or for measurement of optical

Table 4.2 Spectral ranges for visible optical window and lens materials (in microns).

Optical material spectral ranges	Start	End
Silica, UV Grade Fused (SiO_2)	0.20	2.5
Silica, Synthetic Fused (SiO_2)	0.23	2.6
Quartz, Crystalline (SiO_2)	0.24	2.6
Quartz, extremely low O-H	0.19	2.7
Glass, Flint (SF 10)	0.38	2.35
Glass, Flint (SF 8)	0.355	2.35
Glass (BK 7)	0.315	2.35
Glass, "Optical Crown"	0.32	2.3
Glass, "Borosilicate Crown"	0.36	2.35
Glass, Pyrex®	0.31	2.5
Glass, Zerodur® Schott	0.40	2.85
Glass, Tempax®	0.36	2.35
Sapphire (Aluminum Oxide) (Al_2O_3) 5 mm is 50 %T at 5.1 microns	0.15	5.1
Sodium Chloride (NaCl)	0.25	16.0
Suprasil 300	0.19	3.6
Diamond (C)	0.22	4.0
Silica, Fused as pure SiO_2 (IR Quality)	0.20	4.0
Quartz, Anhydrous	0.20	2.75
Glass, Silica, Fused "Water Free" (SiO_2); 10 mm is 82%T at 3.15 microns	0.15	3.15
Glass, Corning Optical Glasses as HPFS® 7978 and 7979 50%T/cm	0.15	4.35
Glass, Corning Optical Glasses as HPFS® 7980; 50%T/cm	0.2	2.6
Glass, Corning Optical Glasses as HPFS® 865X and 797X 50%T/cm	0.15	2.6
Glass, ESCO Optical Glasses as S1-UVA and S1-UVB Working Range (Band 1)	0.17	2.2
Glass, ESCO Optical Glasses as I2-IR Working Range	0.25	3.6
Glass, ESCO Optical Glasses as G1 and A1 Working Range	0.27	2.5
Glass, ESCO Optical Glasses as BK7 Working Range	0.35	2.0

reflection properties of materials in the visible spectral region. For example, certain optical mirror or lens materials, paints or coatings. For the visible region, these measurements are referred to as transflectance or reflection/absorption. As may be observed in Figure 4.7 for specular reflection measurements the incident angle and reflection measurement angle are the same. If the incident angle and the reflection measurement angle are different other reflective interactions will be measured, such as diffuse reflection, interactance, or transflectance. In these types of measurements an inelastic photon interaction occurs and an absorption due to interaction with the sample is the most likely result.

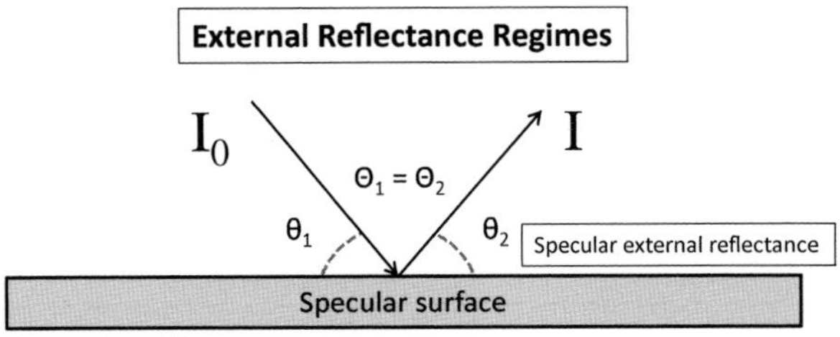

Fig. 4.7 Specular surface reflection. reflectance regimes.

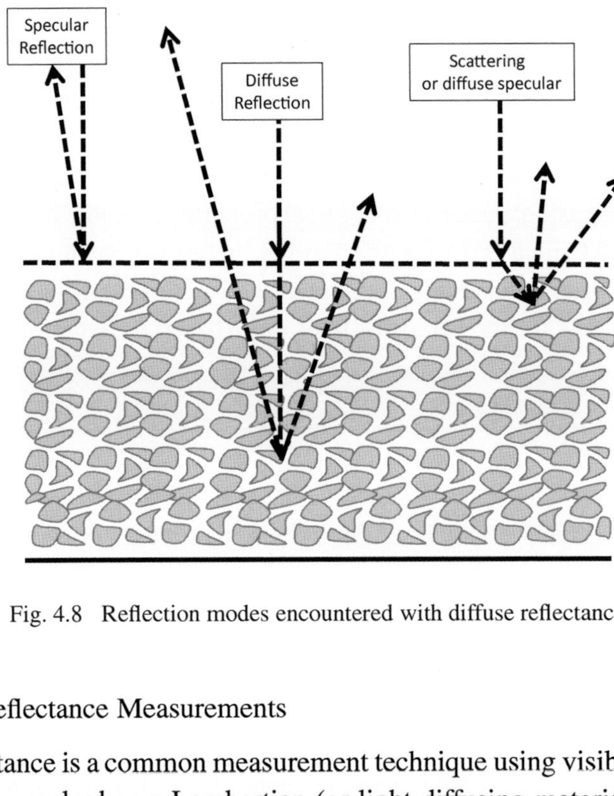

Fig. 4.8 Reflection modes encountered with diffuse reflectance.

(d) Diffuse Reflectance Measurements

Diffuse reflectance is a common measurement technique using visible spectroscopy. The method is used when a Lambertian (or light-diffusing material), is measured. Optical effects primarily occur to the surface of the sample, such as specular reflection, Mie scattering, and diffuse reflection (Figure 4.8). There are detailed discussions regarding the use of the integrating sphere and various spectral data treatments for reflectance measurements in Chapter 7 of this volume and several other volumes of this text set.

(e) Abrasion Measurement Techniques

Very hard surfaces can be studied by the abrasion of the surface with a sheet of abrasive material, such as silicon carbide or carborundum paper. Following a roughening of the surface, diffuse reflectance may be used to measure the material. This technique is described in more detail in Chapters 4, for Volumes 3 and 4. Refer to Chapter 7 of this volume and Volume 3 and the index for detailed descriptions of the theory and application of the integrating sphere, used for reflectance measurements.

4.1.3 *The Properties of Fiber Optics*[5]

4.1.3.1 *Typical Applications*

Optical fibers are useful for remote or process measurements using optical spectroscopy; particularly visible, near infared, and the higher frequency infrared (typically above 1,000 cm^{-1}). The basic properties of fiber optics include materials, construction, dimensions, and overall optical properties. Visible fiber optic materials consist of low-OH silica (SiO_2) with minimal inclusions, such as entrapped air. A fiber bundle consists in cladding layer(s) and a coating layer for protection. See Volume 3, Chapter 4 for the details of fiber optic based measurements.

References

1. J. Workman, *The Academic Press Handbook of Organic Compounds: visible, IR, Raman, and UV-VIS Spectra Featuring Polymers, and Surfactants.* 3 Volume Set: Vol. 1, Methods and Interpretation; Vol. 2, UV-Vis and visible Spectra; Vol. 3, IR and Raman Spectra (Academic Press, Boston, 2000).
2. R.D. Braun, *Introduction to Instrumental Analysis* (McGraw-Hill Book Company, New York, 1987).
3. J. Workman and A. Springsteen, Applied Spectroscopy: A Compact Reference for Practitioners (Academic Press, Boston, 1998).
4. Multiple commercial manufacturers exist for referencing the various sampling systems, including: http://www.starnacells.com/d_cells_s/rect/T001.html
5. J. Hecht, *Understanding Fiber Optics*, 3rd edn. (Prentice Hall, New Jersey, 1999).

Chapter 5

Data Acquisition for Visible Spectra

Contents

5.1 Recommended Spectrum Acquisition, Presentation Format and Data Manipulation Procedures

5.1.1 *Recommended Spectrum Acquisition Parameters*

Quality visible spectrophotometers provide a wavelength coverage over the ultraviolet and visible region from 190 nm to approximately 900 nm. Sample measurement techniques include transmittance or diffuse reflection sample presentation (when using an integrating sphere accessory). A modern visible spectrometer will scan from 1 to 2500 nm/min. with variable total scan time and signal to noise specifications. Spectral resolution or bandpass is often settable from less than 0.1 nm to 5 nm or more. High quality instruments provide a signal-to-noise ratio (S/N) of 10,000:1 or better (0.0001 Abs.). Note that for visible work a halfwidth of less than 5–6 nm has no real advantage due to the broad nature of visible absorption bands.

Documentation should be maintained for all analyses, following good laboratory practices (GLP) guidelines, which include laboratory notebooks, either paper or electronic and recorded measurement parameters, analyst, results, and corroborating signatures.[1]

5.1.2 *Recommended Spectral Range*

Unless special circumstances dictate otherwise, visible spectra are recorded from a minimum of 360 nm to 780 nm (the ASTM International definition) or to 770 nm (the ISO 12099 definition). However typical research grade commercial visible spectrometers will have a scan range of 190 nm to either 900 nm or 1100 nm. The spectral range covered is limited based upon the number of octaves that may be covered with basic optical systems, detectors, and stray light (cut-on) filters. Visible spectroscopy instruments are restricted by the grating, resolution, and detector used; along with the basic optical design criteria.

With modern visible spectroscopy instruments, it is normal to measure the full spectral range with each scan. When calibration or data transfer is required then data may later be truncated (or windowed) so that one spectrometer collects the identical spectral range and data points as another spectrometer. Such data management allows easier compatibility of databases developed over time and allows detailed study of spectra or instrument diagnostics at a later time.

5.1.3 *Recommended Data Presentation Formats*

The normal intensity scale obtained for a raw measurement is T/%T, or R/%R converted to Absorbance (A) using Beer's law (described in detail elsewhere in this volume). If an abbreviated or expanded scale is used, it is important to ensure that the scale limits are presented, preferably with immediate scale markings shown. Note that for all numerical operations on spectral data, it is necessary to perform the operations on the absorbance form of the spectrum, including baseline corrections, spectral subtractions, and any numerical scaling of data. An important exception is the numerical and/or digital treatment of noise. Noise is essentially linear over the entire scale in reflectance (%R), or transmittance (%T) and is logarithmic in the absorbance scale. All processing that assumes a linear distribution of noise, such as digital smoothing or digital signal processing, must be applied to the reflectance or transmittance forms of the data; then converted to absorbance in order to compute a proper correction.

The standard linear wavelength scale is normally used for visible data: electronic transitions and overtone absorption data are associated with wavelength (nanometer or microns) form of the scale (by tradition). However, it is entirely appropriate to represent visible spectra in frequency or wavenumber space, and is often done in astrophysics, physics, or optical technologies.

5.1.4 *Spectral Data Manipulation*

Absorbance spectra for analytical use are recorded using ratioed spectral data. This consists of the sample spectrum, the reference spectrum, and the dark signal spectrum. The use of Beer's law for spectroscopic measurements is shown in the following description. To convert the light reflected or transmitted from a sample (I) ratioed to the incident energy (I_0) to Absorbance (A), as a linear estimate of spectral response to concentration, the following equations are used. If only an internal reference is used for spectral collection, then the absorbance spectrum with respect to wavelength is computed as:

$$A = \log_{10}\left(\frac{I_0}{I}\right) = \log_{10}\left(\frac{1}{T}\right) = \log_{10}\left[\left(\frac{R_I - D_{R_I}}{S - D_S}\right)\right] \tag{5.1}$$

If an external standard material is used to calibrate the internal reference material, then the absorbance spectrum with respect to wavelength is computed as:

$$A = \log_{10}\left(\frac{I_0}{I}\right) = \log_{10}\left[\left(\frac{R_I + R_\Delta - D_{R_I}}{S - D_S}\right)\right] \tag{5.2}$$

where:

$$R_\Delta = \frac{(R_E - D_{RE})}{(R_I - D_{RI})} \tag{5.3}$$

and where S is the sample measurement; D_S is the Dark measurement for the Sample; R_I is the internal Reference Measurement; D_{RI} is the Dark Measurement for the Internal Reference Sample; R_E is the measurement of the external standard reference material for calibration; D_{RE} is the Dark Measurement for the external standard reference material; and R_Δ is the correction factor between the dark corrected R_E and R_I. The final spectrum is simplified to the ratio of (Internal Reference corrected by External Reference minus Dark) divided by (Sample minus Dark). Note that Dark is a measurement where no energy from the source is allowed to the detector (it is blocked). The Dark measurement represents the dark current changes in the instrument during a measurement that relate to electronic noise where the detection electronics, computational electronics, and control electronics perform basic measurement functions with no imputed energy reaching the detector (i.e., the source is turned off or blocked using a shutter closure during the Dark measurement).

For spectral appearance purposes, digital smoothing and nominal baseline corrections are acceptable if they improve overall quality of the final spectra for qualitative evaluation or quantitative analysis. If there are any doubts in terms of acceptability for data processing, the original raw data should be archived. All

Table 5.1 Typical spectroscopic data file formats and extensions.

Data format name	Extension
ASCII Table	(.csv)
Excel	(.xls)
JCAMP-DX	(.dx)
MatLab	(.mat)
mzData	(.XML)
Perkin Elmer	(.sp)
Plain Text	(.txt)
Spectra-Calc (Archival)	(fixed point .spc)
Thermo Galactic	(.spc)
XLM Marked-up text	(.XML)

documentation concerning data manipulation should be retained with the spectra in a digital format.

5.1.5 *Data Formatting*

A standard data format is essential for the utilization of visible spectral data. Data from various instruments is routinely combined for quantitative calibration transfer and utilization of spectral libraries for qualitative searches for the purpose of identification.

In general, there has not been a universal adoption of a single standardized format for visible spectroscopic data. Ideally, one would produce a reproducible standard spectrum for a given material using a prescribed method of sample preparation. The standard spectrum should be independent of operator or instrument manufacturer. Readers are referred to the standard procedures for sample preparation as defined in consensus standards, such as the ASTM *Annual Book of Standards*.[2] Each instrument manufacturer may have from 1–10 (or more) data formats including older versions of their software. A list of the most typical spectroscopy software formats is given in Table 5.1.

5.1.6 *Summary*

This chapter has focused on the issues of sampling as they pertain to routine sampling for qualitative and quantitative visible spectroscopic analysis. There are many routine specialized approaches to sampling that may be adopted for research applications. These are typically experiment dependent, and their success may be somewhat limited to the application for which they are customized. For this reason, such examples have been generally excluded from this text.

References

1. Guidance for Industry Good Laboratory Practices Questions and Answers, U.S. Department of Health and Human Services Food and Drug administration Office of Regulatory affairs, June 1981 (Minor editorial and formatting changes made December 1999 & July 2007).
2. ASTM (American Society for Testing and Materials) Method E169-04 (2009). "Standard Practices for General Techniques of Ultraviolet-Visible Quantitative Analysis", ASTM Committee E 13, 1916 Race Street, Philadelphia, PA 19103.

Chapter 6

Data Analysis and Presentation for Visible Spectroscopy

Contents

This chapter covers a variety of mathematical data treatments common to visible spectroscopy. It is intended to be a reference chapter for descriptions and explanations of each type of mathematical function common to visible methods. Details of multivariate analysis and statistics are included in other volumes of this set. The reader is referred to the index for individual topics related to chemometrics (multivariate analysis). Topics such as matrix mathematics, regression, partial least squares, quantitative analysis, qualitative analysis, and other regression and calibration related topics are included in other volumes.

6.1 Baseline Correction Algorithms

Additional descriptions and figures for baseline correction may be found in the index.

6.1.1 *Baseline Offset Correction*

Offset correction is performed by selecting a single point or multiple points along the spectrum and adding or subtracting a y-value (i.e., intensity value) from the point or points to correct the baseline offset. This preprocessing step is used to align the baseline of two or more spectra, causing them to overlap; or it is used to bring the minimum point to zero. A single point offset of $+\ 0.1$A for all wavelengths is shown in Figure 6.1.

6.1.2 *Derivatives*

Derivatives are used to remove offset or some slope characteristics in the baseline which are the result of background differences or scattering. The reader is referred to the index for a detailed section on derivative methods and spectroscopy.

6.1.3 *Flat Baseline Correction (Two-point baseline correction)*

Two data points are selected on the signal, and a line connecting these points is subtracted from the signal. This process removes first-order uniform offset and will remove some slope effect.

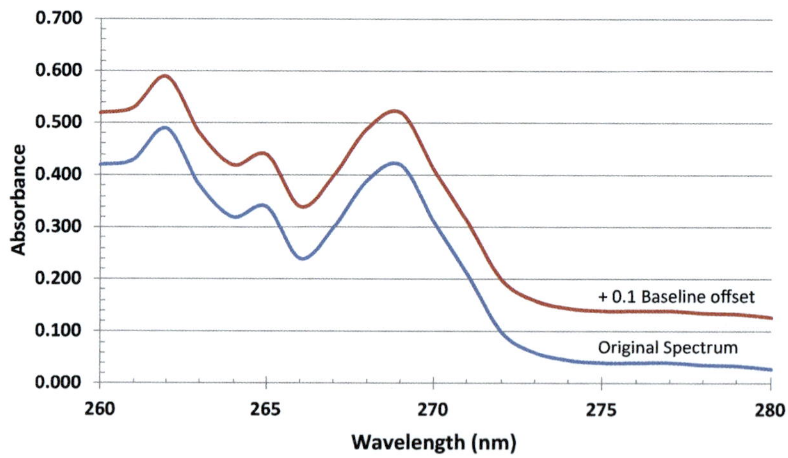

Fig. 6.1 Single point baseline correction of +0.1 Absorbance (A) unit.

6.2 Data Analysis: Plotting Data for Visual Assessment

Human pattern recognition powers enable the spectroscopist to assess characteristics of data rapidly and accurately. When performing calibration or data mining, the various plotting of data sets or features will allow rapid evaluation of the quality and types of data under evaluation. Therefore this section discusses many of the techniques used for manual and visual data review to determine the characteristics of spectra.

There are various plotting techniques for data that demonstrate the character of spectral features and the relationships between variables. Several examples will be illustrated in this section.

6.2.1 *Using Two-Dimensional Data Plots for Visual Data Interpretation*

The main uses of residual plotting to interpret the efficacy of predictive calibration models involves the use of several types of graphics. These include the following basic types:

- Predicted vs. Actual
- Residual vs. Actual

6.2.2 *Predicted versus Actual Plot*

The predicted versus actual plot is made by plotting the reference or actual values for each sample as the abscissa (X axis) versus the spectroscopic method (predicted value) as the Y axis (ordinate). This X-Y plot demonstrates the basic correlation between the estimated value using the analytical method and the reference values or primary reference chemistry as a comparison. It also indicates precision and fitness to the actual (reference) values where a perfect line with no residuals is a perfect fit (Figure 6.2).

6.2.3 *Residual versus Actual Plot*

The predicted (spectroscopic value) residual versus actual (reference value) plot is a powerful visual tool for diagnosing issues associated with evaluating quantitative methods. To generate this plot one plots the reference value as the abscissa (X axis) and the difference between the spectroscopic method and the reference method as the ordinate value (Y axis) for each test or prediction sample. Figure 6.3 demonstrates the basic prediction residuals versus the reference results for a prediction set that is

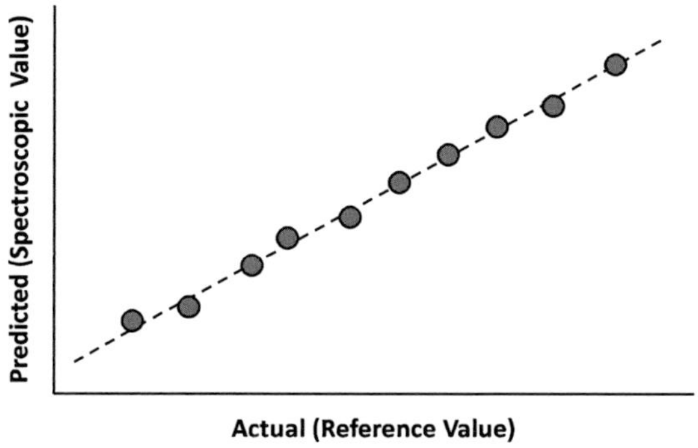

Fig. 6.2 Predicted versus actual plot: a strong positive correlation is shown with good fit for predicted values versus reference values.

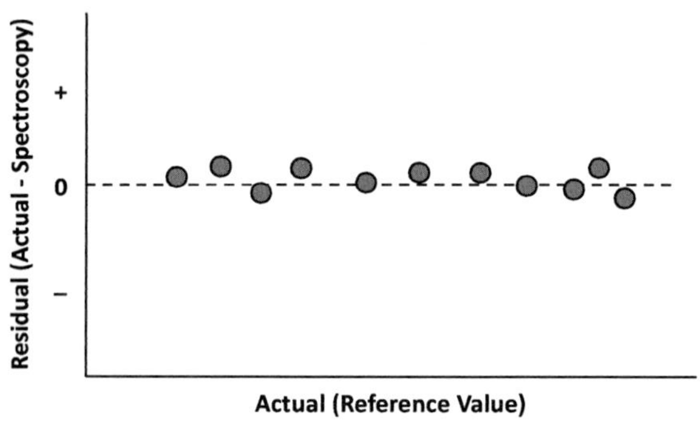

Fig. 6.3 Residual versus actual plot: a strong positive correlation is shown with good (precision), no slope or bias differences; no curvature to data for residual values versus reference values.

predicting accurately. There is no slope or bias differences between the reference values and the predicted values.

6.3 Data Preprocessing: Scaling, Smoothing, and Normalization

Multiple methods are used for preparation of spectroscopic data either for visual evaluation or application to algorithms for qualitative or quantitative analysis.

6.3.1 *Scaling Methods*

6.3.1.1 *Mean Centering*

The mean spectrum for a set of spectra is subtracted from all the spectra in the set. This technique is used to remove the larger (or bulk) spectral features in order to view or calibrate the remaining spectral information. This remaining information

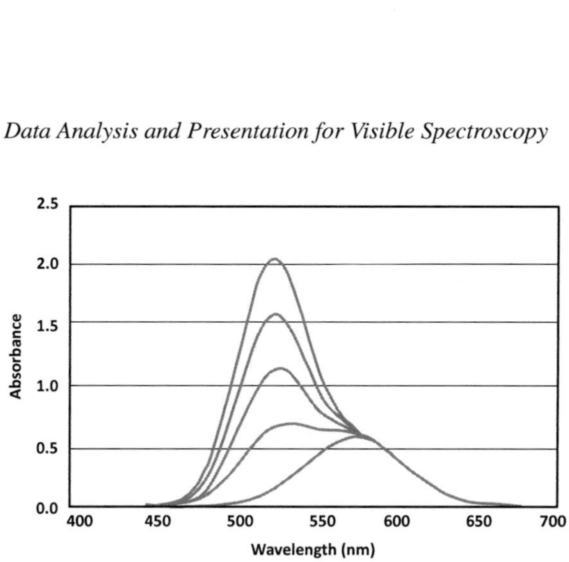

Fig. 6.4 A set of 5 spectra with two components present.

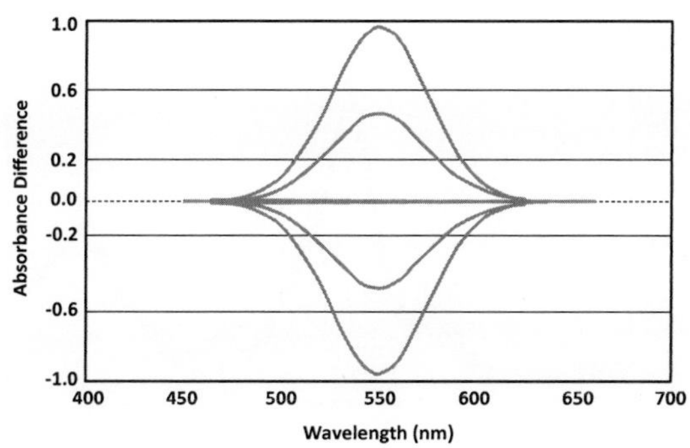

Fig. 6.5 The set of 5 spectra with the mean absorbance at each wavelength subtracted from each spectrum shown in Figure 6.4.

contains the detailed chemical features of the spectra. Figure 6.4 shows a set of spectra, with Figure 6.5 showing the same spectra with the mean absorbance values subtracted at each data point. Note the central spectrum in Figure 6.4 represents the middle absorbance of the five spectra and thus forms a straight line after mean centering, as shown in Figure 6.5.

6.3.1.2 *Autoscaling*

The mean spectrum of a set of spectra is subtracted from all the spectra (mean centering) with an additional step of dividing all the spectra in the teaching set by the standard deviation of absorbance values at each wavelength. This technique is used to enhance the basic chemical information in spectra for manual viewing or for use in multivariate analysis. Figure 6.6 shows a set of spectra in absorbance space; Figure 6.7 shows the same set of spectra after such an autoscaling process.

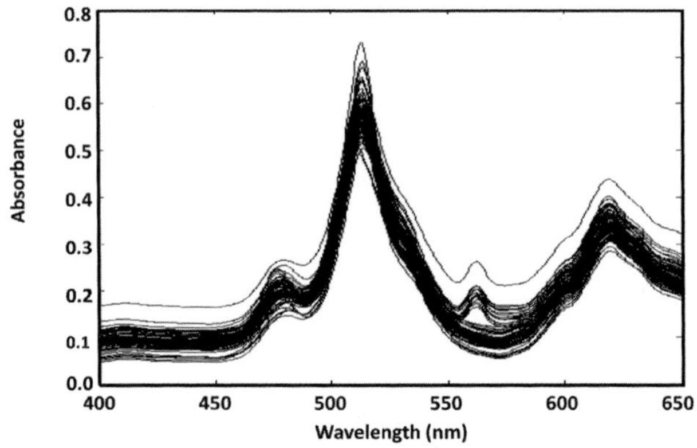

Fig. 6.6 Set of spectra as measured in Absorbance space.

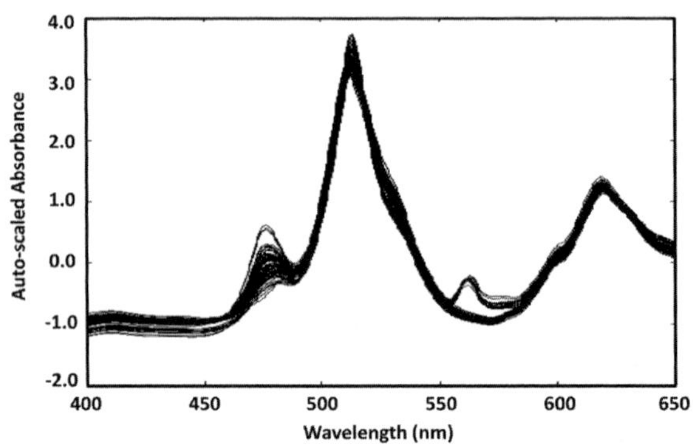

Fig. 6.7 Set of spectra from Figure 6.6 after autoscaling.

6.3.2 *Smoothing Algorithms*

Smoothing eliminates the white noise within spectral signatures due to both random and structured variation in signals. Smoothing allows enhanced manual viewing and multivariate processing by eliminating spectral variation due to random measurement noise. Volume 3, Sections 6.8 and 6.9 provide a detailed description of Savitzky-Golay smoothing and the reader is referred to the index to locate other coverage of this topic. In the following text there is a brief description of the most common applications of smoothing within spectroscopy.

6.3.2.1 *Boxcar Smoothing*

Boxcar smoothing is an algorithm used to improve the signal-to-noise ratio in spectral data by averaging successive data points to remove random variation or noise. The use of this smoothing may broaden bands and remove some fine structure or poorly resolved small spectral bands in the data. Over smoothing will remove both important spectral features and create an x-axis (i.e., wavelength) shift in spectral data.

6.3.2.2 *Fourier-Domain (FFT) Smoothing*

Fourier-domain smoothing involves a Fourier transformation of the signal, the application of a filter function (with a set filter factor), and then performing a reverse Fourier transform to the data. A triangular filter function is generally applied. The FFT smoothing is able to remove high frequency random noise from the signal with a minimum effect on real spectral features. If overfiltering is applied additional spectral artifacts may appear, which have no chemical meaning.

6.3.3 *Normalization*

6.3.3.1 *Normalization by Means of a Pathlength Correction*

Individual pathlength data is used as a scalar multiplier term for correction of an individual spectrum or group/set of spectra of varying pathlengths or varying effective pathlengths.

6.3.3.2 *Normalization by Area*

For spectral normalization by area, all band areas are set to a single integrated area value for the purpose of visual signal comparison and/or correlation techniques. It is most useful for searching for the presence of various chemical components in a mixture spectrum or for spectral qualitative analysis when comparing spectral shapes of mixtures of materials.

6.3.3.3 *Normalization by Means of a Reference Band*

For applying normalization by means of a reference band a set of spectra used for multivariate calibration are ratioed to a peak height or by a factor for peak area of a reference band. The reference band must be of consistent height or area and will correct the spectral signal for anomalies in the measurement conditions. The ratioed spectra will be corrected for use in quantitative analysis when the spectral baseline is poorly resolved.

6.3.3.4 *Normalization Using the Kubelka-Munk Transform*

The Kubelka-Munk transform (KMT) is applied as a linearization function to signals with scattering and absorptive characteristics as often encountered in diffuse reflectance. This relationship is defined as:

$$\text{Spectral Signal (KMT)} = \frac{k}{s} = \frac{(1 - R_{\lambda_i})^2}{2R_{\lambda_i}} \tag{6.1}$$

where k is the absorptive coefficient; s is the scattering coefficient; R is the reflectance signal from the sample; and λ_i is the wavelength where the signal is measured as Reflectance with respect to wavelength (i.e., the reflectance spectrum).

6.4 Derivative and Smoothing Applications in Spectroscopy

6.4.1 *First and Second Derivative Nomenclature*

Note this discussion of derivatives for spectroscopic measurements begins with the common linearization of reflectance (R) or transmission data (T) to absorbance as given by:

$$A = -\log_{10} R_l \quad \text{and} \quad A = -\log_{10} T_l \tag{6.2}$$

where A is absorbance expressed as reflectance or transmission when R or $T = I/I_o$.

Absorbance ratio has been used for quantitative spectroscopy, initially being introduced for NIR.[1] It is the ratio of absorbance at one wavelength divided by the absorbance at a second wavelength. This ratio method is common to infrared spectroscopists as using it results in a term which compensates for baseline offset. The ratio of transmission data is also useful for normalizing or reducing baseline offset in spectroscopic measurements. A typical absorbance ratio is given as:

$$\frac{A_{\lambda_1}}{A_{\lambda_2}} \tag{6.3}$$

Standard derivative nomenclature for first and second order derivatives is as follows. A Gaussian shaped band and its first derivative are illustrated in Figure 6.8.

$$\text{First derivative} = f'(x) = \frac{dy}{dx} \tag{6.4}$$

$$\text{Second derivative} = f''(x) = \frac{d^2y}{dx^2} \tag{6.5}$$

The use of the moving-averaged-segment convolution (MASC) method for computing derivatives in spectroscopy, brings about the expression below describing a first

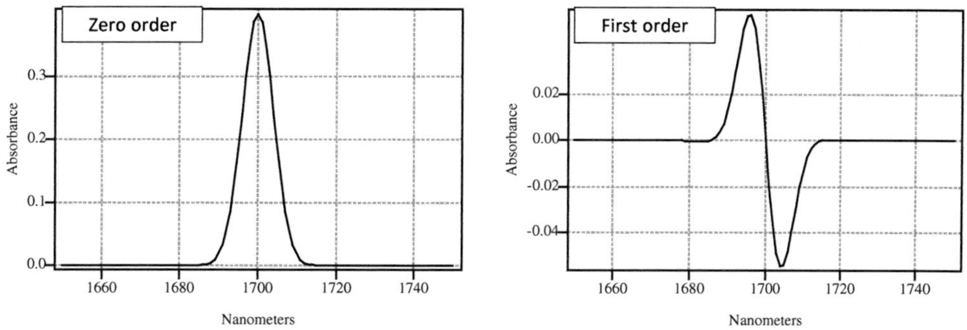

Fig. 6.8 Spectral shapes as zero order Gaussian band (left) and first derivative of band (right).

derivative term as:

$$A_{\lambda_2} - A_{\lambda_1} = A_{\lambda_{1+\Delta\lambda}} - A_{\lambda_{1-\Delta\lambda}} \tag{6.6}$$

where the derivative is given as the difference in absorbance values at 2 different wavelengths; the position of each wavelength being determined as the gap ($\Delta\lambda$) distance + or − from a center wavelength (λ_1).

The MASC form of second derivative is shown below.[2,3] In this case, the second derivative term is defined by the sum of absorbances at two wavelengths ($\lambda_{1+\Delta\lambda}$, and $\lambda_{1-\Delta\lambda}$), minus 2 times the absorbance at a center wavelength (λ_1). In this case the second derivative gap size is designated as $\Delta\lambda$ (delta wavelength). The second derivative preprocessing step is quite effective in removing slope and offset variations in spectral measurement baselines. It also "assists" the calibration mathematics in defining spectral regions where small response changes can be useful in calibration modeling. Without the use of derivatives, these regions would not be beneficial for use in calibration.

$$A_{\lambda_1} + A_{\lambda_3} - 2A_{\lambda_2} = A_{\lambda_{1-\Delta\lambda}} + A_{\lambda_{1+\Delta\lambda}} - 2A_{\lambda_1} \tag{6.7}$$

Other derivative forms and formats are used to express computations of derivative spectra. These are a general form of the derivatives used in derivative processing software for spectrometers. These include the first derivative spectrum as a central difference method.

$$A'_{\lambda} = \frac{A_{\lambda+\Delta} - A_{\lambda}}{\lambda_1 - \lambda_2} = \frac{A_{\lambda+\Delta} - A_{\lambda}}{\Delta_{\lambda}} \tag{6.8}$$

Where Δ is the number of wavelength spaces between A_{λ} and $A_{\lambda+\Delta}$.

A central difference method for computing the first derivative spectrum (Figure 6.8) is used to mitigate for the typical shifts resulting from computing the derivative of spectral data using other equation forms. For this nomenclature

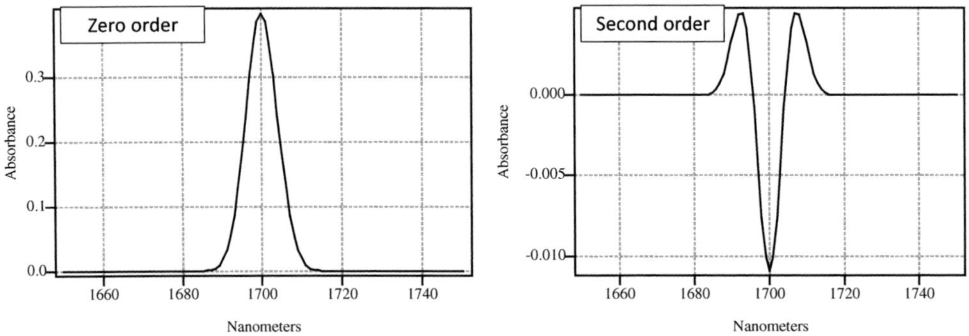

Fig. 6.9 Spectral shapes as zero order Gaussian band (left) and second derivative of band (right).

the $\lambda + \Delta$ represents a center wavelength plus a wavelength gap, represented by (Δ). Therefore $\lambda - \Delta$ represents the central wavelength minus the designated wavelength gap.

$$A'_\lambda = \frac{A_{\lambda+\Delta} - A_{\lambda-\Delta}}{2(\Delta\lambda)} \tag{6.9}$$

The method for computing the second derivative spectrum computation (Figure 6.9) is given as:

$$\begin{aligned} A''_\lambda &= \frac{(A_{\lambda+\Delta} - A_\lambda) - (A_\lambda - A_{\lambda-\Delta})}{(\Delta\lambda)^2} \\ &= \frac{(A_{\lambda+\Delta} - 2A_\lambda + A_{\lambda-\Delta})}{(\Delta\lambda)^2} \end{aligned} \tag{6.10}$$

where Δ is the number of wavelength spaces (gap) between A_λ and $A_{\lambda+\Delta}$ and $A_{\lambda-\Delta}$.

6.5 A Simple Smoothing Function

6.5.1 *Savitzky-Golay Derivative Function of Instrument Software*

Derivative spectra allow enhanced visual identification of small spectral features. Using first- through fourth-order derivatives allow the analyst to observe and study small spectral features which may not be apparent using direct absorbance or transmittance spectral data. One of the best known procedures for producing derivative spectra is the Savitzky-Golay convolution method (Anal. Chem. 36, 1627, 1964).[4,5] This is the method used with many scanning spectrophotometers as the appropriate method for derivative spectra and smoothing.

When using the Savitzky-Golay convolution method on a spectrometer, the user may select an additional set of functions to include first-through fourth-derivative, and a sensitivity setting. The sensitivity function represents a derivative sensitivity, or data interval of 1 nm through 10 nm; each sensitivity number representing 1 nm (see Volume 3, Section 6.9 for details.)

6.6 Visible Instrument Optical Quality Performance Tests

The following series of tests is used to qualify or validate instrument performance and to determine which issues are problematic due to deficiencies in instrument alignment or calibration functions. These tests are related to alikeness in measurement performance between instruments and to overall accuracy, and precision (as repeatability and reproducibility). Note that the terms optical density (O.D.) and absorbance units (AU or Au) are synonyms. (Note that "Optical density" is found in historical documents, and is still used in physics, and biomedical and optical engineering, but not often in analytical chemistry.) Standard methods and practices for calibration include: ISO 17025, ASTM E275-08(2013), ASTM E169-04(2009), ASTM E925-09(2014), and ASTM E958-13.[6–10]

6.6.1 *Wavelength Accuracy Test*

Verify the wavelength accuracy of the spectrophotometer using suitable reference standards. The results must be consistent with the instrument manufacturing specifications, and for the application in use. For visible spectrometers, reference standards used include glass materials with rare earth oxide compounds included, and liquids under standard measurement conditions. For both ultraviolet and visible wavelength accuracy and precision tests, materials used include those shown in Tables 6.1 and 6.2, the nominal (measurand) wavelengths are given for wavelength calibration emission lamps, and solid materials used for testing alignment, respectively. Note that the percent uncertainty is computed as follows:

$$\text{Uncertainty } (\%) = [(\text{Measured Wavelength} - \text{NIST})/\text{NIST}] \times 100\% \quad (6.11)$$

and further U (Uncertainty) is given as:

$$\text{Uncertainty (nm)} = (\text{Measured Wavelength} - \text{NIST}) \quad (6.12)$$

For a more detailed NIST uncertainty value, the equation 6.13 is used.

Table 6.1 Calibration emission lamp standards used for UV-Vis wavelength testing.

Lamp type	Nominal wavelengths (in nm)	Specified uncertainty (± % from NIST)	Allowed deviation (± nm)
Deuterium lamp	486.0	1.0%	1 nm
	656.1	1.0%	3 nm
Mercury vapor lamp	253.7	1.0%	1 nm
	302.25	1.0%	1 nm
	313.16	1.0%	1 nm
	334.15	1.0%	1 nm
	365.48	1.0%	3 nm
	404.66	1.0%	3 nm
	435.83	1.0%	3 nm
	547.07	1.0%	3 nm
	576.96	1.0%	3 nm
	579.07	1.0%	3 nm

NIST uncertainty is a true measure of uncertainty unlike the typical manufacturer report as either precision or accuracy. For example, NIST uncertainty has been calculated from Equation (6.13).[11]

$$U = \sqrt{A^2 + B^2 + C^2} \tag{6.13}$$

Where A = twice the largest standard deviation of measurement of multiple emission lines (measurands)versus the spectrometer measured values over a period of 31 days (or some designated period); B = twice the standard deviation of the uncertainty in the peak selection method used; and C is the maximum variation in the standard due to temperature changes over a specified range and conditions. (Note: The number 2 (twice) is referred to as the k value also known as the *coverage factor*).[12]

A list of NIST standard materials for calibrating UV-Vis spectrophotometers is included in Tables 6.1 through 6.3.[13]

For the wavelength accuracy test, take repeat measurements of the same emission lamp, filter, or liquid sample by placing it in the sample beam and not mechanically moving the sample over a normal measurement cycle for the instrument. For example, a 10–30 second measurement cycle may be typical. Then calculate the first derivative of each of the replicate spectra — compute the inflection or zero-crossing positions for the center band at the peak absorbance near the reference wavelength position (λ_{ref}) specified (see above tables of nominal or measurand values for emission lamps and standards; see Tables 6.1 through 6.3, and Tables 0.21a and 0.21b in Front Material Section). These tables give UV-Vis Gas Emission Sources and

Table 6.2 Standards used for UV-Vis wavelength testing.

Material	Nominal wavelengths (in nm)	Specified uncertainty (± % from NIST)	Allowed deviation (± nm)
NIST SRM 2035a	334.6	0.2%	0.7 nm
	345.4	0.2%	0.7 nm
	360.8	0.2%	0.7 nm
	374.5	0.2%	0.7 nm
	386.1	0.2%	0.7 nm
	402.5	0.2%	0.7 nm
	417.9	0.2%	0.7 nm
	485.4	0.2%	0.7 nm
	537.7	0.2%	0.7 nm
	583.4	0.2%	0.7 nm
	642.4	0.2%	0.7 nm
	747.7	0.2%	0.7 nm
Holmium oxide quartz filter	279.2	1.0%	1 nm
	360.9	1.0%	3 nm
	453.7	1.0%	3 nm
	536.5	1.0%	3 nm
	637.7	1.0%	3 nm
Didymium glass filter	440.4	1.0%	3 nm
	481.0	1.0%	3 nm
	513.4	1.0%	3 nm
	684.5	1.0%	3 nm
	879.3	1.0%	3 nm
Holmium oxide in perchlorate ($HClO_4$) solution	241.15	1.0%	1 nm
	287.15	1.0%	1 nm
	361.5	1.0%	3 nm
	536.3	1.0%	3 nm

Peak Positions, in nanometers, all within this Volume. Next, calculate the standard deviation of difference of the wavelength positions for thc zero crossings for scan-to-scan within (n) replicate samples, and the mean spectrum position ($\overline{\lambda}_i$) for the measured (λ_{ij}) versus reference (λ_{ref}) wavelength values. The standard deviation (s_i) is calculated as:

$$s_i = \sqrt{\frac{\sum_{j=1}^{n} (\lambda_{ij} - \lambda_{ref})^2}{n}} \tag{6.14}$$

The mean difference for wavelength accuracy is determined by:

$$\text{Wavelength Accuracy (as mean difference)} = \overline{\lambda}_i - \lambda_{ref} \tag{6.15}$$

Table 6.3 NIST standard reference materials (SRMs) for calibrating UV-Vis spectrometers.[13]

SRM No.	Description	Unit Size	Wavelength Range (in nm)
931g	Liquid Absorbance Filters, UV-VIS	set (12)	302 to 678
935a	Potassium Dichromate, UV Absorbance Standard	15 g	235 to 350
1935a	Potassium Dichromate Solution/UV Absorbance Standard	set (10)	235, 247, 313, 350
2031b	Metal-on-Fused-Silica Neutral Density Filters (250 nm–635 nm)	set (3)	250 to 635
2035a	Ultraviolet-Visible-Near-Infrared Wavelength/ Wavenumber Transmission Standard	each	334 to 805 and 971 to 1960

where ($\overline{\lambda}_i$) is the average wavelength peak position for the scan-to-scan set; and (λ_{ref}) is the nominal (or measurand) reference wavelength position for the reference standard. The results are reported as Wavelength (λ) precision and accuracy as shown. This may be accomplished for multiple wavelengths depending upon the standard references measured.

	Nominal Reference Value (λ_{ref})	Precision (scan-to-scan standard deviation from reference, Eq. (6.14))	Accuracy (as mean difference from reference, Eq. (6.15))
Scan-to-Scan	—		
Average	—		

6.6.2 *Wavelength Repeatability Test*

Verify the wavelength repeatability of the spectrophotometer using suitable reference standard(s), such as those listed in Tables 6.1 through 6.3.

Take repeat measurements of the same emission lamp, filter, or liquid sample by placing it in the sample beam and not mechanically moving the sample over a normal measurement cycle for the instrument. For example, a 10-30 second measurement cycle may be typical. Then calculate the first derivative of each of the replicate spectra — compute the inflection or zero-crossing positions for the center band at the peak absorbance near the reference wavelength position (λ_{ref}) specified. (See Tables 6.1–6.3 of nominal or measurand values for emission lamps and standards).

The standard deviation as wavelength repeatability is calculated as:

$$s_i = \sqrt{\frac{\sum_{j=1}^{n} (\lambda_{ij} - \overline{\lambda}_i)^2}{n-1}} \tag{6.16}$$

where (s_i) is the standard deviation for the scan-to-scan wavelength precision or repeatability for scan-to-scan measurements, and where (λ_{ij}) are individual wavelength shifts of the zero-crossover for sample i and scan-to-scan number j; ($\overline{\lambda}_i$) is the average wavelength value for the scan-to-scan set; n is the number of replicate measurements (pool all scan-to-scan data).

The mean spectrum wavelength position ($\overline{\lambda}_i$) is calculated as:

$$\overline{\lambda}_i = \frac{\sum_{i}^{n} \lambda_i}{n} \tag{6.17}$$

The results are reported as: Wavelength (nm) Repeatability

	Mean wavelength ($\overline{\lambda}_i$), Eq. (6.17)	Precision/Repeatability (s_i), Eq. (6.16)
Scan-to-Scan		

6.6.3 *Absorbance/Response Accuracy Test*

Verify the response accuracy of the spectrophotometer using a suitable standard, for example, a set of pre-specified reference neutral density (ND) filters (such as NIST SRM 930e, see reference 14) with nominal (measurand) absorbance unit values. This reference standard must be provided with reference measurements of two or more separated wavelength positions.

For this test, repeat measurements of the same photometric standard are completed by placing it in the sample beam and not mechanically moving the sample over a normal measurement cycle for the measurement period. Then calculate the absorbance units (AU) for the entire spectrum and specifically at the two measured reference points of, for example, 440.0 nm, 465.0 nm, 546.1 nm, 590.0 nm, or 635.0 nm (for SRM 930d). See index and Chapter 8 in this volume for more details.

The reference AU for each wavelength position (A_{440nm} and A_{635nm}) is measured for each scan for each sample (n) and for the mean spectrum ($\overline{A}_i$) at each wavelength location over the measurement period. The statistics are calculated as:

$$s_{440nm} = \sqrt{\frac{\sum_{j=1}^{n} (A_{ij} - A_{440nm})^2}{n}} \quad \text{and} \quad s_{635nm} = \sqrt{\frac{\sum_{j=1}^{n} (A_{ij} - A_{635nm})^2}{n}} \tag{6.18}$$

where (s_{nm}) is the standard deviation (precision) for the scan-to-scan absorbance units at a specified wavelength (AU) accuracy for the set of measurements, and where (A_{ij}) are individual measurements of the absorbance units for sample i through scan-to-scan replicate measurement number j; (A_{nm}) are the reference values for the reference material at each of 440.0 nm and 635.0 nm; n is the replicate measurement number. (Remember to pool all scan-to-scan data.)

The mean difference for photometric accuracy at each wavelength position is determined by:

$$\text{Photometric Accuracy (as mean difference)} = \overline{A}_{nm} - A_{nm} \tag{6.19}$$

where ($\overline{A}_{nm}$) is the average photometric value for the scan-to-scan set; and (A_{nm}) is the reference photometric value at each of 440.0 nm and 635.0 nm. The results are reported as Absorbance/Response (Photometric) Accuracy (in AU). These can be computed for multiple calibrated wavelength or wavenumber positions if desired.

	Nominal Reference Value A_{440nm}	Precision as s_{440nm}, Eq. (6.18)	Accuracy (as mean difference) 440 nm, Eq. (6.19).	Nominal Reference Value A_{635nm}	Precision as s_{635nm}, Eq. (6.18).	Accuracy (as mean difference) 635 nm, Eq. (6.19)
Scan-to-Scan	—	—		—	—	
Average	—		—	—		—

6.6.4 *Absorbance/Response Repeatability Test*

Verify the response accuracy of the spectrophotometer using a suitable standard, for example, a set of pre-specified reference neutral density (ND) filters (such as NIST SRM 930e, see reference 14) with nominal (measurand) absorbance unit values. This reference standard must be provided with reference measurements of two or more separated wavelength positions.

For this test, repeat measurements of the same photometric standard is completed by placing it in the sample beam and not mechanically moving the sample over a normal measurement cycle for the measurement period. Then calculate the absorbance units for the entire spectrum and specifically at the two measured reference points, for example, 440.0 nm and 635.0 nm. The absorbance units are measured for each scan (i.e., scan-to-scan for each sample). Calculate the mean and standard deviation of the AU at the two wavelength positions for scan-to-scan (within replicate samples). This statistic is calculated for both 440.0 nm and 635.0 nm wavelengths as:

$$s_i = \sqrt{\frac{\sum_{j=1}^{n} (A_{ij} - \overline{A}_i)^2}{n - 1}} \tag{6.20}$$

where (s_i) is the standard deviation for the scan-to-scan absorbance units (AU) repeatability for the scan-to-scan measurements, and where (A_{ij}) are individual measurements of the absorbance for sample i and scan-to-scan number j; ($\overline{A}_i$) are the mean measured values for the reference sample absorbance values at each of 440.0 nm and 635.0 nm; n is the replicate number of spectra (pool all scan-to-scan data). The results are reported as follows. This can be repeated using a different calibrated set of wavelengths or wavenumbers as needed.

Absorbance/Response (Photometric) Repeatability (in AU).

	Mean Absorbance at 440 nm $\overline{A}_i$	Repeatability s_{440nm}, Eq. (6.20).	Mean Absorbance at 635 nm $\overline{A}_i$	Repeatability s_{635nm}, Eq. (6.20).
Scan-to-Scan				

6.6.5 *Stray Light Test*

The concept of stray light and the computations involved in computing stray light are described in the various volumes of this reference set; the reader is referred to the index for additional details. To measure the stray light in an instrument one is also referred to ASTM E387 test method.[15] This method uses two solutions to completely cut-off wavelengths of light from specific regions, indicating that any stray light will add to the cut-off band area indicating light leakage from other wavelengths (i.e., stray light). The solutions used are given in Table 6.4.

The basic method to measure and compute stray light as percent transmittance of stray light is as follows. Place the cut-off filter in the beam of the instrument and measure the scan in percent transmittance. Repeat the measurement by placing a beam blocker in the instrument. The measurement should be made for a minimum of ±10 nm on either side of the cut-off wavelength for the filter (e.g., 650 nm for Methylene Blue solution), see Figure 6.10. Taking the percent transmittance

Table 6.4 Solutions used to measure stray light and cut-off wavelengths.

Solution type	Cut-off wavelength
Potassium Chloride (KCl), 12g/L Water	200 nm
Sodium Chloride (NaCl)	205 nm
Lithium Carbonate (Li_2CO_3), 13 g/L Water	227 nm
Potassium Iodide (KI), 10g/L Water	260 nm
Sodium Iodide (NaI), 10g/L Water	260 nm
Acetone (pure Spectroscopy grade)	326 nm
Sodium Nitrite ($NaNO_2$), 50 g/L Water	390 nm
Methylene Blue, 0.1 g/L Water	650 nm

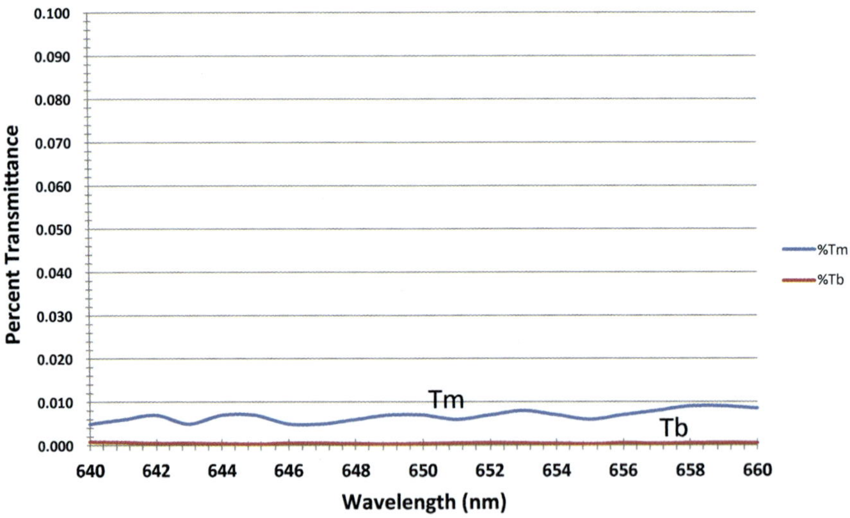

Fig. 6.10 Stray light measurement for cut-off filter near 650 nm. For the example shown the stray light is less than 0.01 %T and is computed as 0.007%T-0.0005%T=0.0065%T at 650 nm. This is equal to %Tm - %Tb.

data from both the filter and blocker measurements, use the equation as follows to compute the stray light (in %T).

$$\%T_S = \%T_m - \%T_b \tag{6.21}$$

Where $\%T_S$ is the percent transmittance as stray light; $\%T_m$ is the measured percent transmittance using the cut-off filter; and $\%T_b$ is the percent measured transmittance using the beam blocker (should be 0%T).

6.6.6 *Photometric Linearity Test*

Verify the photometric linearity of the spectrophotometer by using a set of reference neutral density filters. Plot the observed response against the expected response. The slope of the line for reference (x) versus measured (y) data should be 1.00 ± 0.05 and the intercept 0.00 ± 0.05. Calculate the slope and intercept using the reference material measurements of 5, 10, 20, 40, 60, and 80 percent transmittance; or 1.3, 1.0, 0.70, 0.40, 0.22, 0.10 AU, respectively. Equations for these computations are given in this text, see Equation (6.22).

The results are reported as a graph of the measured linear response against the expected response at the two measured wavelengths; record full spectral data; and include the following table: Linearity at Wavelength #1 ($\lambda 1$) and Wavelength #2 ($\lambda 2$). Other wavelengths may additionally be selected as needed.

Slope at $\lambda 1$	Intercept at $\lambda 1$	Slope at $\lambda 2$	Intercept at $\lambda 2$

Note the slope (b) and intercept (a) for the data set of x_i (actual) and y_i (measured) pairs of measurements for each wavelength position is given as:

$$b = \frac{\sum_i \{(x_i - \overline{x})(y_i - \overline{y})\}}{\sum_i (x_i - \overline{x})^2} \quad \text{and} \quad a = \overline{y} - b\overline{x} \tag{6.22}$$

6.6.7 *Photometric Noise Test*

Determine the photometric noise by using a reference neutral density filter. Repeat measurements of the same reference standard by placing it in the sample beam and not mechanically moving the sample over a typical measurement period. The photometric noise is computed as the standard deviation of the spectral response, and must be consistent with the model performance specifications for the application in use. This statistic is calculated for a single spectrum averaged over a standard measurement period as:

$$s_i = \sqrt{\frac{\sum_{j=1}^{n} (A_{ij} - \overline{A}_{ij})^2}{n-1}} \tag{6.23}$$

where (s_i) is the standard deviation (noise) for the *averaged* spectrum comprised of a number of scan-to-scan measurements for each wavelength, and where (A_{ij}) are individual absorbance measurements i for the averaged spectrum at wavelength j; ($\overline{A}_i$) is the average absorbance units value for the averaged spectrum at each measured wavelength (j); and n is the replicate number of spectra measured. This can be reported at one or more wavelengths or over the entire measurement region.

The results are reported as: Photometric Noise.

	Mean ($\overline{A}_i$)	Photometric noise (s_i), Eq. (6.23)
Averaged spectrum		

6.6.8 *Signal Averaging Test*

Determine the photometric noise by measuring a reference neutral density filter and *report results in transmittance*. Repeat measurements of the same reference standard by placing it in the sample beam and not mechanically moving the sample over the entire measurement period. This signal averaging test is to be completed using three methods:

(a) Random noise test

This test excludes short-, medium-, and long-term drift; slope, and background curvature with time using measurements of alternating background and sample measurement spectra. This test simulates "dual beam" conditions, when using a single beam instrument, and excludes most of the impact from longer term periodic instrument drift, e.g., for $n = 2$, measure background, then measure sample, then background, then sample; reference each spectrum, then average the 2 referenced spectra — repeat this sequence for the appropriate number of co-added spectra: 1, 2, 4, 16, 64, 256, etc.; compute the background corrected spectra by referencing alternate (i.e., sandwiched) spectra for averaged scans, then compute the standard deviation using Equation (6.23).

(b) Noise test (including medium- or short-term drift)

Take background measurements of the same number of scans as sample measurement used for co-added result, for example: measure 1, 2, 4, 16, 64, 256, etc. as alternate background co-added set and then sample co-added set, e.g., for $n = 2$, measure 2 scans as background followed in sequence by 2 scans of the reference sample, ratio these and calculate the standard deviation; for $n = 4$, measure 4 background and then 4 sample spectra, average these, and ratio as a single spectrum, continue this sequence and calculate the standard deviation using Equation (6.23).

(c) Noise test (including long-term drift)

Measure background at start of run and then measure samples in sequence using only the original background. Thus generate average spectra from r number of scans, across entire number of scans available, e.g., for $n = 4$: average scans 1–4, 5–8, etc.; for $n = 16$: average scans 1–16, 17–32, etc. Then calculate the standard deviation across the averaged spectra using Equation (6.23).

(d) Signal Averaging test

Signal Averaging Test — Obtain a series of replicate scan-to-scan spectra in transmittance or reflectance mode, and compute a subset of replicate scans and process as described below. Do this for the following number of scans: 1, 4, 16, 64, 256, 1024, 4096, 16384, etc., up to the maximum measurement time of interest. Ratio each pair of sample and background spectra and calculate the noise level using Equation (6.23) at multiple wavelengths. Irrespective of the wavelengths selected for noise measurements, the noise level should be reduced by a factor of 2 for each

Table 6.5 Signal averaging reportage table.

Number of scans	Expected noise reduction factor	Measured photometric noise (s_i)	Measured noise reduction factor
1	1	—	—
4	1/2	—	—
16	1/4	—	—
64	1/8	—	—
256	1/16	—	—
1024	1/32	—	—
4096	1/64	—	—
16384	1/128	—	—
65536	1/256	—	—

successive ratioed spectrum; for example, if 1 scan gave a noise level of 1, 4 scans would give 1/2, 16 would give 1/4, 64 would give 1/8 and so on until signal averaging fails. The percent noise level for each successive ratioed spectrum should be a factor of 2 lower; for example, 1, 1/2, 1/4, 1/8, 1/16, 1/32, 1/64, 1/128, etc. (see results reporting in Table 6.5).

Failure of Signal Averaging — Report the number of scans and the measurement time for each set of scan-to-scan data used in the particular ratioed spectrum and the noise level. Report a failure when the computed/measured noise level is a minimum of twice (2 times) that of the expected noise reduction. All spectrometers have a limit to their practical signal averaging capability, often set by residual interference fringing by optical components, by the apodization-determined feet of the moisture interferences, by electronic noise floor due to amplifier and detector performance, or mechanical spectrometer alignment or servo errors.

The results are reported as a Photometric noise signal averaging test at each wavelength with a table reported for each of multiple wavelengths (preferably across the full spectral range), as demonstrated for reportage in Table 6.5.

6.6.9 *Resolution Test*

A basic resolution test is made by comparing the Absorbance of a peak height to the absorbance at a peak trough and designating a threshold ratio as the measure of adequate resolution. For example, in ultraviolet-visible spectrometers there is a resolution test used by the European Pharmacopoeia that defines adequate resolution for a spectrophotometer as determining the absorbance ratio for a solution of 0.02% W/v toluene in hexane. The peak is measured at 269 nm and the trough at 266 nm. The ratio for passing this test is > 1.5. In summary, the ratio of absorbance at 269 nm

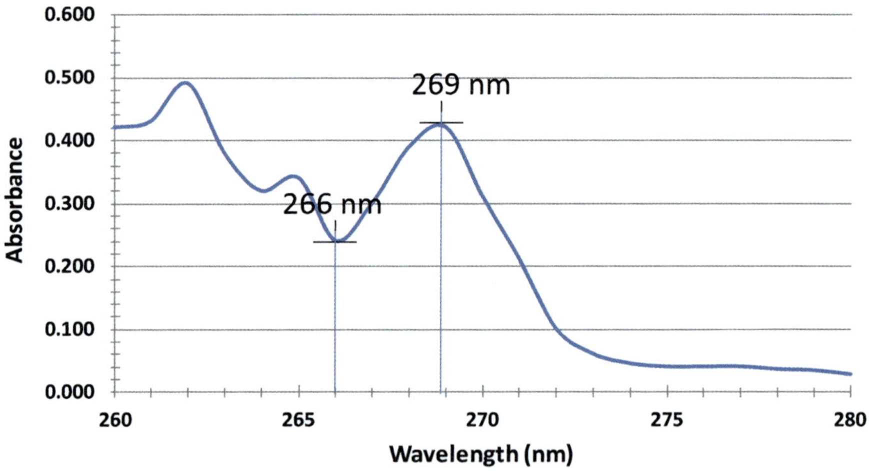

Fig. 6.11 Basic resolution test as a ratio of absorbance measurements for peak and trough of a spectral band. Resolution Ratio = Absorbance at 269 nm/Absorbance at 266 nm. This must be greater than 1.5 for passing value using the resolution test.[16]

divided by the absorbance at 266 nm must exceed 1.5 for passing.[16] The basic form for resolution testing is illustrated in Figure 6.11.

6.6.10 *Summary Specifications for Instrument Performance Testing*

General specifications for comparing instruments should meet basic minimum pre-established criteria (Table 6.6). These criteria are based on the actual use of the spectrophotometer and the accuracy required for measurements for a high signal to noise medical application. General requirements for each spectrometer should depend on the use, application, and overall performance requirements. The specifications here are used for illustrative purposes only. If extremely high performance and 'alikeness' is required then comparison statistics are more important. Table 6.6 describes basic performance criteria that indicate a reasonable alikeness between two or more instruments. Specific calibrations and prediction performance criteria will vary and so then will the comparative instrument performance metrics.

6.7 Peak Selection Approaches (Peak Picking)[17,18]

6.7.1 *Absolute Peak Maxima*

The absolute peak selection method finds the maximum absorbance level, for absorbance spectra, or the minimum transmittance level, for transmittance spectra, and identifies that as the peak position as illustrated in Figure 6.12.

Table 6.6 Basic instrument performance specifications for visible spectrophotometry.

	Test Criteria	Specifications
1.	Wavelength accuracy	±0.20 nm
2.	Wavelength repeatability	<0.05 nm
3.	Absorbance/response accuracy	±0.004A at 1A
4.	Absorbance/response repeatability	<0.001 AU (1 sigma)
5.	Stray light test	<0.01 %T
6.	Photometric linearity	Slope: 1.00 ± 0.02; Intercept: ±0.02 (Absolute)
7.	Photometric noise	RMS <0.001 AU for 0.1%T ND filter
8.	Signal Averaging Test	
	8.1. Random Noise Test	Must pass method to 1024 scans
	8.2. Noise Test (including medium- or short-term drift)	Must pass method to 500 scans
	8.3. Noise Test (including long-term drift)	Must pass method to 480 scans
9.	Resolution Test	A 269nm/A 266 nm > 1.5

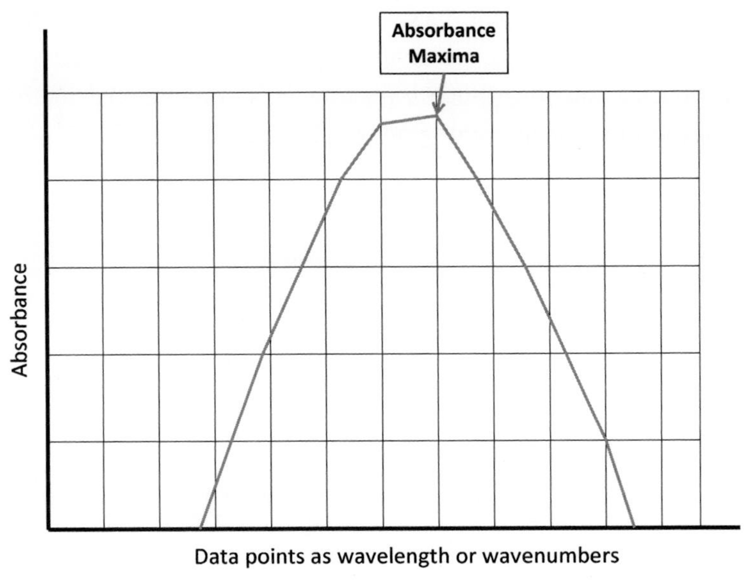

Fig. 6.12 Absorbance maxima as peak location.

6.7.2 *Peak Selection with Smoothing*

In this peak selection technique a smoothing function is applied to the spectral data and the smoothed data maxima is selected as the peak position location. A simple rectangular smoothing technique may be applied for each data point, using a minimum of 3 original data points per smoothed data point. For basic smoothing (i.e., shift and multiply technique) a specified number of adjacent points from an absorbance spectrum are used to compute a point of the smoothed spectrum. The multiple points from the original data are combined to compute the single smoothed data points. The process is iterated for the specific number of points specified. Basic smoothing is performed using the rectangular sliding-average smooth (an unweighted smoothing algorithm). For this technique each of the smoothed data points is determined using the following equation; this example is for three smoothing points.

$$A_S = \frac{A_{\lambda-\Delta} + A_{\lambda} + A_{\lambda+\Delta}}{3} \qquad (6.24)$$

Where A_S is the smoothed absorbance data point based on the absorbance values of three total data points. Note that $A_{\lambda-\Delta}$ (is the absorbance determined for the adjacent data point less 1 position); A_{λ} (is the absorbance for the original central data point to be replaced by the smoothed data computation (A_S)); and $A_{\lambda+\Delta}$ (is the absorbance data for the adjacent data point plus 1 position). These three original absorbance values are summed and divided by 3 (the number of data points to use in the smoothing calculation). Such a rectangular computational method may be derived for any number of smoothing points (Figure 6.13).

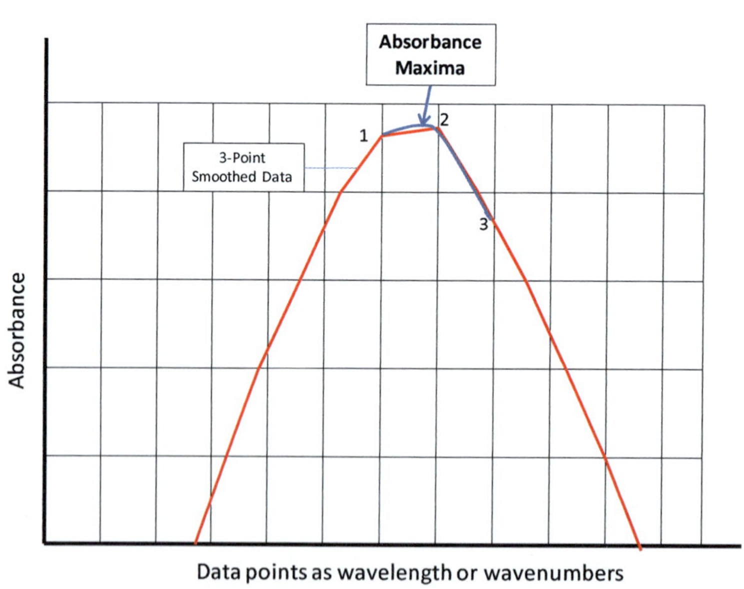

Fig. 6.13 Absorbance maxima of smoothed data as peak location.

6.7.3 *Interpolation*

For interpolation peak finding a cubic spline or similar function is fitted to a fixed number of data points near the peak and the absorbance maxima is selected as the peak (Figure 6.14). The cubic spline interpolation uses a designated number of data points and fits the interpolation function as:

$$y = a + bx + cx^2 + dx^3 \quad (6.25)$$

6.7.4 *Centroid (Center of Mass)*

For center of mass peak selection the center point is selected for the area or mass of the peak information. The peak is located at the center of the area specified (Figure 6.15). A vertical line is drawn from the center and the x-axis (wavelength) position is determined. This method is error prone when the band is not isolated or is asymmetrical.

6.7.5 *First Derivative Zero Cross-Over*

The maximum absorbance for any peak may be located using the first derivative cross-over point (Figure 6.16). A central difference method for computing the first derivative spectrum is used to mitigate for the typical shifts resulting from computing the derivative of spectral data using other equation forms (Equation 6.26). For this

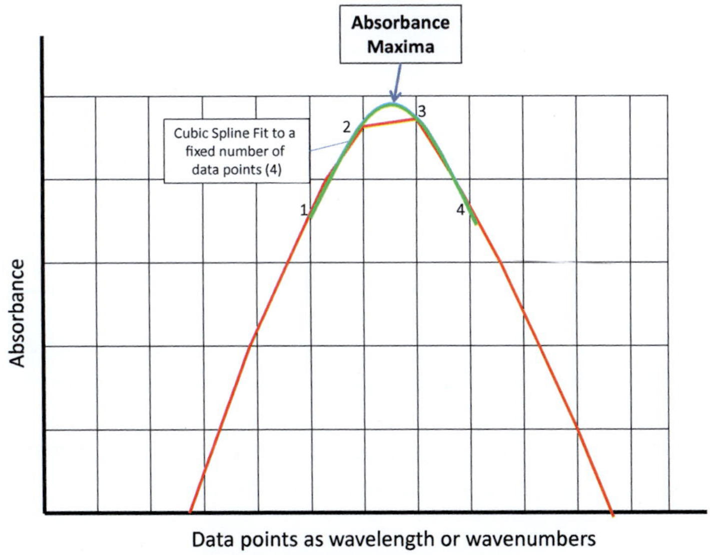

Fig. 6.14 Peak position as absorbance maxima for 4-point cubic spline interpolation.

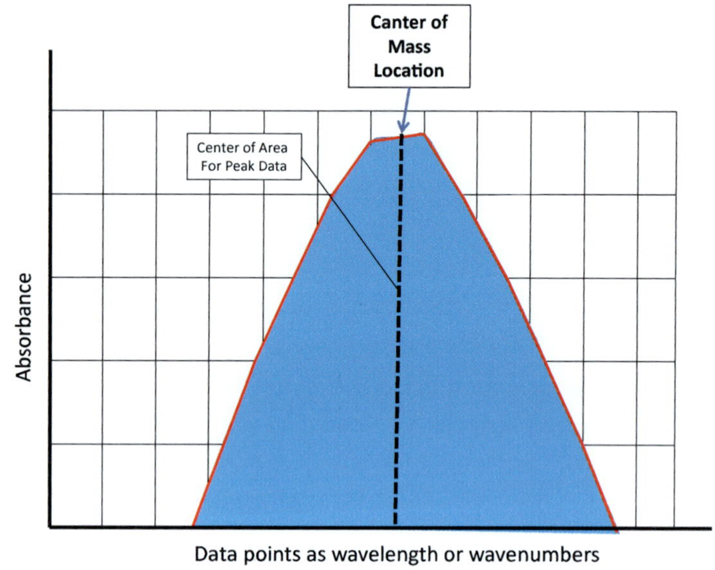

Fig. 6.15 Center of mass as peak location.

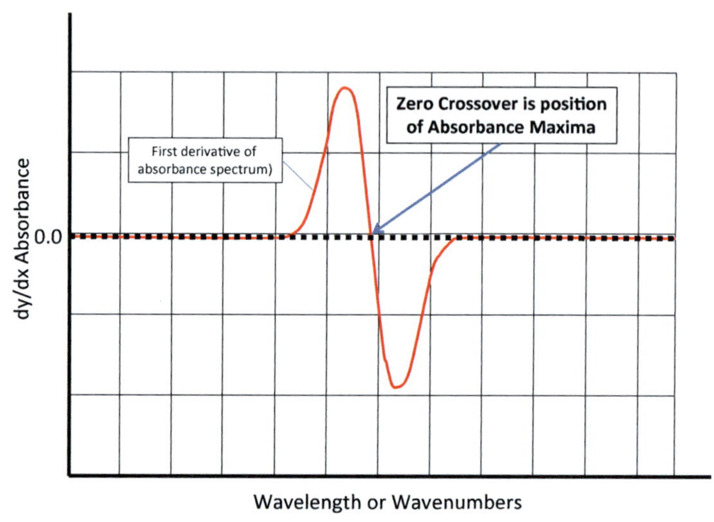

Fig. 6.16 First derivative cross-over point as the peak location.

nomenclature the $\lambda + \Delta$ represents a center wavelength plus a wavelength gap, represented by (Δ). Therefore $\lambda - \Delta$ represents the central wavelength minus the designated wavelength gap.

$$A'_\lambda = \frac{A_{\lambda+\Delta} - A_{\lambda-\Delta}}{2(\Delta\lambda)} \tag{6.26}$$

The method for computing the second derivative spectrum computation is given as:

$$A''_\lambda = \frac{(A_{\lambda+\Delta} - A_\lambda) - (A_\lambda - A_{\lambda-\Delta})}{(\Delta\lambda)^2} = \frac{(A_{\lambda+\Delta} - 2A_\lambda + A_{\lambda-\Delta})}{(\Delta\lambda)^2} \tag{6.27}$$

where Δ is the number of wavelength spaces (gap) between A_λ and $A_{\lambda+\Delta}$ and $A_{\lambda-\Delta}$.

6.8 Qualitative Analysis and Conformity Index

Qualitative analysis is a series of techniques that provide a means for identifying a material or compound being measured, and to some extent the purity of that material or compound under test. The closeness in matching a test spectrum of material to a known reference spectrum of a pure material or mixture provides the means for the qualitative assessment. A perfect match of a test sample spectrum to a reference sample spectrum provides the confidence that the materials are identical. The resolution of an instrument may be increased to better define the alikeness or differences. Also specific areas of a spectrum may be windowed or selected to compare only regions of interest to better resolve any differences between a test material spectrum and a reference material spectrum.

A series of algorithms are used to determine the distance (D) or alikeness (correlation) of a test spectrum to a reference spectrum. An explanation of these methods for a test and reference spectrum is demonstrated in the following text material.

6.8.1 *Euclidean Distance*

The Distance Formula

When computing the Euclidean Distance for spectral distance comparison we compare the X and Y values for each data point for each spectrum and sum the differences to find the Euclidean Distance D. The average distance may also be reported when specified. To begin we note Figure 6.17 showing an illustration of a test spectrum (unknown) and a reference spectrum (known material).

This relationship holds even when x_1 or y_1 or both are negative, and the distance between two points (x_1, y_1) and (x_2, y_2) is given by:

$$D^2 = |x_2 - x_1|^2 + |y_2 - y_1|^2 = (x_2 - x_1)^2 + (y_2 - y_1)^2 \tag{6.28}$$

and then D is given as:

$$D = \sqrt{(x_2 - x_1)^2 + (y_2 - y_1)^2} \tag{6.29}$$

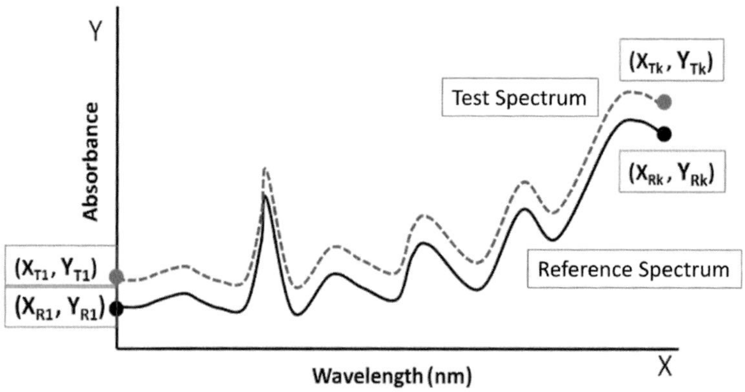

Fig. 6.17 Test spectrum and reference spectrum in X (wavelength or wavenumbers), and Y space (absorbance or amplitude).

So for our multi-dimensional spectra the same formula is used for as many data points on the X (wavelength) and Y (amplitude) axes as relevant. To derive the equations used referring to the reference (known) spectrum data points as (X_{R1}, Y_{R1}) to the final point in the spectral vector as (X_{Rk}, Y_{Rk}); and for the test (unknown) spectrum data points as (X_{T1}, Y_{T1}) to the final point in the spectral vector as (X_{Tk}, Y_{Tk}).

The distance squared formula is as:

$$D^2 = |X_{R1} - X_{T1}|^2 + |Y_{R1} - Y_{T1}|^2 + |X_{R2} - X_{T2}|^2 + |Y_{R2} - Y_{T2}|^2 + \cdots + |X_{Rk} - X_{Tk}|^2 + |Y_{Rk} - Y_{Tk}|^2 \quad (6.30)$$

Since the X values are all identical for each data point set as the wavelength registration, then all the X terms become zero (0), leaving the Distance squared equation as:

$$D^2 = |Y_{R1} - Y_{T1}|^2 + |Y_{R2} - Y_{T2}|^2 + \cdots + |Y_{Rk} - Y_{Tk}|^2 \quad (6.31)$$

and then the spectral distance as D is given as:

$$D = \sqrt{|Y_{R1} - Y_{T1}|^2 + |Y_{R2} - Y_{T2}|^2 + \cdots + |Y_{Rk} - Y_{Tk}|^2} \quad (6.32)$$

The distance may also be reported as the Average Distance or

$$\overline{D} = \frac{D}{n} \quad (6.33)$$

where n is the number of data points.

6.8.2 *Mahalanobis Distance Measurements*

The Mahalanobis Distance statistic (or more correctly the square of the Mahalanobis Distance), D^2, is a scalar measure of where the spectral vector **a** lies within the multivariate parameter space used in a calibration model. The Mahalanobis distance is used for spectral matching, for detecting outliers during calibration or prediction, or for detecting extrapolation of the model during analyses. Various commercial software packages may use D instead of D^2, or may use other related statistics as an indication of high leverage outliers, or may call the Mahalanobis Distance by another name. D^2 is preferred here since it is more easily related to the number of samples and variables. Model developers should attempt to verify exactly what is being calculated. Both mean-centered and not mean-centered definitions for Mahalanobis Distance exist, with the mean-centered approach being preferred. Regardless of whether mean-centering of data is performed, the statistic designated by D^2 has valid utility for qualitative calculations.

If **a** is a spectral vector (dimension f by 1) and **A** is the matrix of calibration spectra (of dimension n by f), then the Mahalanobis Distance is defined as:

$$D^2 = a^t(AA^t)^+a \tag{6.34}$$

For a mean centered calibration, **a** and **A** in equation (6.34) are replaced by $\mathbf{a} - \bar{\mathbf{a}}$ and $\mathbf{A} - \bar{\mathbf{A}}$, respectively.

The Mahalanobis Distance statistic provides a useful indication of the first type of extrapolation. For the calibration set, one sample will have a maximum Mahalanobis Distance, D^2_{max}. This is the most extreme sample in the calibration set, in that, it is the farthest from the center of the space defined by the spectral variables. If the Mahalanobis Distance for an unknown sample is greater than D^2_{max}, then the estimate for the sample clearly represents an extrapolation of the model. Provided that outliers have been eliminated during the calibration, the distribution of Mahalanobis Distances should be representative of the calibration model, and D^2_{max} can be used as an indication of extrapolation. Techniques for matching sample spectra using Mahalanobis distance include references 19–23.

6.8.3 *Correlation Methods*

6.8.3.1 *Matching Index*

The general method for comparing two spectra (test versus reference), where the reference is a known compound; or the mean spectrum of a set of known spectra, is given as the M.I. (Match Index). The M.I. is computed by comparing the vector dot products between the test and reference spectra. The theoretical values for these dot products range from −1.0 to +1.0, where −1.0 is a perfect negative (inverse) correlation, and +1.0 is a perfect match. Since for visible spectroscopy only positive absorbance values are used to compute the dot product, the values for the match index must fall within the 0.0 to +1.0 range. The method, or variations thereof, is described in various papers.[24–28] The mathematics are straightforward and are demonstrated below.

The match index (M.I.) is equal to the cosine of the angle (designated as α) between two row vectors (the test and reference spectra) projected onto a two-dimensional plane, and is equivalent to the correlation (r) between the two spectra (row vectors).

$$M.I. = \cos\alpha = \left(\frac{T \bullet R}{|T||R|}\right) \tag{6.35}$$

Where T is the test spectrum row matrix, and R is the reference spectrum row matrix.

Note the following:

$$(T \bullet R) = \sum_{i=1}^{n} T_i R_i \tag{6.36}$$

where T_i represents the individual data points for the test spectrum (designated as the absorbance values of spectrum T from wavelengths i = 1 through n), and R_i represents the individual data points for the reference spectrum (designated as the absorbance values of spectrum R from wavelengths i = 1 through n).

And where:

$$|T||R| = \left(\sum_{i=1}^{n} T_i^2\right)^{1/2} \left(\sum_{i=1}^{n} R_i^2\right)^{1/2} \tag{6.37}$$

Note, the angle (α), in degrees, between two vectors can be determined from the match index (M.I.) using:

$$\alpha = \cos^{-1}(M.I.) \tag{6.38}$$

6.8.3.2 *Correlation Matching*

The "alikeness" of one test spectrum (or series of spectra) to a reference spectrum can be determined by calculating a point-by-point correlation between absorbance data for each test and reference spectrum. The correlation matching can be accomplished for all data points available or for a pre-selected set only. The more alike the test and reference spectra are, the higher (closer to 1.00) are the r (correlation coefficient) and R^2 (coefficient of determination) values. A perfect match of the two spectra would produce r or R^2 values of 1.00000. The sensitivity of the technique can be increased by pre-treating the spectra as first to higher order derivatives and then calculating the correlation between test and reference spectra. Full spectral data can also be truncated (or reduced) to include only spectral regions of particular interest, a practice which will further improve matching sensitivity for a particular spectral feature of interest. Sample selection using this technique involves selecting samples most different from the mean population spectrum for the full sample set. Those samples with correlations of the lowest absolute values (including negative correlations) are selected first and then samples of second lowest correlation are selected (and so on) until the single sample of highest correlation is found. The distribution of spectra about the mean is assumed to follow a normal distribution with a computable standard deviation. This assumption indicates that a uniformly distributed sample set can be selected based upon the correlation between test spectra and the mean spectrum of a population of spectra.[29]

6.8.3.3 *Conformity Index*

Conformity index may be established using a pre-defined set of criteria related to identification and qualification of materials used in regulated environments or where high quality and safety are primary goals for characterizing raw materials and ingredients. Conformity may be expressed in the following terms using spectral references:

1. Euclidean Distance of reference sample spectrum to test sample spectrum
2. Mahalanobis Distance of reference sample spectrum to test sample spectrum
3. Correlation of reference sample spectrum to test sample spectrum

Set parameter measurements to be within upper and lower control limits. These limits are established by product quality personnel. For example, the user may establish that the fat, protein, and fiber content must be within certain ranges.

The final conformity index may be established using a variety of criteria such as follows: analysis of various chemical, physical, and solubility properties within specifications; spectral matching with reference material within specifications (e.g., Euclidean Distance, Mahalanobis Distance, or Correlation Matching). Conformity Index should be reported as a spectral distance measurement with warning and rejection (non-conforming) limits for high and low limit values, and should also include a potential list of analysis values with warning and rejection (non-conforming) limits for high and low limit values.

NOTE: Qualitative analysis is determined as the distance between a reference sample spectrum (known) and a test sample spectrum (unknown). The distance measures for reference versus unknown should be selectable from the following:

- Euclidean Distance (Equation (6.32))
- Average Euclidean Distance (Equation (6.33))
- Mahalanobis Distance (Equation (6.34))
- Correlation Match Index (Equation (6.35))
- Alpha Distance (Equation (6.38))

The conformity index is determined by selecting warning and action limits as thresholds for distance measures. Also Quantitative measures may be included in establishing the conformity index as options. These should also include warning and action limits as thresholds for conformance.

6.9 Data Preprocessing: Smoothing

6.9.1 *Introduction*

Smoothing is useful for removing random variation (white noise) in spectra to reveal the underlying structure of spectral bands.[4] There is a detailed section on smoothing in this text and the reader is referred to this topic in the index. Derivative preprocessing may be combined with smoothing to remove the effects of offset between spectra, but not to remove baseline slope or other effects due to particle size or energy scattering differences.[4,30] There is a special section on smoothing and derivatives to which the reader is referred (See Main Index for smoothing or derivatives). Each successive derivative increases the noise by a factor of 10 and so also adds structural artifacts into the spectrum based on the fine detailed structure of the spectrum undergoing derivative processing. Refer to index for these topics. Comparison of scattering correction algorithms has been demonstrated and useful examples are found in two references cited.[31,32]

6.10 Spectrum Smoothing

6.10.1 *Rectangular (unweighted smoothing)*

For basic smoothing (i.e., shift and multiply technique) a specified number of adjacent points from an absorbance spectrum are used to compute a point of the smoothed spectrum. The multiple points from the original data are combined to compute the single smoothed data points. The process is iterated for the specific number of points specified. Basic smoothing is performed using the rectangular sliding-average smooth (an unweighted smoothing algorithm). For this technique each of the smoothed data points is determined using the following equation; this example is for three smoothing points.

$$A_S = \frac{A_{\lambda-\Delta} + A_\lambda + A_{\lambda+\Delta}}{3} \qquad (6.39)$$

Where A_S is the smoothed absorbance data point based on the absorbance values of three total data points. Note that $A_{\lambda-\Delta}$ (is the absorbance determined for the adjacent data point less 1 position); A_λ (is the absorbance for the original central data point to be replaced by the smoothed data computation (A_S)); and $A_{\lambda+\Delta}$ (are the absorbance data for the adjacent data point plus 1 position). These three original absorbance values are summed and divided by 3 (the number of data points to use in the smoothing calculation). Such a rectangular computational method may be derived for any odd number of smoothing points.

6.10.2 *Triangular (weighted smoothing)*

This smoothing technique is like the rectangular or unweighted smoothing method with the addition of weighting factors for giving more weight to the center data point and down weighting the influence of adjacent points. This technique requires the divisor to be the sum of the weighting integers. So for a five point triangular smooth we use the equation as follows.

$$A_S = \frac{A_{\lambda-2\Delta} + 2A_{\lambda-\Delta} + 3A_\lambda + 2A_{\lambda+\Delta} + A_{\lambda+2\Delta}}{9} \qquad (6.40)$$

Where A_S is the smoothed absorbance data point based on the absorbance values of five total data points. Note that $A_\lambda - \Delta$ and $A_\lambda - 2\Delta$ (are the absorbance values determined for the adjacent 2 data points less 1 and 2 positions, respectively), and A_λ (is the absorbance for the original central data point to be replaced by the smoothed data computation (A_S)). Note that $A_\lambda + \Delta$ and $A_\lambda + 2\Delta$ (are the absorbance data for the adjacent 2 data points plus 1 and 2 positions, respectively). The product and sum for these five original absorbance values are divided by 9 (i.e., the sum of the number of the weighting integers as $1 + 2 + 3 + 2 + 1 = 9$). Such a rectangular computational method may be derived for any odd number of smoothing points.

6.11 X and Y Plots

6.11.1 *Conventional Plots*

Data plots of X versus Y have a variety of presentation formats based upon the application and context and are given in Figure 6.18. The following X and Y plots are used specifically for quantitative data presentation.

6.12 Analysis of Variance Testing for Flow Cells

6.12.1 *Introduction*

The following experiment will allow initial Analysis of Variance (ANOVA) evaluations for cuvette insertion to spectrometers. This test will determine the error contribution of the variance from inserting and using different physical cuvettes of the same nominal pathlength while making quantitative measurements with a spectrophotometer.

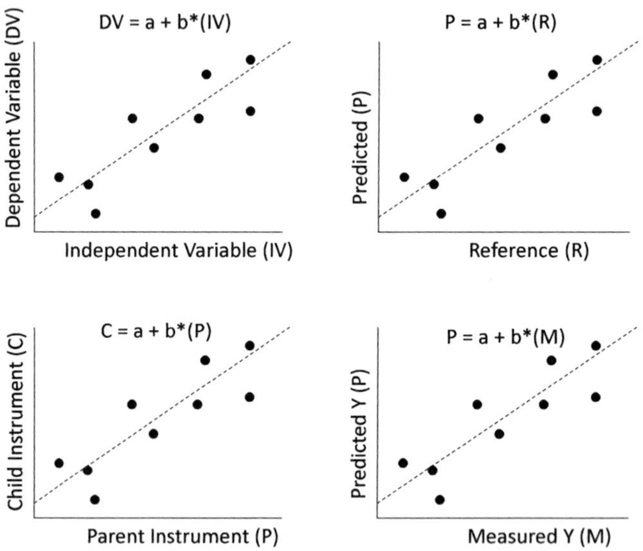

Fig. 6.18 A series of conventional X-Y plots as depicted in journal publications, textbooks and software for Independent Variable (X-axis) versus Dependent Variable (Y-axis) (upper left); Reference (Lab) Value versus Predicted (spectroscopic data) Value (upper right); Parent (original calibration) Instrument versus Child (calibration transfer) Instrument (lower left); and Measured (Lab) Value versus Predicted (spectroscopic) Value (lower right). See X and Y plots or regression in the index for related topics.

Create standard cuvette configurations containing solvent as follows for either static or flowing sampling system tests. For the static cuvette standards the ends (openings) must be filled with solvent and sealed in such a way that they do not leak or cause contamination by chemical sealant leaching. All bubbles must be eliminated from any liquid samples.

Make up a minimum of five (5) cuvettes containing solvent or deionized water and label them C1-C5. (Be certain to measure the physical pathlength of each cuvette and monitor solvent temperature during the measurement period. Note each experiment will have a comment regarding both pathlength and temperature.

NOTE: DURING MEASUREMENTS DO NOT REMOVE OR MOVE THE CUVETTE FOR THE ENTIRE TEST PERIOD UNLESS OTHERWISE DIRECTED IN THIS TEST PROTOCOL. DO NOT MOVE THE INSTRUMENT. DO NOT CHANGE ANY MEASUREMENT OR DATA ACQUISTION SETTINGS DURING THE TEST PERIOD. RECORD ANY UNUSUAL EVENTS, SUCH AS POWER BROWN OUT, HIGH HUMIDITY, UNUSUAL VIBRATION, IMPACT TO THE INSTRUMENT, OR INSTRUMENT FAILURES. IF SUCH EVENTS OCCUR, REMEASURE THE SPECIFIC SAMPLE.

6.12.2 *Instrument Variance Test (timed)*

Instrument variance test: Measure one cuvette combination with a fixed cuvette pathlength (in mm) for the following sets of continuous data: 5 minutes for temperature equilibrium and 3 times 3 sets of complete scan data. Each set consists in 1 scan time, plus 1 wait time. The 3 times 3 sets comprises a total of 9 scans and 9 wait times. The cuvette must remain in the exact SAME orientation (DO NOT TOUCH THE CUVETTE DURING MEASUREMENT RUN). Room temperature and cuvette temperature must be recorded at regular intervals over the entire test period. Measured mechanical pathlength (in mm) must be noted for each cell used. Use these data for calculation of the following. Note the equations for variance, standard deviation, pooled variance, and pooled standard deviation are given in the text.

6.12.2.1 *Graph Average Spectrum for Each of the Three Time Periods and Display as Overlay*

6.12.2.2 *Calculate Spectral Variance due to Instrument for one Cuvette Combination and Sum as Vector (a) and Scalar (b) Values (use Local (Replicate) Means for within Run Variance Calculations). Calculate Pooled Variance (c) and Pooled Standard Deviation (d) for Entire Group*

6.12.2.3 *Calculate Predicted Value Variance due to Instrument for One Cuvette Combination and as a Vector (a) Comprised of Scan-To-Scan Predictions Over Time, and Single Scalar (b) Values (Use Local (Replicate) Means for Within Run Variance Calculations). Calculate Pooled Variance (c) and Pooled Standard Deviation (d) for Entire Group*

6.12.3 *Sample Temperature Variance Test*

Sample temperature test: Measure one cuvette combination with a fixed cuvette pathlength for 30 minutes of continuous data by ramping temperature over 5 degrees Celsius in one degree increments, over the full expected temperature range, using a 6-minute period for each temperature ramp, representing 3 times 3 sets of complete scan data. Each set consists in 1 scan time, plus 1 wait time. The 3 times 3 sets comprises a total of 9 scans and 9 wait times. (DO NOT TOUCH CUVETTE DURING MEASUREMENT RUN). Room temperature and cuvette temperature must be recorded at 1-minute intervals over the entire test period during temperature ramp. Use these data for calculations of the following.

6.12.3.1 *Calculate Spectral Variance due to Temperature and Sum as Vector (a) and Scalar (b) Values (Use Local (Replicate) Mean for Variance Calculation). Calculate Pooled Variance (c) and Pooled Standard Deviation (d) for Entire Group*

6.12.3.2 *Calculate Predicted "Analyte" Value Variance due to Temperature for One Cuvette/Cassette Combination and as a Vector (a) Comprised of Scan-To-Scan Predictions Over Time, and Single Scalar (b) Values (Use Local (Replicate) Means for Within Run Variance Calculations). Calculate Pooled Variance (c) and Pooled Standard Deviation (d) for Entire Group*

6.12.4 *Cuvette Pathlength Variance Test*

Pathlength Variance Test: Measure each of five (5) cuvette/cassette combinations with as much variation in cuvette pathlength as practicable (i.e., full range of −5% relative to +5% if available) of continuous data each (5 minutes for temperature equilibrium and 3 sets of scan data collections with the cuvette/cassette combination in the exact SAME orientation (DO NOT TOUCH DURING EACH INDIVIDUAL MEASUREMENT RUN). Room temperature and cuvette temperature must be recorded at regular intervals over the entire test period. Pathlength must be noted for each cell used.

6.12.4.1 *Calculate Spectral Variance due to Cuvette Pathlength for Each Cuvette Combination and Sum as Vector (a) and Scalar (b) Values (Use Local (Sample) Mean for Variance Calculation and for Comparison, n = 3 Values). Calculate Pooled Variance (c) and Pooled Standard Deviation (d) for Group*

6.12.4.2 *Calculate Predicted "Analyte" Value Variance due to Pathlength for Each Cuvette/Cassette Combination and Sum as a Vector (a) Comprised of Scan-To-Scan Predictions Over Time, and Single Scalar (b) Values (use Local (Sample) Mean for Variance Calculation and for Comparison, n = 3 Values). Calculate Pooled Variance (c) and Pooled Standard Deviation (d) for Group*

6.12.4.3 *Plot Predicted Value Results (Median for Each Cuvette) vs. Pathlength for Each Cuvette Combination (5 Data Points)*

6.12.5 *Cuvette/Cassette Combination Insertion Variance Test*

If a special sampling cassette is used (e.g., disposable for medical device, etc.) perform the following. For each of the five (5) cuvette/cassette combinations: Measure in a single orientation for 5 minutes for temperature equilibrium plus 1 spectral scan; reorient the cuvette combination by removing the unit and reinserting it in ***exactly the same position*** and re-measure. Measure again for 5 minutes equilibrium and 1 scan; repeat this procedure three (3) total times for each cuvette combination. Room temperature and cuvette temperature must be recorded at regular intervals over the entire test period. Pathlength must be noted for each cell used.

6.12.5.1 *Graph Average Spectral Variance vs. Wavenumber Results for Cuvette/Cassette Insertions Data and Display as Overlay (as abs. Spectral Variance)*

6.12.5.2 *Calculate Spectral Variance due to Insertion for Each Cuvette/Cassette Combination and Sum as Vector (a) and Scalar (b) Values (Use Local (Same Cuvette/Cassette Combination) Mean for Variance Calculation). Calculate Pooled Variance (c) and Pooled Standard Deviation (d) for Entire Group*

6.12.5.3 *Calculate Predicted "Analyte" Value Variance due to Insertion for Each Cuvette/Cassette Combination and Sum as a Vector (a) Comprised of Scan-To-Scan Predictions Over Time, and Single Scalar (b) Values (Use Local (Same Cuvette/Cassette Combination) Mean for Variance Calculation). Calculate Pooled Variance (c) and Pooled Standard Deviation (d) for Entire Group*

6.12.5.4 *Plot Predicted Results (Median Values) for Each Cuvette/Cassette Combination (5 Data Points)*

6.12.6 *Data Processing and Interpretation*

The data is processed for each test by calculating the variance and root mean square error (standard deviation) for each test set in several ways. This is accomplished by using a series of background corrected spectra for each test set where every spectral data point (as an absorbance value) at a specified wavelength (nm) is represented as (y_i), and where $(\bar{y}_i)$ represents the mean absorbance value for that test set at a specified wavelength (nm). As a guideline, all spectra are comprised of a sample spectrum ratioed to a background spectrum. The ratioed spectra are then used for processing. Single variance spectra and pooled variance spectra are calculated with respect to nanometer measurements. These calculations are computed for each nanometer for a test set of N spectra. This is calculated for variance and standard deviation as:

Variance:

$$S^2 = \frac{\sum_{i=1}^{N} (y_i - \bar{y}_i)^2}{N - 1} \tag{6.41}$$

Standard Deviation:

$$S = \sqrt{\frac{\sum_{i=1}^{N} (y_i - \bar{y}_i)^2}{N - 1}} \tag{6.42}$$

Such calculations result in a variance or standard deviation plot versus nanometers for differences from the mean spectrum as indicators of total variance. When plotted graphically these variance calculations reveal spectral changes relative to nanometer position. These values are calculated for individual cuvettes using the above equations.

The calculations are repeated for predicted values using standard analyte calibrations with resulting prediction models for each cuvette and each set of measurements.

Pooled variances and standard deviations are also computed by combining the measurements for several tests using identical or different numbers of cuvettes (1 to k) for j replicate measurements over multiple test sets using the equations as:

Pooled Variance:

$$S_P^2 = \frac{\begin{array}{c}\sum_{j=1}^{N1} (y_{1j} - \bar{y}_j)^2 + \sum_{j=1}^{N2} (y_{2j} - \bar{y}_2)^2 \\ + \sum_{j=1}^{N3} (y_{3j} - \bar{y}_3)^2 + \cdots + \sum_{j=1}^{Nk} (Y_{kj} - \bar{y}_k)^2\end{array}}{N1 + N2 + N3 + \cdots + Nk - k} \tag{6.43}$$

Pooled Standard Deviation:

$$S_P = \sqrt{\frac{\sum_{j=1}^{N1} (y_{1j} - \overline{y}_1)^2 + \sum_{j=1}^{N2} (y_{2j} - \overline{y}_2)^2 + \sum_{j=1}^{N3} (y_{3j} - \overline{y}_3)^2 + \cdots + \sum_{j=1}^{Nk} (y_{kj} - \overline{y}_k)^2}{N1 + N2 + N3 + \cdots + Nk - k}} \tag{6.44}$$

These tests will provide detailed data to qualify and quantify instrumental and cuvette interaction in terms of:

1. Instrument variance over timed experiment;
2. Cuvette pathlength variance (effect of pathlength on spectra);
3. Cuvette insertion variance, within versus between cuvettes (this measures the affect of the cuvette holder on overall measurement variance);
4. Sample temperature measurement variance (this test evaluates the affect of temperature on the measurement and plots temperature change over time).

6.12.7 *Summary Possible with Test Series*

In addition to the detailed variances described in #1-4 above, one may rank the measurement error contributions as to their overall significance in adding to the total measurement error budget. One may assess the contribution of each noise source to the spectral variation and how each source propagates through to the final measurement error. There are multiple other statistical analyses that can be performed to classify type of noise and overall error contributions from each noise source.

6.13 Analysis of Variance Testing for Flow Sampling Systems

6.13.1 *Introduction*

The following experiments will allow initial variance testing to determine the critical "noise" characteristics and degree of contribution for each variance source to the overall measurement error. The variance contributors identified for this testing will be those primarily associated with the Sample Access System and the flow cell, comprising the sampling system in total. The primary suspects within the sampling system comprising the variables contributing to measurement noise with the greatest affect on measurement results include the following:

6.13.1.1 *Clear Liquids*

1. Sample volume change in cell;
2. Dilution effects;

3. Chemical composition (non-additive potential to deviate from Beer's law) — this can include pH and ionic composition sensitive absorption bands;
4. Entrained air (bubbles: both micro- and macro-scale);
5. Cuvette thickness (cell pathlength);
6. Cuvette orientation (including precision of windows and surfaces, and positioning errors);
7. Cuvette window (fused silica): impurities, optical clarity, and flatness of optical surfaces.

For scattering materials one would include all of the above and the effects of scattering particles, making the scattering effects the largest contributor to measurement variation. The list in priority of error contribution for flowing sampling systems might be as the following list and (Table 6.7).

6.13.1.2 *Scattering Uniform Bead Solutions or Oil Emulsions*

1. Scattering effects (well-defined as Compton and Raleigh);
2. Sample volume change in cell;
3. Dilution effects;
4. Chemical composition (non-additive potential to deviate from Beer's law) — this can include pH and ionic composition sensitive absorption bands;
5. Entrained air (bubbles: both micro- and macro-scale);
6. Cuvette thickness (cell pathlength);
7. Cuvette orientation (including precision of windows and surfaces, and positioning errors);
8. Cuvette window (fused silica): impurities, optical clarity, and flatness of optical surfaces

Main measurement variation causes:

a) <u>SPECTRA</u> — Variable pathlength: caused by fluctuations in sample temperature, sample density (number) and dimensions (shape) of scattering particles, and flow cell (cuvette) inner dimensions.

b) <u>PREDICTED VALUES</u> — Non-modeled or non-calibrated spectral interferences, including unmodeled changes in spectral band shapes. Note: Compton-like x-axis shifts are not modeled using conventional chemometric approaches. Multivariate regression techniques assume x-axis alignment and accommodate only for model variances in spectral amplitude associated with concentration (y-block) data.

Table 6.7 Showing the suspected causes of variation resulting from a flow sampling access system. This table could be used for a medical device for measuring blood as a scattering medium (presented as an example).

Measurement variation observed	Cause(s)	Spectral variation effect(s)
Scattering effects (variable)	Flow rate variability - Shear effects (changes in shape, quantities, and optical properties of scattering centers)	Variable pathlength (l) for A = elc multiplicative effect; offset, slope change, band shifts (x-axis), and spectral 'distortions'
Sample volume change in cell;	Sample Temperature and flow rate	Variable pathlength (l) for A = ecl multiplicative effect
Dilution effects;	Flow rate variability - mixing rate, intravenous treatments	Variable concentration of scattering centers (as number 1 above)
Chemical composition (non-additive potential to deviate from Beer's law) — this can include pH and ionic composition sensitive absorption bands;	Different blood phenotypes, exogenous and endogenous interferences, disease states, intravenous treatments	Non-modeled or non-calibrated interferences, band shapes, and variable pathlength effects
Entrained air (bubbles: both micro- and macro-scale);	Fluid drawing variability, leaks in tubing joints	Variable concentration of scattering centers (as number 1 above)
Cuvette thickness (cell pathlength);	Manufacturing tolerances	Variable pathlength (l) for A = elc multiplicative effect
Cuvette orientation (including precision of windows and surfaces, and positioning errors);	Cuvette and optical design (design to required precision)	Variable I_0 term in $A = -\log_{10}(I/I_0)$, as well as unmodeled features introduced into the spectrum
Cuvette window (fused silica): impurities, optical clarity, and flatness of optical surfaces.	Cuvette design to required precision	Spectral features showing on some cuvettes that are not present on others

Comparison of Sample Access Components In comparing any existing system configuration (Config. A) or procedure (Proc. A) to a proposed change in the system (Config. B), e.g., tubing, pump roller components, etc.; or procedure changes (Proc. B), e.g., number of revolutions, flow sequence, flow rate transition, etc. the following tests are conducted.

These tests will evaluate changes in sample temperature at point of measurement, sample flow rate, coefficient of shear, sample settling rate, and dilution effects.

For these tests one must create standard test solutions with the following materials. Note: All bubbles must be eliminated from each of the liquid samples.

One blank solution containing standard solvent or deionized water (SB); and one solution containing standard solvent (known molar concentration) solution or deionized water with a low concentration level of sample analyte (SL) and one with a high concentration level of sample analyte material (SH). The quantities of analyte material must be representative of the high and low concentrations of typical samples. (Be certain to measure pathlength and monitor temperature during measurement period. Note: each experiment will have a comment regarding both pathlength and temperature.)

NOTE: DURING MEASUREMENTS DO NOT REMOVE OR MOVE THE FLOW CUVETTE DURING THE ENTIRE TEST PERIOD. DO NOT MOVE THE INSTRUMENT. DO NOT CHANGE ANY MEASUREMENT OR DATA ACQUISTION SETTINGS DURING THE TEST PERIOD. RECORD ANY UNUSUAL EVENTS, SUCH AS POWER BROWN OUT, HIGH HUMIDITY, UNUSUAL VIBRATION, AND INSTRUMENT TAMPERING OR FAILURES.

6.13.2 *Instrument System Stability Test for Config. A Versus Config. B Conditions*

For each available system make measurements using SB, SL, and SH containing materials under standard measurement use conditions related to data acquisition and processing rates (e.g. standard for proposed use conditions). Collect these data over a multi-hour period recording spectra. The final absorbance spectra will be created by ratioing sample spectra to the reference material (solvent) spectra as described in the Data Processing and Interpretation section of this procedure. Room temperature and cuvette temperature must be recorded at regular intervals over the entire test period. Pathlength must be noted for each flow cell used.

6.13.2.1 *Sample Temperature Variance Test*

Place reservoir of each material (i.e., SB, SL, and SH) into the refrigerator and let the temperature equilibrate overnight (record temperature of reservoir following cooling process). Remove each reservoir one at a time and place each reservoir into the instrument and record measurements over a two-hour period. Repeat for each material, room temperature and cuvette temperature must be recorded at regular intervals over the entire test period. Pathlength must be noted for each cell used.

a) Data Processing and Interpretation

The data is processed for each test by calculating the variance and root mean square error (standard deviation) for each test set in several ways. This is accomplished by using a series of background corrected spectra for each test set where every spectral data point (as an absorbance value) at a specified wavelength (nm) is represented as (y_i), and where $(\overline{y}_i)$ represents the mean absorbance value for that test set at a specified wavelength (nm). The ratioed spectra are then used for processing. Single variance spectra and pooled variance spectra are calculated with respect to wavelength measurements. These calculations are computed for each wavenumber for a test set of N spectra. This is calculated for variance and standard deviation as:

Variance:

$$S^2 = \frac{\sum_{i=1}^{N} (y_i - \overline{y}_i)^2}{N - 1} \tag{6.45}$$

Standard Deviation:

$$s = \sqrt{\frac{\sum_{i=1}^{N} (y_i - \overline{y}_i)^2}{N - 1}} \tag{6.46}$$

Such calculations result in a variance or standard deviation plot versus wavenumbers for differences from the mean spectrum as indicators of total variance. When plotted graphically these variance reveal spectral changes relative to wavenumber position. These values are calculated for individual materials (i.e., SB, SL, and SH) using the above equations.

The calculations are repeated for predicted values using standard analyte prediction models for each cuvette and each set of measurements.

Pooled variances and standard deviations are also computed by combining the measurements for several tests using identical or different numbers of cuvettes (1 to k) for j replicate measurements over multiple test sets using the equations as:

Pooled Variance:

$$S_P^2 = \frac{\begin{array}{c}\sum_{j=1}^{N1} (y_{1j} - \overline{y}_1)^2 + \sum_{j=1}^{N2} (y_{2j} - \overline{y}_2)^2 \\ + \sum_{j=1}^{N3} (y_{3j} - \overline{y}_3)^2 + \cdots + \sum_{j=1}^{Nk} (Y_{kj} - \overline{y}_k)^2\end{array}}{N1 + N2 + N3 + \cdots + Nk - k} \tag{6.47}$$

Pooled Standard Deviation:

$$S_P = \sqrt{\frac{\begin{array}{c}\sum_{j=1}^{N1} (y_{1j} - \overline{y}_1)^2 + \sum_{j=1}^{N2} (y_{2j} - \overline{y}_2)^2 \\ + \sum_{j=1}^{N3} (y_{3j} - \overline{y}_3)^2 + \cdots + \sum_{j=1}^{Nk} (y_{kj} - \overline{y}_k)^2\end{array}}{N1 + N2 + N3 + \cdots + Nk - k}} \tag{6.48}$$

These tests will provide detailed data to qualify and compare system changes for:

1. Multi-hour system stability (system stability over multi-hour use test);
2. Sample temperature measurement variance (this test evaluates the effect of temperature on the measurement system and plots temperature versus spectral changes over time).

b) Summary possible with test series

In addition to the detailed variances described above, one may rank the measurement error contributions as to their overall significance in adding to the total measurement error budget. One may assess the contribution of each configuration or procedural noise source to the spectral variation and how each source propagates through to the final measurement error. There are multiple other statistical analyses that can be performed to classify the type of noise and overall error contributions from each noise source.

6.14 Instrument Quality Performance Tests[33,34]

Accuracy and precision as concepts are represented in Figure 6.19. These are analogous to accuracy and repeatability, respectively. This illustration also demonstrates the concepts of biased and unbiased analysis results. For specifics on instrument performance testing for visible spectrophotometers refer to Section 6.6 of this chapter, entitled, "Visible Instrument Optical Quality Performance Tests."

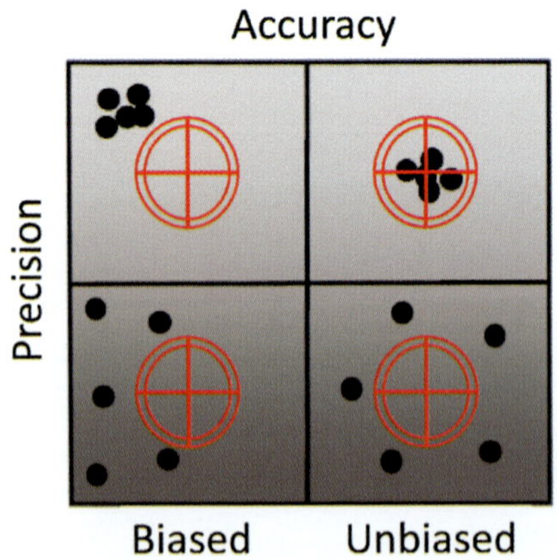

Fig. 6.19 An illustration of the concepts of accuracy and precision as well as biased and unbiased results.

6.14.1 *Wavelength Accuracy*

Verify the wavelength accuracy of the spectrophotometer using a suitable reference standard, for example NIST SRMs.

6.14.2 *Wavelength Repeatability*

Verify the wavelength repeatability of the spectrophotometer using a suitable standard.

6.14.3 *Absorbance/Response Accuracy*

Verify the response accuracy of the spectrophotometer using a suitable standard.

6.14.4 *Absorbance/Response Repeatability*

Verify the response repeatability of the spectrophotometer using a suitable standard.

6.14.5 *Photometric Linearity*

Verify the photometric linearity of the spectrophotometer by using a set of transmittance or reflectance standards. The slope of the line should be 1.00 ± 0.05 and the intercept 0.00 ± 0.05.

6.14.6 *Photometric Noise*

Determine the photometric noise (1) with no sample in the spectrometer beam, and (2) by using a reference standard. Scan the air and the standard in accordance with the spectrophotometer use recommendation and calculate the photometric noise, either peak to peak, or for a given wavelength, the standard deviation of the responses.

6.15 Final Check on Instrument/Calibration Performance

When the instrument passes all other quality and performance tests, the final test evaluation is based on measurements of the analyte in the sample matrix of interest. Spectra of test samples should be collected using exactly the same procedures as were used to collect spectra of the calibration samples. Reference values for the test samples should be obtained using the same reference method as was used for the calibration samples. Spectra should be analyzed using the multivariate model to produce estimates of the component concentrations or properties, and the statistics described below should be calculated.[35,36]

The tests may be performed by taking ten (10) test samples, with 5 replicates each, and measuring them in static mode on a fully calibrated instrument. The following are reported.

6.15.1 *Standard Error of Validation (SEV)*

Measure ten (10) static reference samples and calculate the SEP (no bias allowed) as Standard Error of Validation (SEV) given by:

$$\mathrm{SEV} = \sqrt{\frac{\sum_{i=1}^{v}\sum_{j=1}^{r_i}(\mathbf{y}_{ij} - \hat{\mathbf{y}}_i)^2}{d.f.}} = \sqrt{\frac{\sum_{i=1}^{v}\sum_{j=1}^{r_i}(\mathbf{y}_{\mathbf{ij}} - \hat{\mathbf{y}}_i)^2}{50}} \tag{6.49}$$

The $d.f.$ (degrees of freedom) is given as fifty (50) or d.f. = n × r is the total number of reference values available for all validation samples. SEV is the standard deviation in the differences between standard reference method and the spectroscopic method as reported values for samples in the validation set.

6.15.2 *Validation of Agreement Between Model and Reference Method*

The SEV value for the reference set must not exceed a pre-set threshold value of k × SEC.

6.15.2.1 *Bias*

The average bias for the estimation of the validation set, $\overline{b}_{\mathrm{v}}$, is calculated as:

$$\overline{\mathrm{b}}_{\mathrm{v}} = \frac{\sum_{i=1}^{v}\sum_{i=1}^{r_i}(\mathbf{y}_{ij} - \hat{\mathbf{y}}_i)}{d.f.} \tag{6.50}$$

where r_i is 1 if individual reference values where used, or is the number of reference values that were averaged for the ith validation sample if averages are used; $d.f.$ is the total number of reference values (samples and replicates) used in the calculation.

6.15.2.2 *Bias Significance*

The standard deviation of the validation errors, SDV, is calculated as:

$$\mathrm{SDV} = \sqrt{\frac{\sum_{i=1}^{v}\sum_{j=1}^{r_i}\left[(y_{ij} - \hat{y}_i) - \overline{b}\right]^2}{\left(\sum_{i=1}^{v} r_i\right) - 1}} \tag{6.51}$$

where r_i is n if individual reference measurements are used in calculating $\hat{\mathbf{y}}$. The *d.f.* (denominator in Eq. 6.51) is precisely n × r − k − 1 where k is the number of factors in the equation.

6.15.2.3 *Significance Test for Validation Bias*

A t test is used to determine if the validation estimates show a statistically significant bias. A t value is calculated as:

$$t = \frac{\bar{b}_V \sqrt{d.f.}}{SDV} \tag{6.52}$$

The t value is compared to critical t values from standard t-table for d.f. (degrees of freedom) used. If the t value is less than the critical t value, then analyses based on the multivariate model are expected to give essentially the same average result as measurements conducted by the reference method, provided that the analysis represents an interpolation of the calibration.

If the t value calculated is greater than the tabulated t value, there is a 95% probability that the estimate from the multivariate model will not give the same average results as the reference method. Validity of the multivariate model is then suspect. Further investigation of the calibration is required to resolve the probable bias that is indicated.

6.15.2.4 *Precision*

Measure five (5) replicate measurements for each sample ($n \times r = 50$) and calculate method precision. The precision of values estimated from a multivariate model is calculated from repeated spectral measurements. The samples used for repeat spectral measurements should span at least 95% of the range of concentration or property values used in the model. When possible, samples should be selected to ensure that some variation on each spectral variable is exhibited among the samples (i.e., that the most diverse population is selected for the validation set). Five (5) spectra should be collected for each sample. The spectra should be analyzed and values estimated. The average estimate for each sample should be calculated, and the standard deviation among the estimates should be obtained. If $\hat{y}_{ij}$ is the estimate for the jth spectrum of r_i total spectra for the ith sample, then the average estimate for this sample is:

$$\bar{\hat{y}}_i = \frac{\sum_{j=1}^{r_i} \hat{y}_{ij}}{r_i} \tag{6.53}$$

The standard deviation of the replicate estimates is calculated as:

$$\sigma_i = \sqrt{\frac{\sum_{j=1}^{r_i} (\hat{y}_{ij} - \bar{\hat{y}}_i)^2}{r_i - 1}} \tag{6.54}$$

6.16 Simple Linear Regression Analysis

6.16.1 *Introduction*

Often there is confusion in multidisciplinary uses of statistical methods due to the variation in terminology, assumptions, and specific use of statistical methods within each scientific or technical discipline. An analytical chemist may look at analytical performance quite differently than a clinical chemist, or a physicist, or a mechanical engineer. An individual from one technical discipline may only be interested in overall error or deviation of one analysis method as compared to another reference method, whereas another individual may be more interested in bias and precision; and still another in tolerance stacking, and so forth.

Combining terminology and methods for analytical chemistry, clinical chemistry, bioengineering, physics, and biochemistry concepts into a single set of statistical parameters would be useful and descriptive to a multidisciplinary team involved in looking at analytical method comparison. This section describes how to perform statistical analysis of quantitative measurement methods. The equations and terminology in this section are consistent with Clinical and Laboratory Standards Institute (CLSI) guidelines. These statistical analyses evaluate the accuracy of a test method compared to a reference method that measures the same analyte. Multiple references yield descriptions and worked problems associated with the individual statistics demonstrated in this section.[37–43]

6.16.2 *Definitions*

A comparison of methods experiment records differences between a test method and a comparative or reference method:

X comparative or reference method
Y test method
x_i observation i from comparative method
y_i observation i from test method

For clarity, this section assumes the comparative method is a traceable reference method that has better precision than the test method, which can be achieved by averaging replicate reference measurements if necessary.

6.16.3 *Measurement Error*

The Measurement Error (e_i) is the test method measurement minus the reference method

$$e = \text{Test Measurement} - \text{Reference Method} \tag{6.55}$$

or equivalently, using the CLSI definitions, the measurement error for the ith observation is:

$$e_i = y_i - x_i \tag{6.56}$$

6.16.3.1 *Accuracy*

Accuracy includes both random and systematic components of a single measurement. Accuracy for a group of observations of the test method relative to the comparative method is calculated as:

$$\text{Accuracy} = \sqrt{\frac{\sum_{i=1}^{n} e_i^2}{n}} \tag{6.57}$$

where n is the number of measurements. A common statistical term for this accuracy calculation is a root mean squared error (RMSE). Similar statistics are used to quantify errors in multivariate calibration and prediction, such as the root mean squared error of prediction (RMSEP, also known as SEP). Note: SEP = the square root of ($SD_r^2 + Bias^2$).

6.16.3.2 *Trueness and Bias*

Trueness is the closeness in agreement between the average value from a large series of measurements and a recognized reference method or traceable standard. The measure of 'trueness' is usually expressed in terms of bias (B)

Bias = average (Test Measurement) – average (Reference Method)

or equivalently, using the CLSI definitions:

$$B = \frac{\sum_{i=1}^{n} y_i - \sum_{i=1}^{n} x_i}{n} = \overline{y} - \overline{x} \tag{6.58}$$

6.16.3.3 *Precision*

Precision is defined as the closeness of the agreement between the test measurement results under specified conditions. In general, medical device manufacturers report precision estimates for *repeatability* and *reproducibility* conditions. These are considered the extreme measures of precision. Repeatability (within-run precision) is the precision of measurements made by the same operator, using the same equipment, in a short period of time. Reproducibility (total precision) is assessed over multiple days and usually includes different operators and devices.

The simplest way to estimate *repeatability* is to compute the standard deviation (SD) of a sequence of repeat measurements on identical test material:

$$SD_{repeatability} = \sqrt{\frac{\sum_{i=1}^{n} y_i^2 - \frac{(\sum y_i)^2}{n}}{n-1}} \tag{6.59}$$

In some samples the analyte level can change due to a chemical reaction. If these chemical reactions are significant contribution to the standard deviation then repeatability can be approximated from the measurement errors:

$$SD_{repeatability} \cong \sqrt{\frac{\sum_{i=1}^{n} e_i^2 - \frac{(\sum e_i)^2}{n}}{n-1}} \tag{6.60}$$

This is an approximation because the repeatability estimate now includes the imprecision of both the test method and the reference method.

6.16.3.4 *Reproducibility*

The *reproducibility* (S_T) of a measurement is a calculation that typically combines repeatability, between-run, and between day standard deviations. The necessary calculations are included in CLSI Document EP5-A2 (as referenced).

6.16.3.5 *Coefficient of Variation*

Precision (expressed in terms of repeatability and reproducibility) should be assessed at concentration levels that span the measuring range and include medical decision levels. The reported results should include the concentration level, number of samples, and precision. Precision should be reported in absolute units (such as mg/dl) and in relative units expressed as a coefficient of variation. The *coefficient of variation* expresses the precision relative to the average reference value ($\overline{x}_i$):

$$CV\% = \frac{SD \cdot 100}{\overline{x}_i} \tag{6.61}$$

Sample data calculations are given in Table 6.8.

6.16.3.6 *Computation of the Regression Line*

a) Pearson Product-Moment Correlation Coefficient (r)

The Pearson product-moment correlation coefficient for x and y data pairs is the alikeness of x to y including their respective differences ratioed to the dispersion (standard deviation) of the dataset. So the same error between x and y computes to a higher correlation when the data is more disperse or has a wider range. Therefore to

Table 6.8 Sample data calculations for reportage. The sample calculations use data from Reference 44 for comparison.

Reference values	Test values	Measurement error	Error squared
0	2.1	2.10	4.41
2	5	3.00	9.00
4	9	5.00	25.00
6	12.6	6.60	43.56
8	17.3	9.30	86.49
10	21	11.00	121.00
12	24.7	12.70	161.29

Statistical Parameter	Calculated Value
Accuracy	8.02
Standard Deviation	4.0390
Bias	7.10
%CV	67.3%
Slope	1.930
Intercept	1.52
R	0.9989
R^2	0.9978

compare correlation between experiments one should use the same data distribution for both. A high correlation does not mean smaller error unless the spread of the data used in the experiments is equivalent.

The correlation coefficient computed using a standard summation notation is defined as:

$$r = \frac{\sum_{i=1}^{n}[(x_i - \overline{x}_i)\cdot(y_i - \overline{y}_i)]}{\sqrt{\sum_{i=1}^{n}(x_i - \overline{x}_i)^2 \cdot \sum_{i=1}^{n}(y_i - \overline{y}_i)^2}} = \frac{sum[(x - \overline{x})\cdot(y - \overline{y})]}{\sqrt{sum(x - \overline{x})^2 \cdot sum(y - \overline{y})^2}} \tag{6.62}$$

b) Coefficient of Determination (R^2)

The Coefficient of Determination, R^2, is the square of the Pearson product-moment correlation coefficient. This statistic represents the amount of variation in the data that is modeled by linear fit of the test and comparative data pairs as a fraction of 1.0.

Note: For a multivariate calibration, this statistic is often termed the coefficient of multiple determination. It specifically reports the total amount of variation in the data that is fully modeled by the calibration equation as a total fraction of 1.0. If the R^2 is 1.00 then 100% of the variation is modeled in the calibration; similarly, an

R^2 of 0.80 indicates 80% of the variation has been modeled using the mathematics selected.

c) Slope (m_0)

This is the slope of the regression line between x and y paired values. A slope of 1.00 indicates perfect agreement between a change in reference value magnitude and a change in test value magnitude. This slope value does not indicate the magnitude of the bias or of the intercept of the regression line between x and y values. It is computed as follows (summation notation is indicated):

$$m_0 = \frac{n \cdot \sum_{i=1}^{n} (y_i \cdot x_i) - \sum_{i=1}^{n} y_i \cdot \sum_{i=1}^{n} x_i}{n \cdot \sum_{i=1}^{n} (y_i^2) - \sum_{i=1}^{n} (y_i)^2}$$

$$= \frac{n \cdot sum(y \cdot x) - sum(y) \cdot sum(x)}{n \cdot sum(y^2) - (sum\ y)^2} \tag{6.63}$$

d) y-Intercept (i)

The y-intercept is the point on the y-axis where the regression line crosses the 0 reference (x) value. It is not the bias which has already been defined as Parameter #3. In summation notation the intercept is computed as follows:

$$i = \frac{\sum_{i=1}^{n} y_i^2 \cdot \sum_{i=1}^{n} x_i - \sum_{i=1}^{n} y_i \cdot \sum_{i=1}^{n} (y_i \cdot x_i)}{n \cdot \sum_{i=1}^{n} (y_i^2) - \sum_{i=1}^{n} (y_i)^2}$$

$$= \frac{sum(y^2) \cdot sum(x) - sum(y) \cdot sum(y \cdot x)}{n \cdot sum(y^2) - (sum\ y)^2} \tag{6.64}$$

The regression line with linear equation is shown in Figure 6.20; regression analysis results are shown in Table 6.8.

These same methods may be used for the computation of Absorbance (X-axis) versus concentration (Y-axis) for a basic calibration. If we have a calibration sample set consisting of the data shown in Table 6.9 we may compose a simple linear regression (Figure 6.21). Note that classic methods generally use Concentration of a standard as the abscissa (or X-Axis) and Absorbance of each calibration sample as the ordinate (or Y-axis) value. This is perfectly acceptable, however if one regresses the Absorbance (as the X-axis) and Concentration (as the Y-axis) one is able to compute the regression equation immediately for use in estimating concentration (Y estimate or $\hat{Y}$). The estimated concentration is computed by inserting the absorbance measured for the test sample as the X value in the calibration linear regression as shown in Equations (6.65) and (6.66).

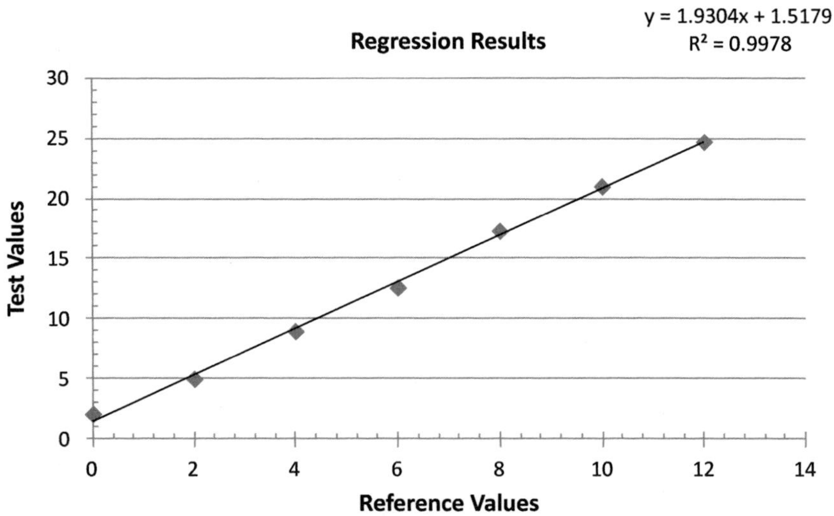

Fig. 6.20 Regression results from data in Table 6.8. (Note linear regression equation is given.)

Table 6.9 Example of basic calibration measurement data.

Measured absorbance	Known concentration
0.15	2.00
0.32	4.00
0.44	6.00
0.59	8.00
0.66	10.00
0.90	12.00
1.18	14.00

The regression analysis yields the following results.

The equation to estimate the concentration of a test sample is based on a set of calibration sample measurement results data as the example shown in Table 6.9. The resulting equation is as:

$$\hat{Y} = \mathrm{Y}_{\mathrm{est}} = 12.141\mathrm{X} + 0.6463 \tag{6.65}$$

So to compute the estimated concentration from a test sample from the calibration the following equation form is used:

$$\text{Concentration} = 12.141(\text{Absorbance}) + 0.6463 \tag{6.66}$$

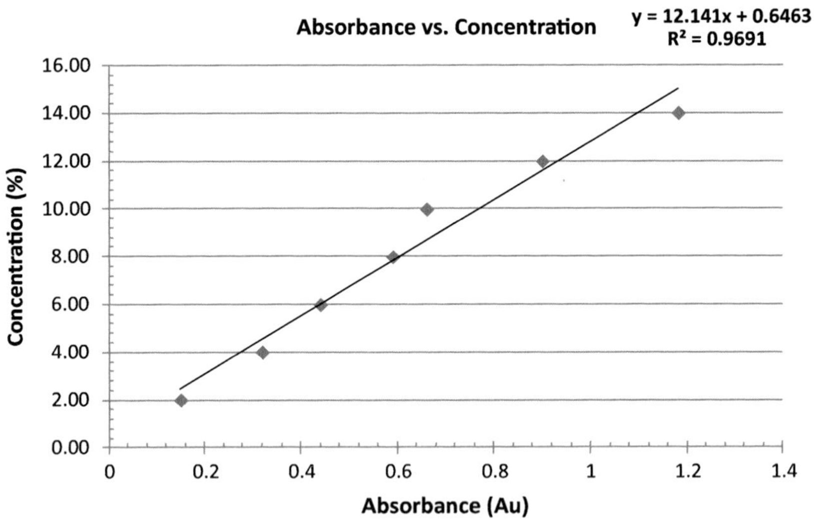

Fig. 6.21 Regression results from data in Table 6.9. (Note linear regression equation is given.)

That is, Equation (6.66) represents a calibration regression equation for estimating the concentration of a test sample from the absorbance measurement of the test sample.[44,45]

References

1. P. Williams and K. Norris (Eds.), *Near-Infrared Technology* (Amer. Assoc. Cereal Chemists, St. Paul, MN, 1987).
2. W. F. McClure and A. M. C. Davies, More on derivatives: Part 1: Segments, gaps and ghosts. NIR news **4**(6) (1994) 12.
3. W. F. McClure, More on derivatives. Part 2: Band shifting and noise. NIR news **5**(1) (1994) 14–16.
4. A. Savitzky and M.J.E.Golay, Smoothing and Differentiation of Data by Simplified Least Squares Procedures. *Anal. Chem.* **36**(8) (1964) 1627–1639.
5. A. Savitzky, "Data processing in analytical chemistry," Anal. Chem. **33**(13) (1961) 25A–32A, 35A–42A.
6. ISO/IEC 17025:2005, "General requirements for the competence of testing and calibration laboratories," International Organization for Standardization, ISO Central Secretariat, 1, ch. de la Voie-Creuse, CP 56, CH-1211 Geneva 20, Switzerland. Reviewed 2010.
7. ASTM E275-08(2013), "Standard Practice for Describing and Measuring Performance of Ultraviolet and Visible Spectrophotometers," ASTM International, West Conshohocken, PA, 2013, www.astm.org.
8. ASTM E169-04(2009), "Standard Practices for General Techniques of Ultraviolet-Visible Quantitative Analysis," ASTM International, West Conshohocken, PA, 2009, www.astm.org.

9. ASTM E925-09(2014), "Standard Practice for Monitoring the Calibration of Ultraviolet-Visible Spectrophotometers whose Spectral Bandwidth does not Exceed 2 nm," ASTM International, West Conshohocken, PA, 2014, www.astm.org.
10. ASTM E958-13, "Standard Practice for Estimation of the Spectral Bandwidth of Ultraviolet-Visible Spectrophotometers," ASTM International, West Conshohocken, PA, 2013, www.astm.org.
11. V.R. Weidner, P.Y. Barnes, and K.L. Eckerle, A Wavelength Standard for the Near Infrared Based on the Reflectance Of Rare-Earth Oxides, J. Research NBS **91**(5), 243–253 (1986).
12. B.N. Taylor and C.E. Kuyatt, Guidelines for Evaluating and Expressing the Uncertainty of NIST Measurement Results, National Institute of Standards and Technology (NIST), Technical Note 1297, 20 pages (1994).
13. From https://www-s.nist.gov/srmors/ [Search UV]
14. From https://www-s.nist.gov/srmors/ [Search SRM 930]
15. ASTM E387-04(2014), "Standard Test Method for Estimating Stray Radiant Power Ratio of Spectrophotometers by the Opaque Filter Method," ASTM International, West Conshohocken, PA, 2014, www.astm.org.
16. European Pharmacopoeia, Qualification of Equipment Annex 3: Qualification of UV-Visible spectrophotometers PA/PH/OMCL (07) 11 DEF CORR, 2007.
17. R. C. Fox, Computer searching of infrared spectra using peak location and intensity data, *Anal. Chem.* **48**(4) (1976) 717–721.
18. L. Brodsky, A. Moussaieff, N. Shahaf, A. Aharoni, and I. Rogachev, Evaluation of Peak Picking Quality in LC−MS Metabolomics Data, *Anal. Chem.* **82**(22) (2010), 9177–9187.
19. H. L. Mark, and D. Tunnell, Qualitative Near-infrared Reflectance Analysis Using Mahalanobis Distances, *Anal. Chem.* **57**(7) (1985) 1449–1456.
20. H. Mark, Normalized Distances for Qualitative Near-Infrared Reflectance Analysis, *Anal. Chem.* **58** (1986) 379–384.
21. ASTM (American Society for Testing and Materials) Method E 1655. "Standard Practice for General Techniques for Qualitative Infrared Analysis", ASTM Committee E 13, 1916 Race Street, Philadelphia, PA 19103.
22. R. G. Whitfield, M. E. Gerber, and R. L. Sharp, Near-infrared spectrum qualification via Mahalanobis distance determination. *Appl. Spectrosc.* **41** (1987) 1204–1213.
23. P. C. Mahalanobis, On the generalized distance in statistics. *Proceedings* of the *National Institute* of *Sciences* of India, Indian Natl. Inst. Science Proc. **2** (1936) 2, 49–55.
24. J. C. Reid and E. C. Wong, Data-Reduction and Search System for Digital Absorbance Spectra, *Appl. Spectrosc.* **20** (1966) 320–325.
25. P. M. Owens and T. L Isenhour, Infrared Spectral Compression Procedure for Resolution Independent Search Systems, *Anal. Chem.* **55** (1983) 1548–1553.
26. K. Tanabe and S. Saeki, Computer Retrieval of Infrared Spectra by a Correlation Coefficient Method, *Anal. Chem.* **47** (1975) 118–122.
27. L. V. Azarraga, R. R. Williams, and J.A. de Haseth, Fourier Encoded Data Searching of Infrared Spectra (FEDS/IRS), *Appl. Spectrosc.* **35** (1981) 466–469.
28. J. A. de Haseth and L. V. Azarraga, Interferogram-Based Infrared Search System, *Anal. Chem.* **53** (1981) 2292–2296.
29. D. Abookasis and J. Workman, *Chemom. Intell. Lab. Syst.* **107**(2) (2011) 303–311.
30. B. G. Osborne, T. Fearn and P. H. Hindle, *Practical NIR Spectroscopy with Applications in Food and Beverage Analysis*. 2nd edn. (Longman Group, Burnt Mill, Harlow, Essex, England, UK, 1993).

31. F. Liu, Y. He and G. Sun, Determination of Protein Content of Auricularia auricula Using Near Infrared Spectroscopy Combined with Linear and Nonlinear Calibrations. *J. Agric. Food Chem.* **57** (2009) 4520–4527.
32. L. Xu, D.-H. Deng and C.-B. Cai, Predicting the Age and Type of Tuocha Tea by Fourier Transform Infrared Spectroscopy and Chemometric Data Analysis. *J. Agric. Food Chem.* **59** (2011) 10461–10469.
33. Reproduced with permission, from NCCLS publication EP5-A2—Evaluation of Precision Performance of Quantitative Measurement Methods; Approved Guideline— Second Edition (ISBN 1-56238-542-9). Copies of the current edition may be obtained from NCCLS, 940 West Valley Road, Suite 1400, Wayne, Pennsylvania 19087–1898, USA.
34. ASTM Standard Practice E1655-00, "Standard Practices for Infrared, Multivariate, Quantitative Analysis," American Society for Testing and Materials International, Barr Harbor Dr., West Conshohocken, PA 19428.
35. N.M. Faber, F. H. Schreutelkamp, and H. W. Vedder, Estimation of prediction uncertainty for a multivariate calibration model," *Spectroscopy Europe* **16**(1) (2004) 17–20.
36. W. J. Youden and E. H. Steiner, *Statistical Manual of the AOAC*, 1st edn. (Association of Official Analytical Chemists, Washington, D.C., 1975).
37. Clinical and Laboratory Standards Institute (CLSI) guidelines: EP21-A, Estimation of Total Analytical Error for Clinical Laboratory Methods; Approved Guideline (2014).
38. CLSI Document EP5-A2, Evaluation of Precision Performance of Quantitative Measurement Methods; Approved Guideline — Second Edition (2006).
39. CLSI Document EP10-A2, Preliminary Evaluation of Quantitative Clinical Laboratory Methods; Approved Guideline — Second Edition (2006).
40. CLSI Document EP15-A2, User Verification of Precision and Trueness; Approved Guideline — Second Edition (2006).
41. CLSI Document EP9-A2, Method Comparison and Bias Estimation using Patient Samples; Approved Guideline — Second Edition (2006).
42. CLSI Document EP10-A2, Preliminary Evaluation of Quantitative Clinical Laboratory Methods; Approved Guideline — Second Edition (2006).
43. CLSI Document EP15-A2, User Verification of Precision and Trueness; Approved Guideline — Second Edition (2006).
44. J. C. Miller and J. N. Miller, *Statistics for Analytical Chemistry*, 2nd edn. (Ellis Horwood, New York, 1992).
45. H. Mark and J. Workman, *Chemometrics in Spectroscopy* (Elsevier/Academic Press, Boston, 2007).

Chapter 7

Applications and Spectral Examples for Visible Spectroscopy

Contents

This chapter describes the main uses of visible spectroscopy, including color measurement, polarization measurements, solar measurements, and colorimetric chemical reaction measurements. Other aspects of visible spectroscopy are also described. Please see the index or other chapters for specific topics related to calibrating spectrophotometers, measuring performance of spectrometers, and definitions of sample measurement geometry.

7.1 Applications of Visible Spectroscopy

A variety of applications are performed using visible spectroscopy. There are a number of chromophores measured using the visible region and a variety of chemical functional groups as well (Table 7.1, and Figures 7.1, 7.2 and Appendix Figures 7.43 through 7.50).

See Appendix section of this chapter for graphical representations of Table 7.1 (as Figures 7.43 through 7.50).

7.2 Color Measurement and Color Coordinate Calculations

Basic color is defined as the visual effect on human perception of different wavelengths of light in the 380 nm to 780 nm wavelength region. Basic colors are defined for wavelength bands as shown in Table 7.2.

7.2.1 *Basic Color Theory and Introduction*

Color measurements using visible spectroscopy between 380 nm to 780 nm attempt to predict or mimic the perception of the human eye to the color of materials. This is made more complex due to the variety of ways that visible light is able to reflect or transmit through an object and the distance and angle of observation of the eye in relation to that object. A variety of color measurement geometry configurations and computational methods for color coordinates makes color matching a challenge for specialists. The technical aspects of color measurements include Standard Observer Angle tables, Standard Illumination (or Standard Illuminants) tables, and specific measurement geometry whereby the visible spectrum is measured. The American Society for Testing and Materials (ASTM) International has created a number of consensus documents to assist with interpreting the various methods used to measure and compute color coordinates.[1–13] The ASTM E308-01, "Standard Practice for Computing the Colors of Objects by using the CIE System," and successive standards assist the spectroscopist with understanding the complexities of the CIE (International Commission on Illumination) color measurement system. The 2° Standard Observer is used for any viewing angle less than 4°, and for greater than 4° the 10° Standard Observer is used. An illustration of the various Standard

Table 7.1 Visible chromophore band positions in alphabetical order (References 12, 13, 30, 31).

Visible chromophore band positions	Start (nm)	End (nm)	Range (nm)
Violet	380	440	60
Indigo	440	470	30
Sky Blue	470	480	10
Blue	480	490	10
Blue/Green	490	495	5
Green	495	560	65
Yellow/Green	560	570	10
Yellow	570	575	5
Yellow/Orange	575	590	15
Orange	590	600	10
Orange/Red	600	620	20
Red	620	700	80
Dark Red	700	780	80
S, z, B (CIE Standard Observer)	420	440	20
M, y, G (CIE Standard Observer)	530	540	10
L, x, R (CIE Standard Observer)	560	580	20
O-H Alkyl alcohol (6ν, no hydrogen bonding)	510	516	6
Aromatic C-H Stretch (5ν)	711	717	6
O-H Alkyl alcohol (4ν, no hydrogen bonding)	738	744	6
Methyl C-H Stretch (5ν)	744	750	6
O-H Phenols (4ν, no hydrogen bonding)	752	765	13
Methylene C-H Stretch (5ν)	759	765	6
O-H Primary Alcohols (4ν)	764	770	6
O-H Water (4ν)	767	773	6
O-H Secondary Alcohols (4ν)	770	776	6
O-H Tertiary Alcohols (4ν)	773	779	6
Alkenes, conjugated RC=C-C=C-R′	450	465	15
Beta-carotene (Vitamin A)	462	468	6
Carotenes: Band 1	420	440	20
Carotenes: Band 2	440	460	20
Carotenes: Band 3	470	495	25
Chlorophyll a: Band 1	420	465	45
Chlorophyll a: Band 2	660	683	23
Chlorophyll b: Band 1	450	480	30
Chlorophyll b: Band 2	640	650	10
International Color (Blue)	439	441	2
International Color (Green)	519	521	2
International Color (Red)	619	621	2
Cu(II) ion	819	821	2
Turbidity measurement standard	899	901	2

(*Continued*)

Table 7.1 (*Continued*)

Visible chromophore band positions	Start (nm)	End (nm)	Range (nm)
Colorimetry: Eriochrome Cyanine R Method for Aluminum	525	535	10
Colorimetry: Silver Diethyldithiocarbamate Method for Arsenic	530	540	10
Colorimetry: Aluminon Method for Beryllium	510	515	5
Colorimetry: Dithizone Method for Cadmium	513	518	5
Colorimetry: N,N-Diethyl-p-phenylenediamine (DPD) Method for Chlorine	490	530	40
Colorimetry: Acidic Diphenylcarbazide Method for Chromium	535	540	5
Colorimetry: Neocuproine Method for Copper	450	460	10
Colorimetry: Chloramine-T Method for Cyanide	570	580	10
Colorimetry: Sodium 2-(parasulfophenylazo)-1,8-dihydroxy-3,6-naphthalene disulfonate (SPADNS) Method for Fluoride	550	580	30
Colorimetry: Leuco Crystal Violet Method for Iodide	585	592	7
Colorimetry: Nesslerization Method for Ammonia or Organic Nitrogen	400	425	25
Colorimetry: Phenate Method for Ammonia Nitrogen	625	630	5
Colorimetry: Cadmium Reduction Method for Nitrate Nitrogen	540	545	5
Colorimetry: Diazotized sulfanilic acid and N-(1-naphthyl)-ethylenediaminedihydrochloride Method for Nitrite Nitrogen	540	545	5
Colorimetry: 4-aminoantipyrine and potassium ferricyanide Method for Phenol	495	500	5
Colorimetry: Vanadomolybdophosphoric Acid Method for Phosphorus	400	470	70
Colorimetry: Stannous Chloride Method for Phosphorus	685	690	5
Colorimetry: Ascorbic Acid Method for Phosphorus	875	880	5
Colorimetry: Diaminobenzidine Method for Selenium	415	420	5
Colorimetry: Molybdosilicate Method for Silica	405	410	5
Colorimetry: Heteropoly Blue Method for Silica (Wavelength 1)	810	815	5
Colorimetry: Heteropoly Blue Method for Silica (Wavelength 2)	640	650	10

(*Continued*)

Table 7.1 (*Continued*)

Visible chromophore band positions	Start (nm)	End (nm)	Range (nm)
Colorimetry: Dithizone Method for Silver (Wavelength 1)	615	620	5
Colorimetry: Dithizone Method for Silver (Wavelength 2)	457	462	5
Colorimetry: Methylene Blue Method for Sulfide	659	664	5
Colorimetry: Tungstophosphoric and Molybdophosphoric acid Method for Tannin	695	700	5
Colorimetry: Tungstophosphoric and Molybdophosphoric acid Method for Lignin	695	700	5
Colorimetry: Chlorine reaction Method for Thiocyanate	475	480	5
Colorimetry: Gallic Acid Method for Vanadium	410	415	5
Colorimetry: Dithizone Method for Vanadium	610	620	10
Colorimetry: Ferric Thiocyanate Method for Chloride	475	480	5
Enzymes: NADH and NADPH (Direct Absorption)	335	340	5
Enzymes: Lactate dehydrogenase (Direct Absorption)	345	350	5
Enzymes: Alkaline phosphatase (Direct Absorption)	545	550	5
Enzymes: NADH and NADPH (Direct Absorption)	335	340	5
Enzymes: Alcohol dehydrogenase (Direct Absorption)	335	340	5
Enzymes: Aldolase (Wavelength 1) (Direct Absorption)	235	240	5
Enzymes: Aldolase (Wavelength 2) (Direct Absorption)	335	340	5
Enzymes: D-Amino acid oxidase (Direct Absorption)	335	340	5
Enzymes: L-Amino acid oxidase (Direct Absorption)	431	436	5
Enzymes: Alpha-Amylase (Color Reaction)	535	540	5
Enzymes: L-Arginase (Color Reaction)	485	490	5
Enzymes: Arylsulfatase (Hydrolysis Reaction)	400	405	5
Enzymes: Catalase (Liberation of H_2O_2)	235	240	5
Enzymes: Cholinesterases (Color Reaction)	335	340	5
Enzymes: Alpha-Chymotrypsin (Hydrolysis Product)	275	280	5
Enzymes: Creatine kinase (Direct Absorption)	335	340	5

(*Continued*)

Table 7.1 (*Continued*)

Visible chromophore band positions	Start (nm)	End (nm)	Range (nm)
Enzymes: Deoxyribonuclease I (Depolymerization product)	255	260	5
Enzymes: Diamine oxidase (Direct Absorption)	335	340	5
Enzymes: Beta-Galactosidase (Hydrolysis Product) (Wavelength 1)	400	405	5
Enzymes: Beta-Galactosidase (Hydrolysis Product) (Wavelength 2)	431	436	5
Enzymes: Glucose oxidase (Color Reaction)	431	436	5
Enzymes: Glucose-6-phosphate dehydrogenase (Direct Absorption)	335	340	5
Enzymes: Glucose phosphate isomerase (Direct Absorption)	335	340	5
Enzymes: Beta-Glucosidase (Direct Absorption)	335	340	5
Enzymes: Beta-Glucuronidase (Color Reaction)	535	540	5
Enzymes: Glutamate-oxaloacetate transaminase (Direct Absorption)	335	340	5
Enzymes: Glutamate pyruvate transaminase (Direct Absorption)	335	340	5
Enzymes: Gamma-Glutamyl transferase (p-nitroalinine method)	395	400	5
Enzymes: Hexokinase (Direct Absorption)	335	340	5
Enzymes: Alpha-Hydroxybutyrate dehydrogenase (Direct Absorption)	335	340	5
Enzymes: Isocitrate dehydrogenase (Direct Absorption)	335	340	5
Enzymes: Lactate dehydrogenase (Direct Absorption)	335	340	5
Enzymes: Leucine amino peptidase (p-nitroalinine method)	400	405	5
Enzymes: Lipase (Color Reaction)	535	540	5
Enzymes: Monoamine oxidase (Color Reaction)	451	456	5
Enzymes: Pepsin (Color Reaction) (Wavelength 1)	573	578	5
Enzymes: Pepsin (Color Reaction) (Wavelength 2)	686	691	5
Enzymes: Pepsin (Color Reaction) (Wavelength 3)	745	750	5
Enzymes: Peroxidase (Color Reaction)	455	460	5

(*Continued*)

Table 7.1 (*Continued*)

Visible chromophore band positions	Start (nm)	End (nm)	Range (nm)
Enzymes: Acid phosphatase (Direct Absorption)	295	300	5
Enzymes: Alkaline phosphatase (Color Reaction)	525	530	5
Enzymes: Pyruvate kinase (Direct Absorption)	335	340	5
Enzymes: Sorbitol dehydrogenase (Direct Absorption)	335	340	5
Enzymes: Trypsin (Direct Absorption)	275	280	5
Enzymes: Urease (Color Reaction) (Wavelength 1)	575	580	5
Enzymes: Urease (Color Reaction) (Wavelength 2)	625	630	5
Enzymes: Xanthine oxidase (Color Reaction)	530	580	50
Gemstones: Aquamarine	535	537	2
Gemstones: Aquamarine, Maxixe	653	655	2
Gemstones: Ruby (Band 1)	465	476	11
Gemstones: Ruby (Band 2)	650	660	10
Gemstones: Ruby (Band 3)	692	694	2
Gemstones: Topaz, Pink	677	682	5
Gemstones: Turquoise	427	432	5
Gemstones: Sapphire, Blue from Australia	450	471	21
Gemstones: Sapphire, Blue from Sri Lanka	445	450	5
Gemstones: Sapphire, Yellow	450	471	21
Gemstones: Sapphire, Green	450	471	21
Gemstones: Emerald (Band 1)	580	630	50
Gemstones: Emerald (Band 2)	635	640	5
Gemstones: Emerald (Band 3)	655	660	5
Gemstones: Emerald (Band 4)	681	683	2
Gemstones: Emerald (Band 3)	430	445	15
Gemstones: Spinel, Blue (Band 1)	458	478	20
Gemstones: Spinel, Blue (Band 2)	555	585	30
Gemstones: Spinel, Blue (Band 3)	630	632	2
Gemstones: Spinel, Red (Band 1)	555	560	5
Gemstones: Spinel, Red (Band 2)	675	680	5
Gemstones: Peridot (Band 1)	445	450	5
Gemstones: Peridot (Band 2)	471	476	5
Gemstones: Peridot (Band 3)	494	495	1
Gemstones: Tourmaline, Rubellite (Band 1)	449	451	2
Gemstones: Tourmaline, Rubellite (Band 2)	456	460	4
Gemstones: Tourmaline, Rubellite (Band 3)	467	472	5
Gemstones: Tourmaline, Rubellite (Band 4)	482	492	10
Gemstones: Tourmaline, Blue-Green (Band 1)	459	461	2

(*Continued*)

Table 7.1 (*Continued*)

Visible chromophore band positions	Start (nm)	End (nm)	Range (nm)
Gemstones: Tourmaline, Blue-Green (Band 2)	497	502	5
Gemstones: Alexandrite, Greenish (Band 1)	640	555	85
Gemstones: Alexandrite, Greenish (Band 2)	653	655	2
Gemstones: Alexandrite, Greenish (Band 3)	678	680	2
Gemstones: Alexandrite, Redish	676	678	2
Gemstones: Amethyst	520	550	30
Gemstones: Apatite, Yellow-Green (Band 1)	575	577	2
Gemstones: Apatite, Yellow-Green (Band 2)	583	585	2
Gemstones: Apatite, Blue (Band 1)	489	491	2
Gemstones: Apatite, Blue (Band 2)	505	507	2
Gemstones: Apatite, Blue (Band 3)	510	512	2
Gemstones: Aventurine, Green	680	682	2
Gemstones: Axinite (Band 1)	413	415	2
Gemstones: Axinite (Band 2)	464	466	2
Gemstones: Axinite (Band 3)	490	492	2
Gemstones: Axinite (Band 4)	510	512	2
Gemstones: Azurite (Band 5)	498	500	2
Gemstones: Chrysoberyl	443	445	2
Gemstones: Coral	493	495	2
Gemstones: Diamond, colorless to slightly yellow (Band 1)	413	415	2
Gemstones: Diamond, colorless to slightly yellow (Band 2)	476	478	2
Gemstones: Diamond, natural brown to green	502	504	2
Gemstones: Garnet, Grossular (Band 1)	503	505	2
Gemstones: Garnet, Grossular (Band 2)	603	605	2
Gemstones: Garnet, Grossular (Band 3)	628	630	2
Gemstones: Jadeite, Natural Green (Band 1)	435	437	2
Gemstones: Jadeite, Natural Green (Band 2)	689	691	2
Gemstones: Kyanite	444	446	2
Gemstones: Opal, Fire (Band 1)	400	590	190
Gemstones: Opal, Fire (Band 2)	640	700	60
Gemstones: Peridot (Band 1)	451	453	2
Gemstones: Peridot (Band 2)	471	473	2
Gemstones: Peridot (Band 3)	490	493	3
Gemstones: Peridot (Band 4)	492	495	3
Gemstones: Peridot (Band 5)	492	497	5
Gemstones: Garnet, Spessartine (Band 1)	410	412	2
Gemstones: Garnet, Spessartine (Band 2)	430	432	2
Gemstones: Tanzanite	593	595	2
Gemstones: Zircon	651	653	2

Visible Spectra-Structure Correlation Charts
From 26,316 cm^{-1} to 12,821 cm^{-1} (380 nm to 780 nm)

Color Key:

O-H Groups (Water, Alcohols)
C-H Alkanes (Aliphatics)
Aromatic C-H (Aromatic Compounds)

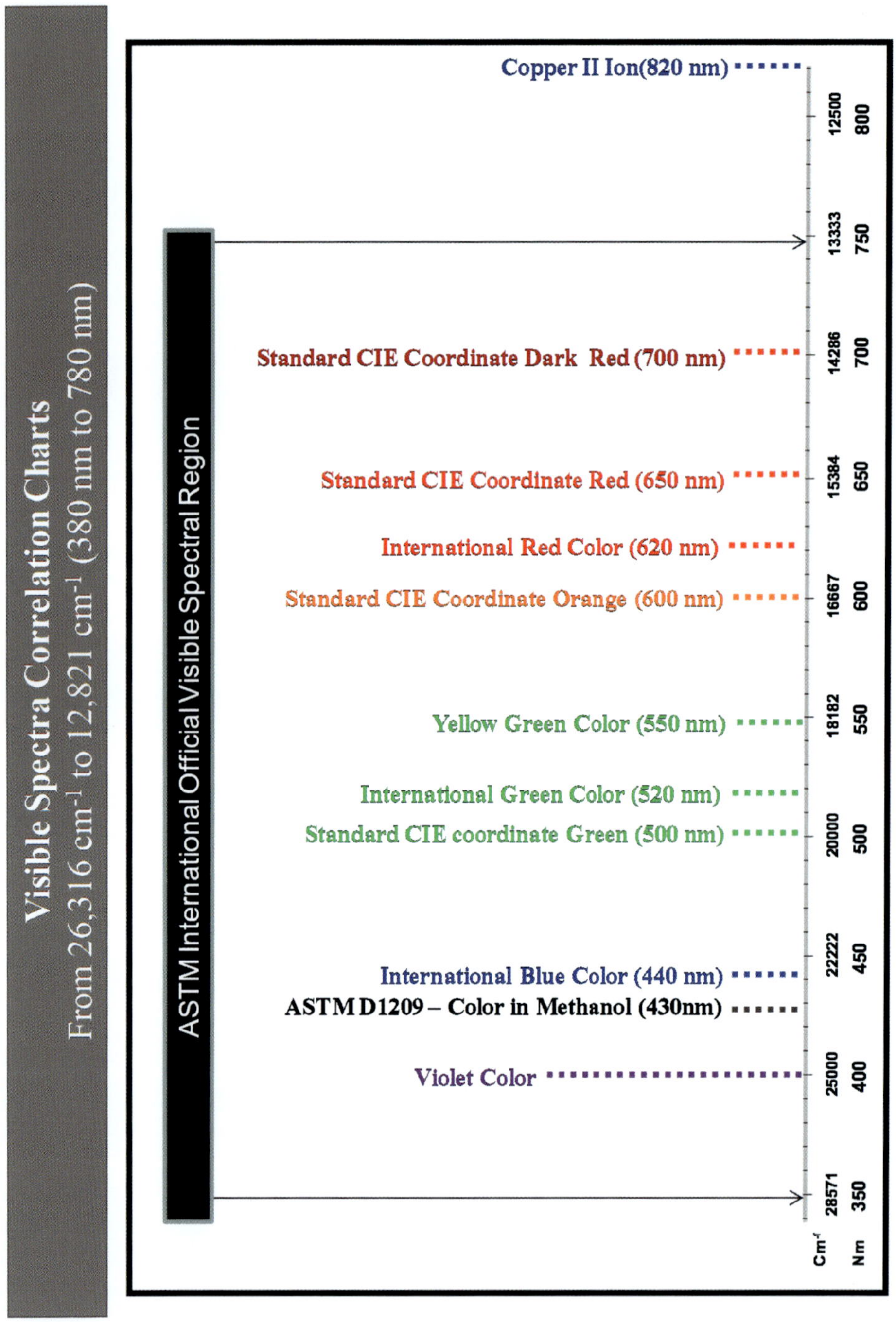

Fig. 7.1 Correlation chart for chemical group by functional structure in the VIS region from 350 to 820 nm.

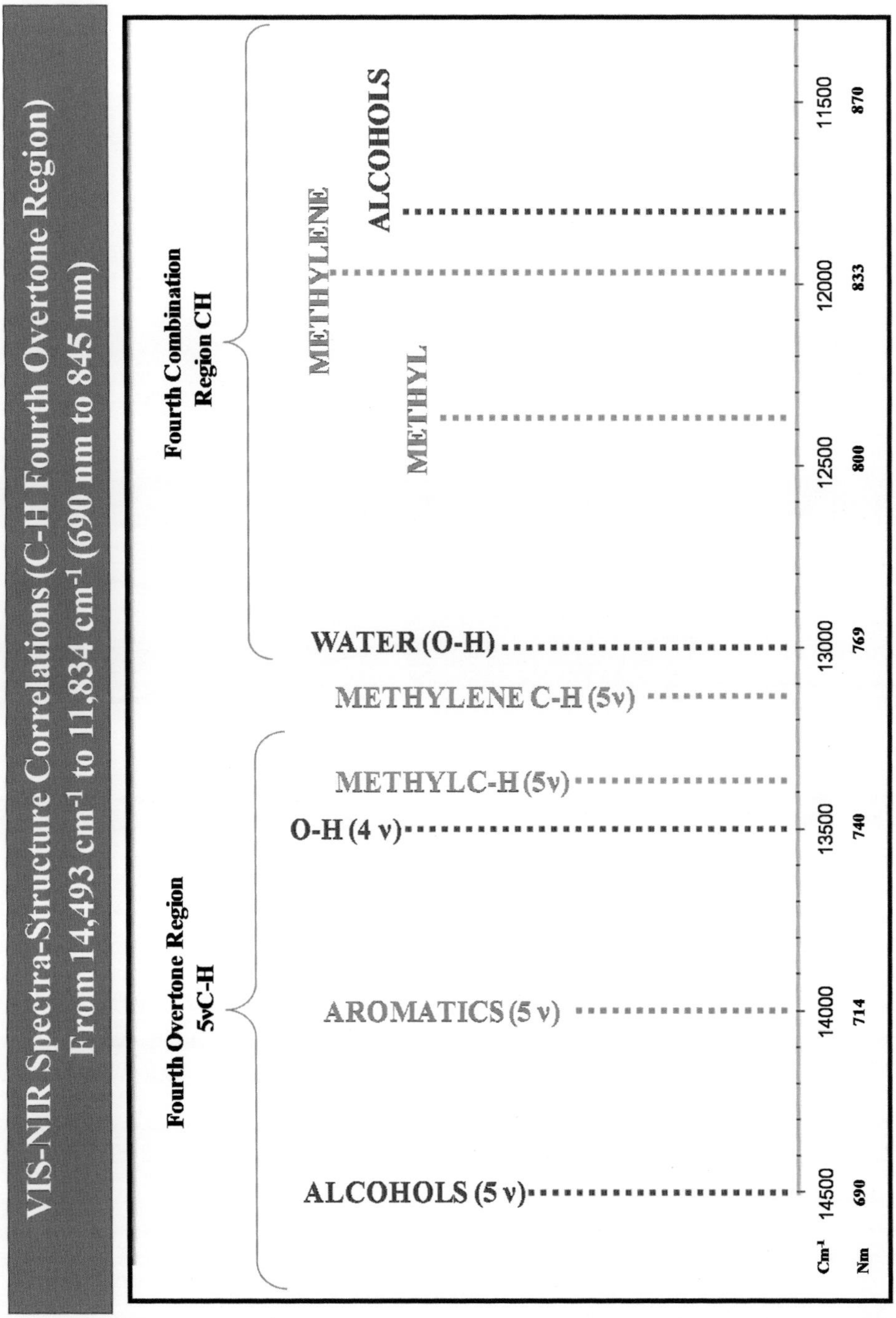

Fig. 7.2 Correlation chart for chemical group by functional structure in the VIS-short-wave NIR region from 690 to 870 nm.

Table 7.2 Basic color definitions versus wavelengths of light.

Color Name	Start (nm)	End (nm)	Range (nm)
Violet	380	440	60
Indigo	440	470	30
Sky Blue	470	480	10
Blue	480	490	10
Blue/Green	490	495	5
Green	495	560	65
Yellow/Green	560	570	10
Yellow	570	575	5
Yellow/Orange	575	590	15
Orange	590	600	10
Orange/Red	600	620	20
Red	620	700	80
Dark Red	700	780	80

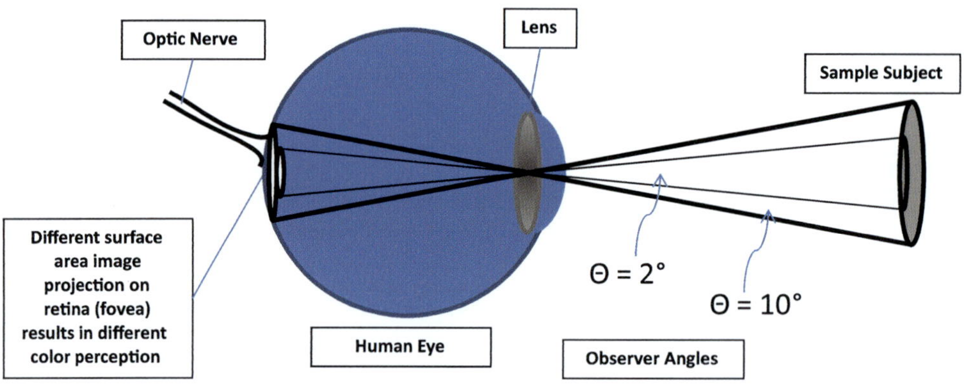

Fig. 7.3 Cartoon illustration of the concepts of 2° and 10° standard observer angles. The larger the sample the greater the projected image onto the fovea of the eye resulting in a basic difference in human color perception.

Observer angles are given in Figure 7.3. It shows the concept of a larger sample size projecting a larger image on the fovea of the retina on the human eye. Color perception is different for a larger appearing sample and thus the distinction in calculations of perceived color for large samples has been devised.

7.2.2 *Measuring the Sample for Color Measurement*

The key aspects of measuring samples for color measurement include: (1) the light source, and (2) the detector positioning relative to the sample. There are multiple geometric arrangements for making color and appearance measurements. These are referred to as the measurement geometry or the optical configuration or

Table 7.3 Typical measurement geometry for color measurements.

Measurement Geometry Name	Angle of Illumination*	Angle of Detection*	Comments
45°/0°	45°	0°	Most Common
d/8°	90°/diffuse	8°	Common
0°/45°	0°	45°	Most Common
22.5°/22.5°	22.5°	22.5°	Common
Diffuse Reflection	0°	45°	Most Common
Diffuse Transmission	0°	135°	Common
Specular Reflection	0°	<5°	Common
Specular Transmission	0°	180°	Most Common

*Relative to normal angle from the sample

design of the measuring instrument. The purpose of the spectrometer is to make a visible spectral measurement of both reference and test samples over the range of 380 nm to 780 nm. The spectrum must be accurate and repeatable for wavelength measurements (better than 0.2 nm accuracy); line width or bandpass (between 5–10 nm with high precision); and accurate in photometric intensity (better than 2–3% Reflection or Transmission) as compared to first principles or standard reference samples of known wavelength and photometric qualities. The typical measurement geometry for spectrometers is given in the following Table 7.3 and illustrated in Figures 7.4 through 7.11.

The following figures illustrate the various sample measurement geometries.

7.2.3 *Computing Color Coordinate Values*

A measurement of the sample is made following the appropriate illumination and sample measurement geometry. The various measurement schema are shown in the specific section on measuring the sample for color measurement. To calculate the color and appearance for any sample one needs to have three critical elements which are all vectors or tables of values as follows: (1) the Spectral power distribution ($S(\lambda)$) of the illuminant (usually either Standard Illuminant D65 or Standard Illuminant A); (2) The color matching functions representing the human eye sensitivity to Red, Green, Blue (RGB) as $\bar{x}$, $\bar{y}$, $\bar{z}$, respectively; and (3) the visible spectrum of the sample in the appropriate measurement geometry ($R(\lambda)$).

To compute the color matching functions as the R G B tristimulus values converted to the X Y Z color matching functions for a 10° Standard Observer and D65 Illuminant, we use the following equations and the illustration from Figure 7.12. The final values are referred to as either the 2° or 10° standard observer color matching functions. There are separate $\bar{x}$, $\bar{y}$, $\bar{z}$ tables for 2° or 10° standard observer. The

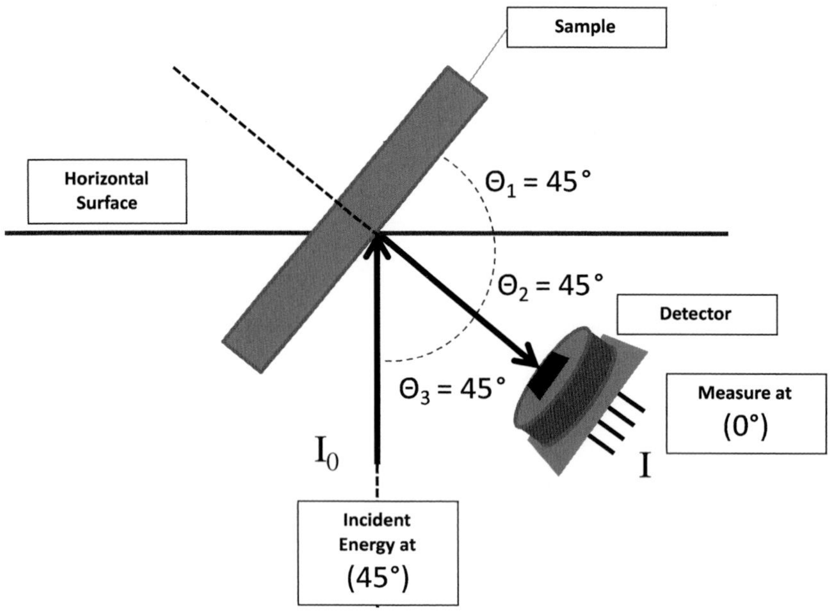

Fig. 7.4 Illustration of the 45°/0° sample measurement geometry.

observer angle definitions are found in a separate section of this text and refer to the field of view (FOV) when the eye is physically viewing a sample. The observer angle refers to the differences in appearance when the field of view on the retina of the eye subtends either a 2° or a 10° angle. To the color calculations this requires a different table of color matching functions representing the human eye sensitivity to Red, Green, and Blue (RGB). These are referred to as either $\bar{x}_2$, $\bar{y}_2$, $\bar{z}_2$ or $\bar{x}_{10}$, $\bar{y}_{10}$, $\bar{z}_{10}$ for the 2° and 10° standard observer tables, respectively.

a) X Y Z Tristimulus Values (CIE 1964 Standard 10° Observer at 5 nm intervals)

To compute the X Y Z Tristimulus values from the visible spectrum of a sample, whether in reflection or transmission one uses the following equations. Note that the symbols will be defined after each set of equations:

$$X = k \cdot \int_{380}^{780} R(\lambda) \cdot S(\lambda) \cdot \bar{x}_{10}(\lambda) d\lambda \tag{7.1}$$

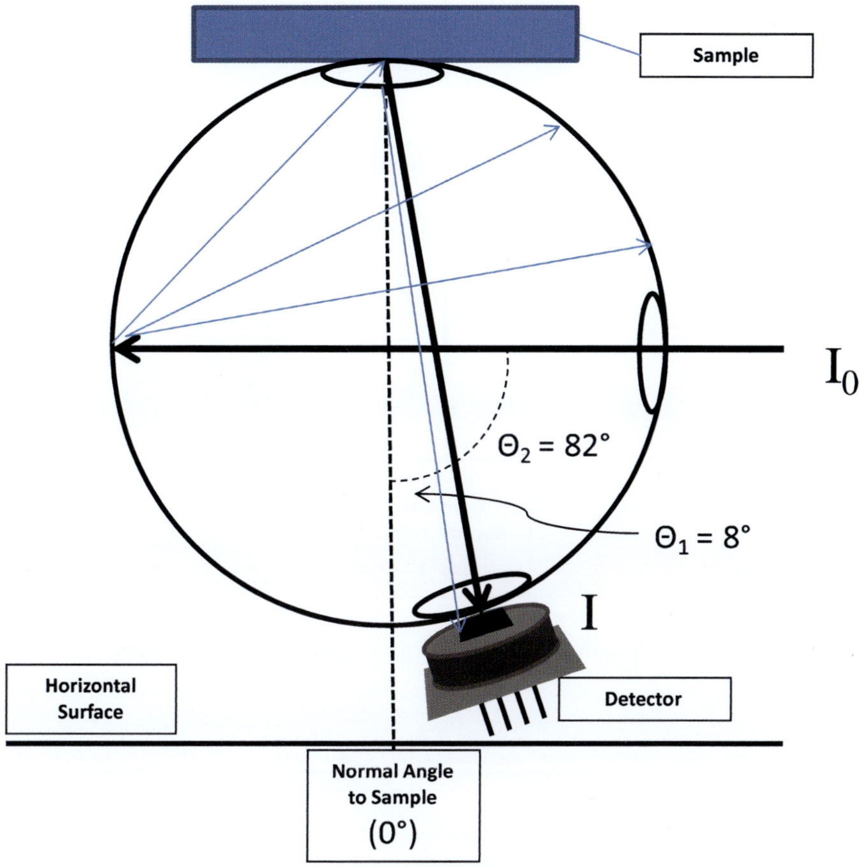

Fig. 7.5 Illustration of the d/8° sample measurement geometry.

$$Y = k \cdot \int_{380}^{780} R(\lambda) \cdot S(\lambda) \cdot \bar{y}_{10}(\lambda) d\lambda \tag{7.2}$$

$$Z = k \cdot \int_{380}^{780} R(\lambda) \cdot S(\lambda) \cdot \bar{z}_{10}(\lambda) d\lambda \tag{7.3}$$

and where

$$k = \frac{100}{\int_{380}^{780} S(\lambda) \cdot \bar{y}_{10}(\lambda) d\lambda} \tag{7.4}$$

Note that $R(\lambda)$ is the reflectance or transmittance visible spectrum of the sample using the appropriate sample measurement geometry. This would be in units of 0.0 to 1.0 for the R or T values. $S(\lambda)$ is the relative Spectral power distribution of the illuminant (generally either Standard Illuminant D65 or Standard Illuminant A).

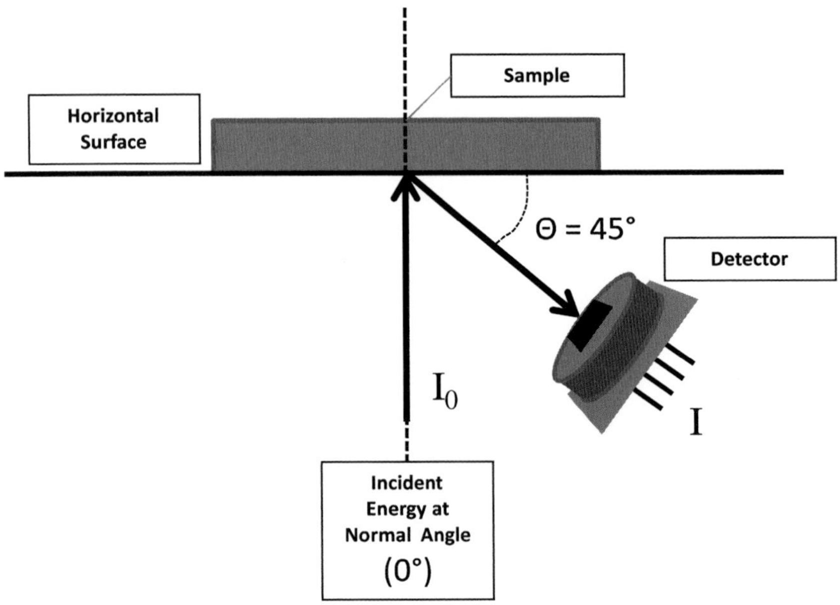

Fig. 7.6 Illustration of the 0°/45° sample measurement geometry.

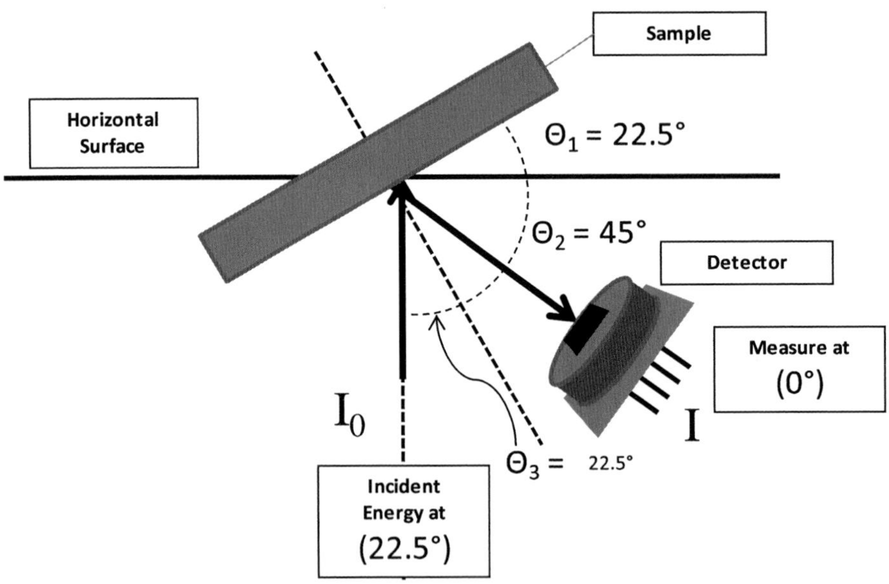

Fig. 7.7 Illustration of the 22.5°/22.5° sample measurement geometry for specular reflection.

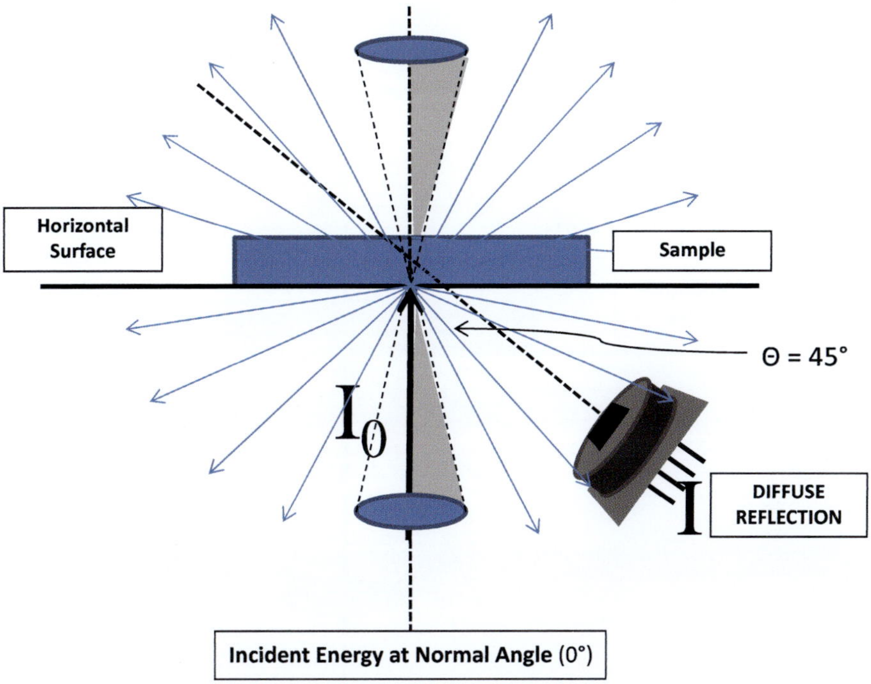

Fig. 7.8 Illustration of the 0°/45° diffuse reflection sample measurement geometry, showing reflection from the sample and direct and diffuse transmittance through the sample.

The color matching functions representing the human eye sensitivity to Red, Green, and Blue (RGB) are given as $\bar{x}_2$, $\bar{y}_2$, $\bar{z}_2$ or $\bar{x}_{10}$, $\bar{y}_{10}$, $\bar{z}_{10}$ for the 2° and 10° standard observer tables, respectively. The example will be computed for the X Y Z Tristimulus values for a specific reflectance spectrum for a red object. Note the following Tables 7.4 through 7.6 showing the actual values used for computations of X Y Z. These include the Spectral Power, $\bar{x}_{10}$, $\bar{y}_{10}$, $\bar{z}_{10}$, and the Reflectance Spectrum of the red sample.

So the computations are made as per the equations for X Y and Z using the D65 illuminant and the CIE 1964 $\bar{x}_{10}$, $\bar{y}_{10}$, $\bar{z}_{10}$ values. The k value is computed by multiplying $S(\lambda) \cdot \bar{y}_{10}$ at each wavelength and then summing the values; k is then determined by computing 100/sum of $S(\lambda) \cdot \bar{y}_{10}$ at each wavelength.

b) X Y Z Tristimulus Values (CIE 1931 Standard 2° Observer at 5 nm intervals)

To compute the X Y Z Tristimulus values from the visible spectrum of a sample whether in reflection or transmission one uses the following equations. Note that

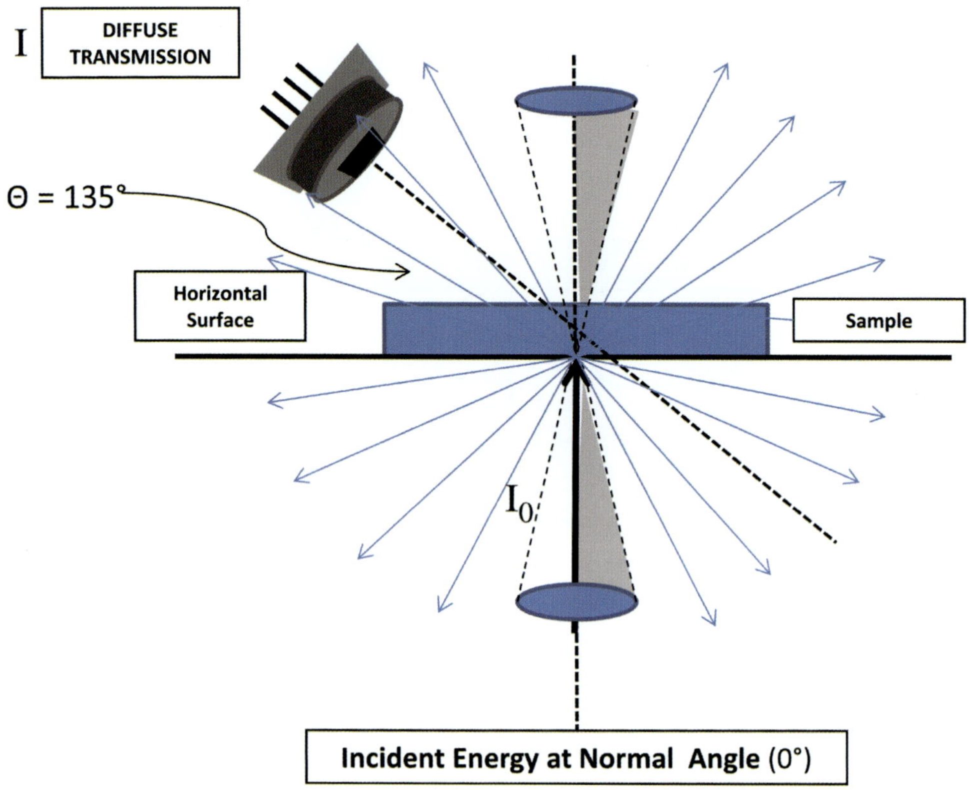

Fig. 7.9 Illustration of a 0°/135° diffuse transmission sample measurement geometry.

the symbols will be defined after each set of equations:

$$X = k \cdot \int_{380}^{780} R(\lambda) \cdot S(\lambda) \cdot \bar{x}_2(\lambda) d\lambda \tag{7.5}$$

$$Y = k \cdot \int_{380}^{780} R(\lambda) \cdot S(\lambda) \cdot \bar{y}_2(\lambda) d\lambda \tag{7.6}$$

$$Z = k \cdot \int_{380}^{780} R(\lambda) \cdot S(\lambda) \cdot \bar{z}_2(\lambda) d\lambda \tag{7.7}$$

and where

$$k = \frac{100}{\int_{380}^{780} S(\lambda) \cdot \bar{y}_2(\lambda) d\lambda} \tag{7.8}$$

Note that $R(\lambda)$ is still the reflectance or transmittance visible spectrum of the sample using the appropriate sample measurement geometry. This would be in units of 0.0

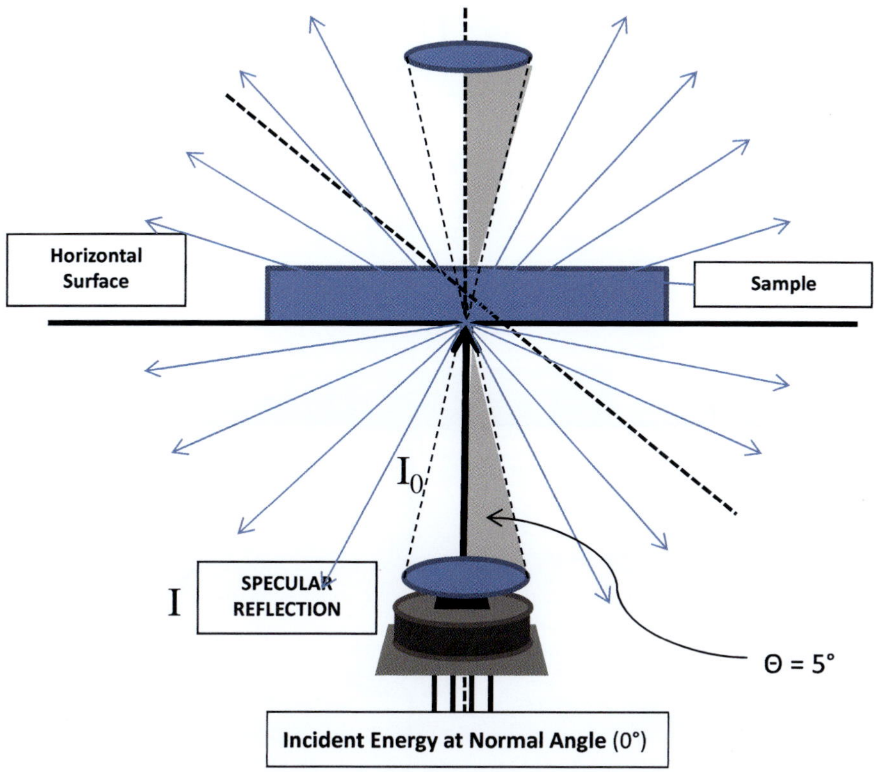

Fig. 7.10 Illustration of a 0°/<5° specular reflection sample measurement geometry.

to 1.0 for the R or T values. S(λ) is the relative Spectral power distribution of the illuminant (generally either Standard Illuminant D65 or Standard Illuminant A). The color matching functions representing the human eye sensitivity to Red, Green, and Blue (RGB) are given as $\bar{x}_2$, $\bar{y}_2$, $\bar{z}_2$ or $\bar{x}_{10}$, $\bar{y}_{10}$, $\bar{z}_{10}$ for the 2° and 10° standard observer tables, respectively. The example will be computed for the X Y Z Tristimulus values for a specific reflectance spectrum for a red object. Note the R(λ) and S(λ) tables are the same for the 2° standard observer, but the Spectral Power tables differ as $\bar{x}_2$, $\bar{y}_2$, $\bar{z}_2$ as in Table 7.7 and as illustrated in Figure 7.13.

Using the X Y Z tristimulus values one is able to compute many other color coordinate systems and these will be described here.

c) xyz Chromaticity Coordinates

The xyz Chromaticity Coordinates use the X Y Z Tristimulus values computed and applied to the following equations. Either X_2, Y_2, Z_2; or X_{10}, Y_{10}, Z_{10} may be used

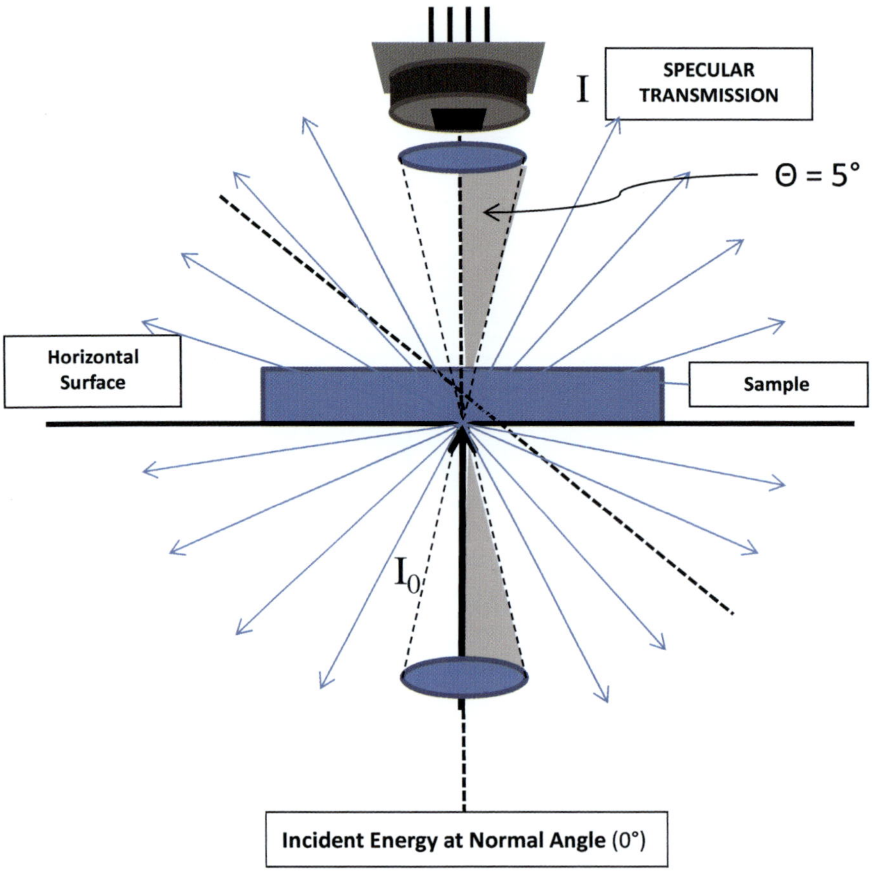

Fig. 7.11 Illustration of a 0°/180° specular transmission sample measurement geometry.

to compute x_2, y_2, z_2; or x_{10}, y_{10}, z_{10}, respectively:

$$x = \frac{X}{X + Y + Z} \tag{7.9}$$

$$y = \frac{Y}{X + Y + Z} \tag{7.10}$$

$$z = \frac{Z}{X + Y + Z} \tag{7.11}$$

The x, y, and z chromaticity coordinates form a color coordinate map. A simple version of this space without the color components is shown in Figure 7.14. The x and y values are computed as above from the Spectral Tristimulus Values $\bar{x}_{10}$, $\bar{y}_{10}$, $\bar{z}_{10}$ of the CIE 1964 Supplementary Standard (10°) Observer, at 5 nm intervals; or from

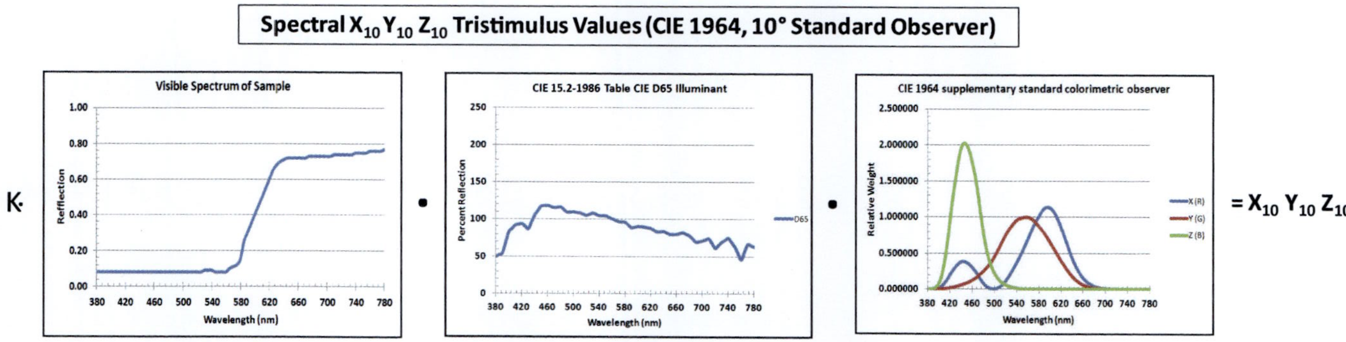

$$K \cdot R(\lambda) \cdot S(\lambda) \cdot \bar{X}_{10} = X_{10}$$
$$K \cdot R(\lambda) \cdot S(\lambda) \cdot \bar{Y}_{10} = Y_{10}$$
$$K \cdot R(\lambda) \cdot S(\lambda) \cdot \bar{Z}_{10} = Z_{10}$$

Fig. 7.12 Spectral X_{10} Y_{10} Z_{10} Tristimulus values (CIE 1964, 10° standard observer, D65 illuminant shown).

Table 7.4. Reflectance spectrum of the Sample from 380 nm to 780 nm.

nm	Reflection	nm	Reflection
380	0.08	585	0.25
385	0.08	590	0.30
390	0.08	595	0.35
395	0.08	600	0.40
400	0.08	605	0.45
405	0.08	610	0.50
410	0.08	615	0.55
415	0.08	620	0.60
420	0.08	625	0.65
425	0.08	630	0.68
430	0.08	635	0.70
435	0.08	640	0.71
440	0.08	645	0.72
445	0.08	650	0.72
450	0.08	655	0.72
455	0.08	660	0.72
460	0.08	665	0.72
465	0.08	670	0.72
470	0.08	675	0.73
475	0.08	680	0.73
480	0.08	685	0.73
485	0.08	690	0.73
490	0.08	695	0.73
495	0.08	700	0.73
500	0.08	705	0.73
505	0.08	710	0.74
510	0.08	715	0.74
515	0.08	720	0.74
520	0.08	725	0.74
525	0.08	730	0.74
530	0.09	735	0.74
535	0.09	740	0.75
540	0.09	745	0.75
545	0.08	750	0.75
550	0.08	755	0.75
555	0.08	760	0.76
560	0.08	765	0.76
565	0.10	770	0.76
570	0.11	775	0.76
575	0.12	780	0.77
580	0.15		

Table 7.5 The Spectral power distribution (S(λ)) of Illuminant D65 and standard illuminant A.

nm	D65	A
380	49.98	9.80
385	52.31	10.90
390	54.65	12.09
395	68.70	13.35
400	82.75	14.71
405	87.12	16.15
410	91.49	17.68
415	92.46	19.29
420	93.43	21.00
425	90.06	22.79
430	86.68	24.67
435	95.77	26.64
440	104.87	28.70
445	110.94	30.85
450	117.01	33.09
455	117.41	35.41
460	117.81	37.81
465	116.34	40.30
470	114.86	42.87
475	115.39	45.52
480	115.92	48.24
485	112.37	51.04
490	108.81	53.91
495	109.08	56.85
500	109.35	59.86
505	108.58	62.93
510	107.80	66.06
515	106.30	69.25
520	104.79	72.50
525	106.24	75.79
530	107.69	79.13
535	106.05	82.52
540	104.41	85.95
545	104.23	89.41
550	104.05	92.91
555	102.02	96.44
560	100.00	100.00
565	98.17	103.58
570	96.33	107.18
575	96.06	110.80

(Continued)

Table 7.5 (*Continued*)

nm	D65	A
580	95.79	114.44
585	92.24	118.08
590	88.69	121.73
595	89.35	125.39
600	90.01	129.04
605	89.80	132.70
610	89.60	136.35
615	88.65	139.99
620	87.70	143.62
625	85.49	147.24
630	83.29	150.84
635	83.49	154.42
640	83.70	157.98
645	81.86	161.52
650	80.03	165.03
655	80.12	168.51
660	80.21	171.96
665	81.25	175.38
670	82.28	178.77
675	80.28	182.12
680	78.28	185.43
685	74.00	188.70
690	69.72	191.93
695	70.67	195.12
700	71.61	198.26
705	72.98	201.36
710	74.35	204.41
715	67.98	207.41
720	61.60	210.37
725	65.74	213.27
730	69.89	216.12
735	72.49	218.92
740	75.09	221.67
745	69.34	224.36
750	63.59	227.00
755	55.01	229.59
760	46.42	232.12
765	56.61	234.59
770	66.81	237.01
775	65.09	239.37
780	63.38	241.68

Table 7.6 Spectral Tristimulus values $\bar{x}_{10}$, $\bar{y}_{10}$, $\bar{z}_{10}$ of the CIE 1964 supplementary standard (10°) observer, at 5 nm intervals.

nm	$\bar{x}_{10}$	$\bar{y}_{10}$	$\bar{z}_{10}$
380	0.000160	0.000017	0.000705
385	0.000662	0.000072	0.002928
390	0.002362	0.000253	0.010482
395	0.007242	0.000769	0.032344
400	0.019110	0.002004	0.086011
405	0.043400	0.004509	0.197120
410	0.084736	0.008756	0.389366
415	0.140638	0.014456	0.656760
420	0.204492	0.021391	0.972542
425	0.264737	0.029497	1.282500
430	0.314679	0.038676	1.553480
435	0.357719	0.049602	1.798500
440	0.383734	0.062077	1.967280
445	0.386726	0.074704	2.027300
450	0.370702	0.089456	1.994800
455	0.342957	0.106256	1.900700
460	0.302273	0.128201	1.745370
465	0.254085	0.152761	1.554900
470	0.195618	0.185190	1.317560
475	0.132349	0.219940	1.030200
480	0.080507	0.253589	0.772125
485	0.041072	0.297665	0.570060
490	0.016172	0.339133	0.415254
495	0.005132	0.395379	0.302356
500	0.003816	0.460777	0.218502
505	0.015444	0.531360	0.159249
510	0.037465	0.606741	0.112044
515	0.071358	0.685660	0.082248
520	0.117749	0.761757	0.060709
525	0.172953	0.823330	0.043050
530	0.236491	0.875211	0.030451
535	0.304213	0.923810	0.020584
540	0.376772	0.961988	0.013676
545	0.451584	0.982200	0.007918
550	0.529826	0.991761	0.003988
555	0.616053	0.999110	0.001091
560	0.705224	0.997340	0.000000
565	0.793832	0.982380	0.000000
570	0.878655	0.955552	0.000000

(*Continued*)

Table 7.6 (*Continued*)

nm	$\bar{x}_{10}$	$\bar{y}_{10}$	$\bar{z}_{10}$
575	0.951162	0.915175	0.000000
580	1.014160	0.868934	0.000000
585	1.074300	0.825623	0.000000
590	1.118520	0.777405	0.000000
595	1.134300	0.720353	0.000000
600	1.123990	0.658341	0.000000
605	1.089100	0.593878	0.000000
610	1.030480	0.527963	0.000000
615	0.950740	0.461834	0.000000
620	0.856297	0.398057	0.000000
625	0.754930	0.339554	0.000000
630	0.647467	0.283493	0.000000
635	0.535110	0.228254	0.000000
640	0.431567	0.179828	0.000000
645	0.343690	0.140211	0.000000
650	0.268329	0.107633	0.000000
655	0.204300	0.081187	0.000000
660	0.152568	0.060281	0.000000
665	0.112210	0.044096	0.000000
670	0.081261	0.031800	0.000000
675	0.057930	0.022602	0.000000
680	0.040851	0.015905	0.000000
685	0.028623	0.011130	0.000000
690	0.019941	0.007749	0.000000
695	0.013842	0.005375	0.000000
700	0.009577	0.003718	0.000000
705	0.006605	0.002565	0.000000
710	0.004553	0.001768	0.000000
715	0.003145	0.001222	0.000000
720	0.002175	0.000846	0.000000
725	0.001506	0.000586	0.000000
730	0.001045	0.000407	0.000000
735	0.000727	0.000284	0.000000
740	0.000508	0.000199	0.000000
745	0.000356	0.000140	0.000000
750	0.000251	0.000098	0.000000
755	0.000178	0.000070	0.000000
760	0.000126	0.000050	0.000000
765	0.000090	0.000036	0.000000
770	0.000065	0.000025	0.000000
775	0.000046	0.000018	0.000000
780	0.000033	0.000013	0.000000

Table 7.7 Spectral Tristimulus values $\bar{x}_2$, $\bar{y}_2$, $\bar{z}_2$ of the CIE 1931 supplementary standard (2°) Observer, at 5 nm intervals.

nm	$\bar{x}_2$	$\bar{y}_2$	$\bar{z}_2$
380	0.001368	0.000039	0.006450
385	0.002236	0.000064	0.010550
390	0.004243	0.000120	0.020050
395	0.007650	0.000217	0.036210
400	0.014310	0.000396	0.067850
405	0.023190	0.000640	0.110200
410	0.043510	0.001210	0.207400
415	0.077630	0.002180	0.371300
420	0.134380	0.004000	0.645600
425	0.214770	0.007300	1.039050
430	0.283900	0.011600	1.385600
435	0.328500	0.016840	1.622960
440	0.348280	0.023000	1.747060
445	0.348060	0.029800	1.782600
450	0.336200	0.038000	1.772110
455	0.318700	0.048000	1.744100
460	0.290800	0.060000	1.669200
465	0.251100	0.073900	1.528100
470	0.195360	0.090980	1.287640
475	0.142100	0.112600	1.041900
480	0.095640	0.139020	0.812950
485	0.057950	0.169300	0.616200
490	0.032010	0.208020	0.465180
495	0.014700	0.258600	0.353300
500	0.004900	0.323000	0.272000
505	0.002400	0.407300	0.212300
510	0.009300	0.503000	0.158200
515	0.029100	0.608200	0.111700
520	0.063270	0.710000	0.078250
525	0.109600	0.793200	0.057250
530	0.165500	0.862000	0.042160
535	0.225750	0.914850	0.029840
540	0.290400	0.954000	0.020300
545	0.359700	0.980300	0.013400
550	0.433450	0.994950	0.008750
555	0.512050	1.000000	0.005750
560	0.594500	0.995000	0.003900
565	0.678400	0.978600	0.002750
570	0.762100	0.952000	0.002100

(*Continued*)

Table 7.7 (*Continued*)

nm	$\bar{x}_2$	$\bar{y}_2$	$\bar{z}_2$
575	0.842500	0.915400	0.001800
580	0.916300	0.870000	0.001650
585	0.978600	0.816300	0.001400
590	1.026300	0.757000	0.001100
595	1.056700	0.694900	0.001000
600	1.062200	0.631000	0.000800
605	1.045600	0.566800	0.000600
610	1.002600	0.503000	0.000340
615	0.938400	0.441200	0.000240
620	0.854450	0.381000	0.000190
625	0.751400	0.321000	0.000100
630	0.642400	0.265000	0.000050
635	0.541900	0.217000	0.000030
640	0.447900	0.175000	0.000020
645	0.360800	0.138200	0.000010
650	0.283500	0.107000	0.000000
655	0.218700	0.081600	0.000000
660	0.164900	0.061000	0.000000
665	0.121200	0.044580	0.000000
670	0.087400	0.032000	0.000000
675	0.063600	0.023200	0.000000
680	0.046770	0.017000	0.000000
685	0.032900	0.011920	0.000000
690	0.022700	0.008210	0.000000
695	0.015840	0.005723	0.000000
700	0.011359	0.004102	0.000000
705	0.008111	0.002929	0.000000
710	0.005790	0.002091	0.000000
715	0.004106	0.001484	0.000000
720	0.002899	0.001047	0.000000
725	0.002049	0.000740	0.000000
730	0.001440	0.000520	0.000000
735	0.001000	0.000361	0.000000
740	0.000690	0.000249	0.000000
745	0.000476	0.000172	0.000000
750	0.000332	0.000120	0.000000
755	0.000235	0.000085	0.000000
760	0.000166	0.000060	0.000000
765	0.000117	0.000042	0.000000
770	0.000083	0.000030	0.000000
775	0.000059	0.000021	0.000000
780	0.000042	0.000015	0.000000

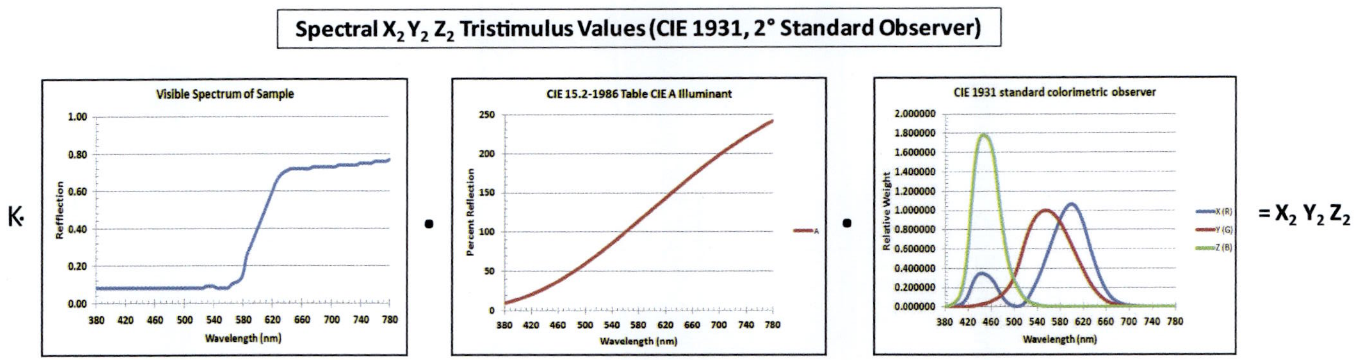

$$K \cdot R(\lambda) \cdot S(\lambda) \cdot \bar{X}_2 = X_2$$
$$K \cdot R(\lambda) \cdot S(\lambda) \cdot \bar{Y}_2 = Y_2$$
$$K \cdot R(\lambda) \cdot S(\lambda) \cdot \bar{Z}_2 = Z_2$$

Fig. 7.13 Spectral $\bar{x}_2$, $\bar{y}_2$, $\bar{z}_2$ tristimulus values (CIE 1931, 2° standard observer, a illuminant shown).

the Spectral Tristimulus Values $\bar{x}_2$, $\bar{y}_2$, $\bar{z}_2$ of the CIE 1931 Supplementary Standard (2°) Observer, at 5 nm intervals.

d) L*a*b* Color Space Coordinates

L*a*b* Color Space coordinates are computed using the X Y Z Tristimulus values for the sample and either a 100% transmission (with no sample present), or 100% reflectance using a highly reflective reference standard. The sample measurement coordinates are represented as X Y Z and the 100% reference standard measurement coordinates as X_0 Y_0 Z_0. So the values of the L*a*b* Color Space coordinates are computed using the following standard expressions. L*a*b* color space is a

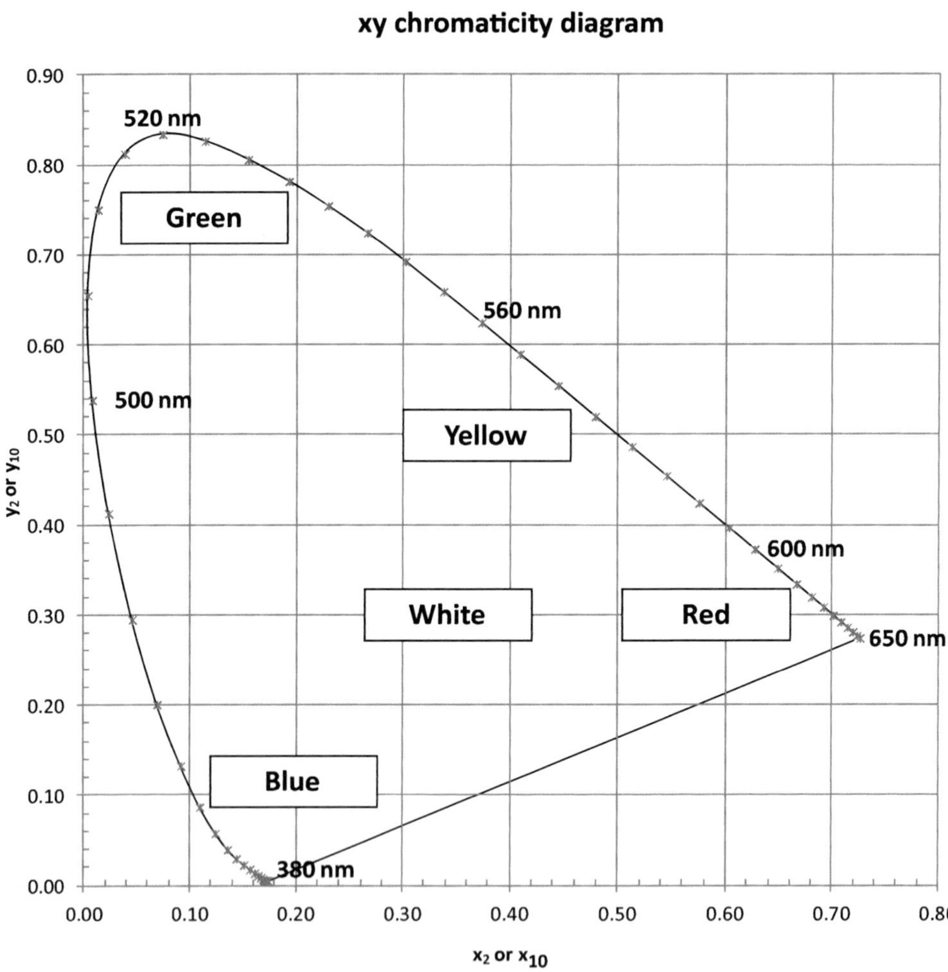

Fig. 7.14 Illustration of the xy chromaticity diagram at 5 nm intervals from 380 nm to 650 nm, indicating major color areas.

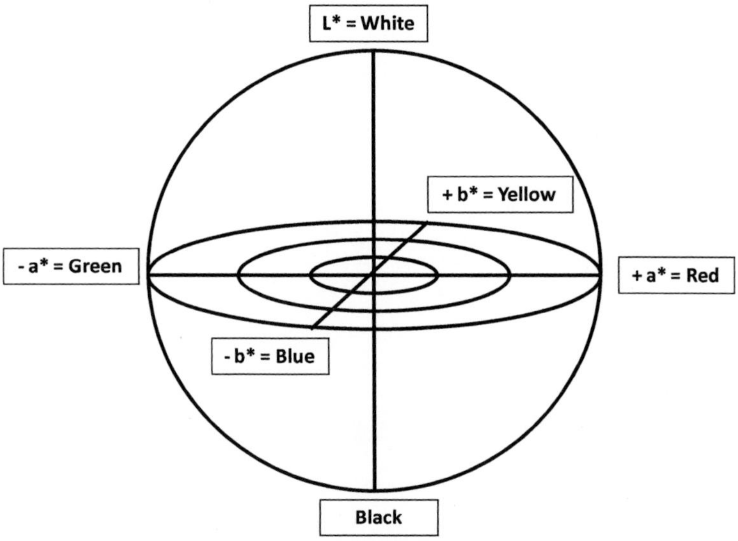

Fig. 7.15 Illustration of the L*a*b* spherical color space.

projection of CIE color coordinates onto a spherical color space with the "poles" of that space being pure white and pure black (i.e., the L* dimension). We draw a line through the center of the sphere representing the dimensions of pure yellow and pure blue (i.e., b* dimension); and pure red and pure green as the a* dimension. The basic diagram of the L*a*b* sphere is shown in Figure 7.15. The two directions at the center of the sphere are represented by pure blue.

The Lightness variable is designated as L* and is computed as:

$$L^* = 116 \cdot \left(\frac{Y}{Y_0}\right)^{\frac{1}{3}} - 16 \tag{7.12}$$

The Chromaticity coordinates are designated as a* and b* and are computed using:

$$a^* = 500 \cdot \left[\left(\frac{X}{X_0}\right)^{\frac{1}{3}} - \left(\frac{Y}{Y_0}\right)^{\frac{1}{3}}\right] \tag{7.13}$$

$$b^* = 200 \cdot \left[\left(\frac{Y}{Y_0}\right)^{\frac{1}{3}} - \left(\frac{Z}{Z_0}\right)^{\frac{1}{3}}\right] \tag{7.14}$$

In an exceptional case where any of the ratios $\frac{X}{X_0}$, $\frac{Y}{Y_0}$, $\frac{Z}{Z_0}$ are less than 0.008856, the following equations are used to compute L*a*b*.

The Lightness variable is designated as L* and is computed as:

$$L^* = 116 \cdot \left(\frac{Y}{Y_0}\right)^{\frac{1}{3}} - 16 \tag{7.15}$$

The Chromaticity coordinates a* and b* are computed using:

$$a^* = 500 \cdot \left[\left(7.787 \cdot \left(\frac{X}{X_0}\right) + \frac{16}{116}\right) - \left(7.787 \cdot \left(\frac{Y}{Y_0}\right) + \frac{16}{116}\right)\right] \tag{7.16}$$

$$b^* = 200 \cdot \left[\left(7.787 \cdot \left(\frac{Y}{Y_0}\right) + \frac{16}{116}\right) - \left(7.787 \cdot \left(\frac{Z}{Z_0}\right) + \frac{16}{116}\right)\right] \tag{7.17}$$

e) Color Difference using L*a*b* Coordinates

The Color difference, sometimes referred to as ΔE^*_{ab} indicates the estimated difference in color space. This color difference is computed as:

$$\Delta E^*_{ab} = \{(\Delta L^*)^2 + (\Delta a^*)^2 + (\Delta b^*)^2\}^{\frac{1}{2}} \tag{7.18}$$

where the delta values are the differences between the color standard and the test sample L*a*b* values.

f) L*C*h Color Space

The L*C*h Color Space uses the L*a*b* spherical coordinates but projects them from three-dimensional spherical space to a three-dimensional cylindrical coordinate space. The lightness coordinate (L*) is identical to the L* value of L*a*b* color space. The terms Metric Chroma (C*) and Metric-Hue Angle (h) are defined by the following formulas:

$$C^* = \{(a^*)^2 + (b^*)^2\}^{\frac{1}{2}} \tag{7.19}$$

$$h = \tan^{-1}\left(\frac{b^*}{a^*}\right) = \arctan\left(\frac{b^*}{a^*}\right) \tag{7.20}$$

Note: h is expressed in degrees, and to convert radians to degrees multiply radians × 57.269°/radians.

g) Metric-Hue-Angle Difference

The Metric-Hue-Angle Difference (ΔH*) is calculated using the reference and test sample a* and b* values from their respective L*a*b* coordinates, as well as the

Metric Chroma (C*) values for reference and test samples. It is computed as follows:

$$\Delta H^* = \{(\Delta a^*)^2 + (\Delta b^*)^2 + (\Delta C^*)^2\}^{\frac{1}{2}} \tag{7.21}$$

Note that the Metric-Hue angle is positive if the test sample ΔH^* is greater than the reference sample; and negative if the test sample ΔH^* is less than the reference sample.

h) Hunter 1948 Lab Color Coordinate Space

Richard S. Hunter developed the Hunter Lab Color Space in 1948. It is based on the tristimulus method and allows color measurement using a basic colorimeter instrument with the Red, Green, and Blue color measures. It relies on using the Tristimulus X Y and Z coordinate space for its calculations. The Hunter Lab is determined as:

$$L = 100 \cdot \left\{\frac{Y}{Y_0}\right\}^{\frac{1}{2}} \tag{7.22}$$

$$a = 175 \cdot \left\{\frac{0.0102 \cdot X_0 \cdot Y_0}{Y}\right\}^{\frac{1}{2}} \cdot \left[\left(\frac{X}{X_0}\right) - \left(\frac{Y}{Y_0}\right)\right] \tag{7.23}$$

$$b = 70 \cdot \left\{\frac{0.00847 \cdot Z_0 \cdot Y_0}{Y}\right\}^{\frac{1}{2}} \cdot \left[\left(\frac{Y}{Y_0}\right) - \left(\frac{Z}{Z_0}\right)\right] \tag{7.24}$$

Note: the X Y and Z values are the tristimulus coordinates for the specified observer (generally 2° or 10°) and the Illuminant (generally D65 or A). The X_0 Y_0 and Z_0 values are the tristimulus values for the same observer and Illuminant for the perfect reflective standard. It is important to note that the L, a, b equations for Hunter color space are different for the 2° Standard Observer with Standard Illuminant C. For these conditions the Hunter Lab coordinates are:

$$L = 10 \cdot Y^{1/2} \tag{7.25}$$

$$a = \frac{17.5(1.02X - Y)}{Y^{1/2}} \tag{7.26}$$

$$b = \frac{7.0(Y - 0.847Z)}{Y^{1/2}} \tag{7.27}$$

i) Color Difference using Hunter Lab Coordinates

The Color difference for Hunter color coordinates, sometimes referred to as ΔE_H indicates the estimated difference in this color space. This Hunter color difference is computed as:

$$\Delta E_H = \{(\Delta L)^2 + (\Delta a)^2 + (\Delta b)^2\}^{\frac{1}{2}} \tag{7.28}$$

where the delta values are the differences between the color standard and the test sample Hunter Lab values.

j) The 1976 CIE UCS (Uniform Color Space) Diagram

This color space is computed directly using the X Y Z Tristimulus Space. Either X_2, Y_2, Z_2; or X_{10}, Y_{10}, Z_{10} may be used to compute the u′ and v′ values. These values are computed as follows, and are designated as u'_2 and v'_2 or u'_{10} and v'_{10} depending on the Tristimulus observer angle values (i.e., 2° or 10°) used.

$$u' = \frac{4X}{X + 15Y + 3Z} \tag{7.29}$$

$$v' = \frac{9Y}{X + 15Y + 3Z} \tag{7.30}$$

k) Determining the L*u*v* Color Space

The L*u*v* color space is also known as the CIELUV color space. In 1976 the CIE wrote the definition for this space and uses the following equations for its computations. These equations use the Y tristimulus values in combination with the CIE 1976 UCS Diagram and the calculations of the u′ and v′ values to compute the L*u*v* values as demonstrated.

$$L^* = 116 \cdot \left(\frac{Y}{Y_0}\right)^{\frac{1}{3}} - 16 \tag{7.31}$$

This applies when $\frac{Y}{Y_0} > 0.008856$

$$u^* = 13L^* \cdot (u' - u'_0) \tag{7.32}$$

$$v^* = 13L^* \cdot (v' - v'_0) \tag{7.33}$$

l) Color Difference using L*u*v*Color Space Coordinates

The Color difference for L*u*v* color coordinates, sometimes referred to as ΔE_{Luv} indicates the estimated difference in this color space. This L*u*v* color difference is computed as:

$$\Delta E_{Luv} = \left\{(\Delta L^*)^2 + (\Delta u^*)^2 + (\Delta v^*)^2\right\}^{\frac{1}{2}} \tag{7.34}$$

where the delta values are the differences between the reference color standard and the test sample L*u*v* color values.

Table 7.8 Color coordinate values for CIE 1964 supplementary standard (10°) observer, at 5 nm intervals; illuminant D65.

Color-matching functions	Color-matching coordinate values		
XYZ =	27.24	18.25	8.59
Yxy =	18.25	0.504	0.337
xyz Chrom =	0.504	0.337	0.159
L*a*b* =	49.80	46.32	27.25
L*C*h=	49.80	53.74	30.47
Hunter (Lab) =	42.72	42.23	16.01
CIE 1976 Lu′v′ =	49.80	0.33	0.50
L*u*v* =	49.80	87.80	21.45

Table 7.9 Color coordinate values for CIE 1964 supplementary standard (10°) observer, at 5 nm intervals; illuminant A.

Color-matching functions	Color-matching coordinate values		
XYZ =	42.17	24.69	2.82
Yxy =	24.69	0.605	0.354
xyz Chrom =	0.605	0.354	0.040
L*a*b* =	56.78	48.29	39.27
L*C*h=	56.78	62.24	39.12
Hunter (Lab) =	49.69	49.68	12.83
CIE 1976 Lu′v′ =	56.78	0.40	0.53
L*u*v* =	56.78	104.59	2.66

m) Summary of Color Coordinate Values

The values of the different color coordinates possible from the example spectrum (Table 7.4) are as shown in Tables 7.8 through 7.11. These include both D65 and A Illuminants each with 10° and 2° Standard Observer.

7.3 Solar Measurements

The use of visible spectroscopy for solar measurements is another high volume use of the technique. There are visible solar measurements using a wavelength range shown in the following Table 7.12. Note that each of these regions may be selected individually to report the specified solar measurements.

Table 7.10 Color coordinate values for CIE 1931 standard (2°) observer, at 5 nm intervals; illuminant D65.

Color-matching functions	Color-matching coordinate values		
XYZ =	28.94	18.90	8.72
Yxy =	18.90	0.512	0.334
xyz Chrom =	0.512	0.334	0.154
L*a*b* =	50.57	49.45	28.54
L*C*h=	50.57	57.09	30.00
Hunter (Lab) =	43.47	45.78	16.83
CIE 1976 Lu′v′ =	50.57	0.34	0.50
L*u*v* =	50.57	94.71	22.35

Table 7.11 Color coordinate values for CIE 1931 standard (2°) observer, at 5 nm intervals; illuminant A.

Color-matching functions	Color-matching coordinate values		
XYZ =	43.73	25.03	2.86
Yxy =	25.03	0.611	0.349
xyz Chrom =	0.611	0.349	0.040
L*a*b* =	57.11	52.71	39.71
L*C*h=	57.11	66.00	36.99
Hunter (Lab) =	50.03	54.73	13.05
CIE 1976 Lu′v′ =	57.11	0.41	0.53
L*u*v* =	57.11	113.56	1.73

Table 7.12 Range of standard solar measurements spectral regions.

Range of measurements	Wavelength (nm)	Wavenumbers (cm^{-1})
Near-Ultraviolet/Visible	300–780	33,333–12,821
Near Infrared	780–2500	12,821–4,000
Full Solar Range	300–2500	33,333–4,000
Solar Astronomy (Visible)	350–850	28,571–11,765

Note: The full solar measurement range is UV-Vis-NIR from 300 nm to 2500 nm.

Standards of optical materials are generally measured at normal incidence for both reflectance and transmittance measurements. This angle is the most straightforward for measurement and negates the problems associated with polarization. Optical coatings are best measured at normal incidence for standardized comparisons. Solar measurement standards such as: ISO 9050, EN 410, ASTM

E903, and EN 14500 all require near normal illumination and at the extreme allow "an angle not exceeding 10 degrees from the normal to the surface." EN 14500 does describe the use of polarized light for measurements made at oblique angles.[14–25]

7.3.1 *Measurement Configurations for Samples and Reference Materials Using an Integrating Sphere*

The following Table 7.13 and figures illustrate the measurements of reflectance or transmittance of various sample types, both opaque and non-opaque. There are several specific measurement conditions required to compute either the reflectance or the transmittance of a test sample for computing the solar measurement parameters. These specific measurements are conducted as follows. Separate figures are shown for either single- or double-beam measurements using an integrating sphere for each measurement type. For reflectance, measure 0% reflectance by having no sample in the sample port or aperture as illustrated in Figures 7.16 and 7.17 for either single or double-beam instruments, respectively. Then measure 100% reflectance by placing a sample equal in reflectance to the inner reflective wall of the integrating sphere (i.e., near 100% reflector) in the sample port(s), as shown in Figures 7.18 and 7.19, respectively. Finally the sample is measured by placing it in the reflectance sample port and comparing it to a standard reference material with calibrated reflectance measurements as shown in Figures 7.20 and 7.21.

For transmittance, measure 0% transmittance by blocking the sample entrance port or aperture as illustrated in Figures 7.22 and 7.23 for either single or double-beam instruments, respectively. Then measure 100% reflectance by placing no sample in the transmittance port with reflectors equal to the inner reflective wall of the integrating sphere (i.e., near 100% reflector) in the reflectance port(s), as shown in Figures 7.24 and 7.25, respectively. Finally the sample is measured by placing it in the sample transmittance port as shown in Figures 7.26 and 7.27.

7.3.2 *Computing Reflectance of Materials for Solar Measurements*

The spectral reflectance of opaque samples is computed as follows:[16]

$$\rho(\lambda) = \frac{(S_\lambda - Z_\lambda)}{(100_\lambda - Z_\lambda)\rho'(\lambda)} \tag{7.35}$$

where S_λ is the test sample reflectance measurement; Z_λ is the 0% reflectance measurement; 100_λ is the 100% reflectance measurement; and $\rho'(\lambda)$ is the calibrated standard reference material measurand values per wavelength (λ).

Table 7.13 Table summarizing the positions of various materials for solar measurement set-up with respect to integrating sphere ports as illustrated in the Figures 7.16 through 7.27. This table provides information for single- and double-beam measurements.

Measurement type	Beam type	Signal measured	Entrance port	Sample port	Reference port
%Reflectance	Single	0%R	None	None	NA
%Reflectance	Double	0%R	None	None	100% Reflector
%Reflectance	Single	100%R	None	100% Reflector	NA
%Reflectance	Double	100%R	None	100% Reflector	100% Reflector
%Reflectance	Single	Test Sample %R	None	Test Sample	NA
%Reflectance	Double	Test Sample %R	None	Test Sample	SRM (Reference Sample)
%Transmittance	Single	0%R	Blocker	100% Reflector	NA
%Transmittance	Double	0%R	Blocker	100% Reflector	100% Reflector
%Transmittance	Single	100%R	None	100% Reflector	NA
%Transmittance	Double	100%R	None	100% Reflector	100% Reflector
%Transmittance	Single	Test Sample %T	Test Sample	100% Reflector	NA
%Transmittance	Double	Test Sample %T	Test Sample	100% Reflector	100% Reflector

NA indicates Not Applicable (i.e., single beam integrating spheres do not use a reference beam port).

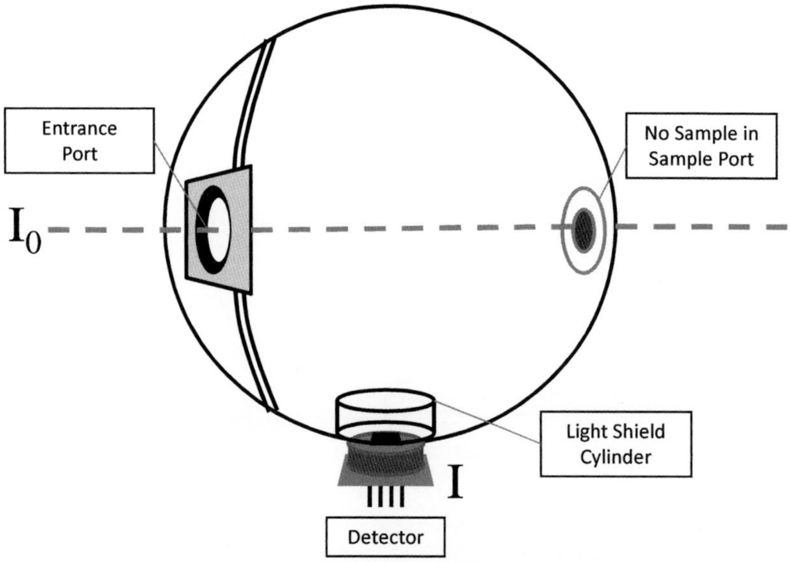

Fig. 7.16 Reflectance measurement set-up for 0% reflectance: Single-beam integrating sphere.

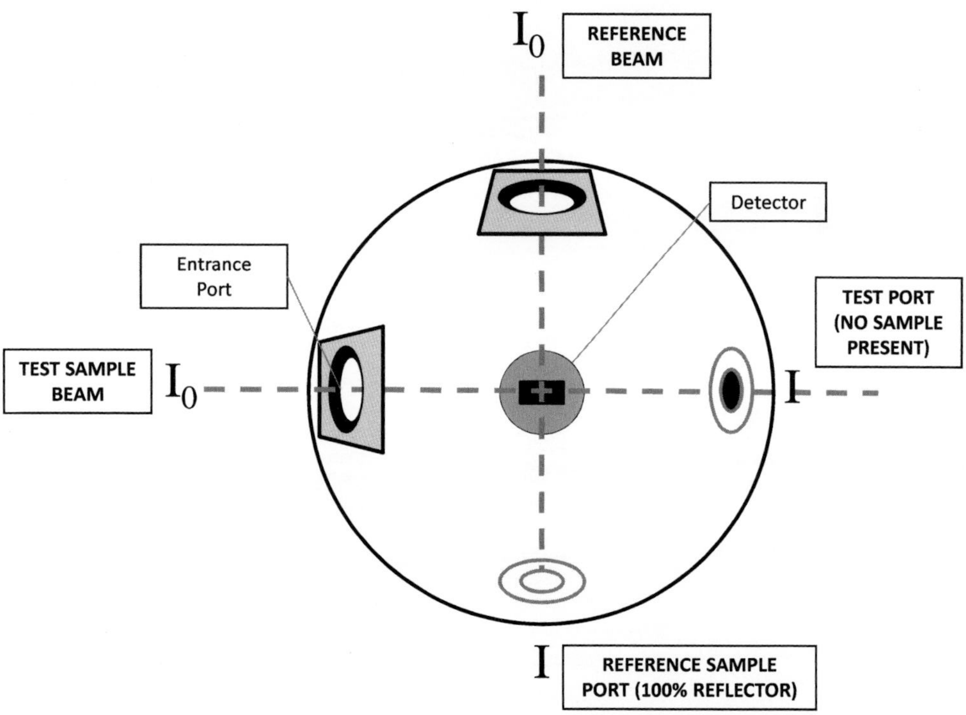

Fig. 7.17 Reflectance measurement set-up for 0% reflectance: Double-beam integrating sphere.

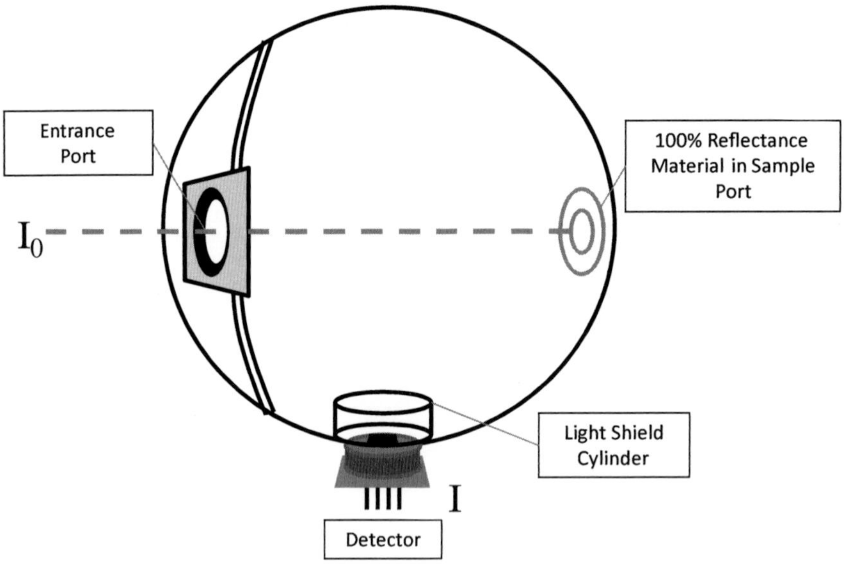

Fig. 7.18 Reflectance measurement set-up for 100% reflectance: Single-beam integrating sphere.

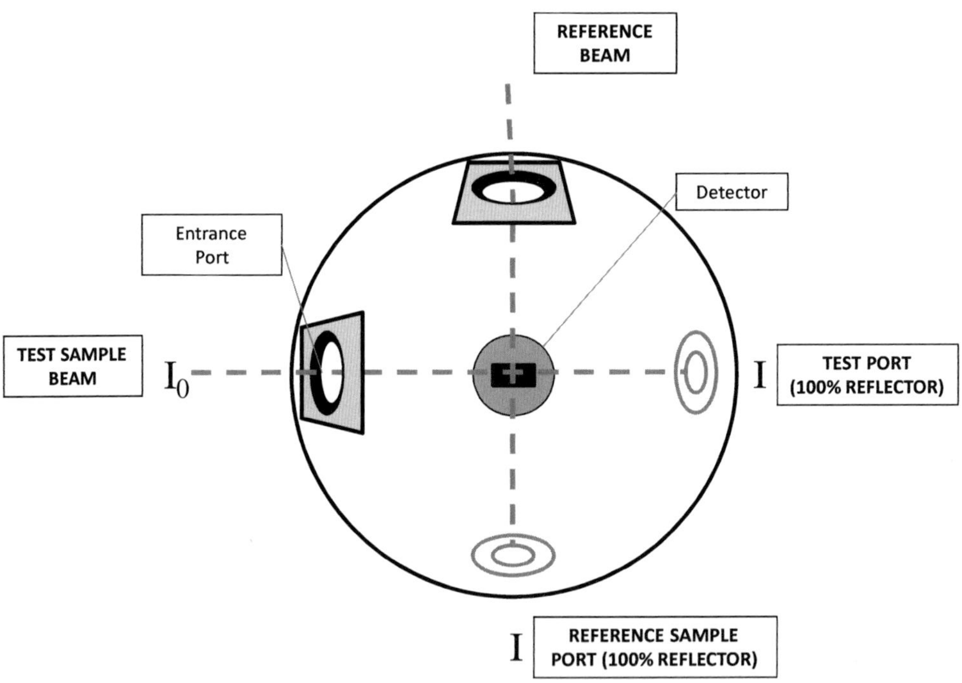

Fig. 7.19 Reflectance measurement set-up for 100% reflectance: Double-beam integrating sphere.

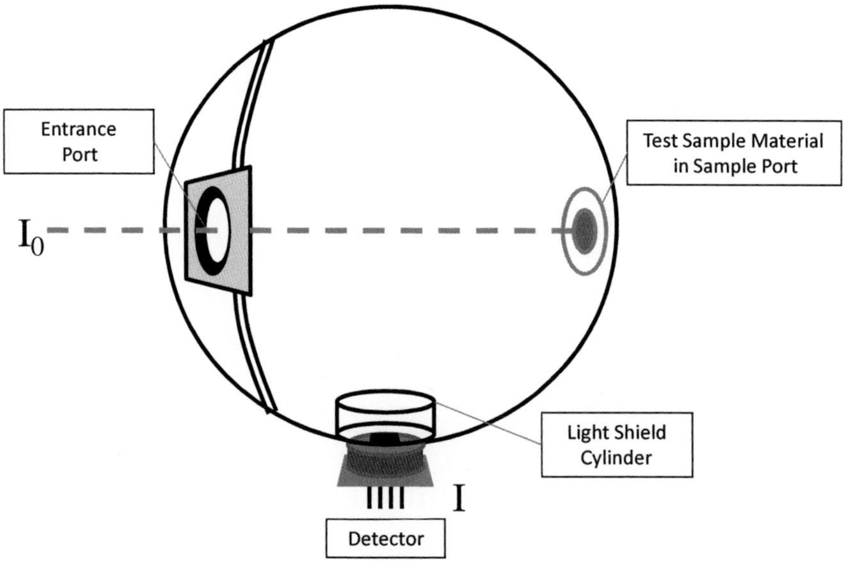

Fig. 7.20 Reflectance measurement set-up for test sample reflectance: Single-beam integrating sphere.

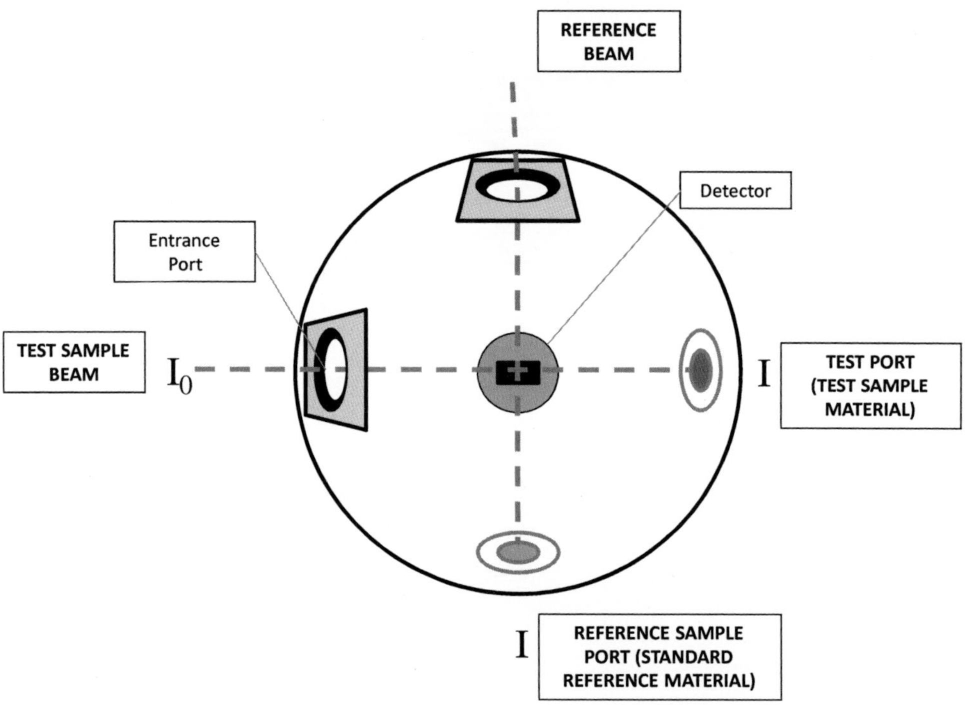

Fig. 7.21 Reflectance measurement set-up for test sample reflectance: Double-beam integrating sphere.

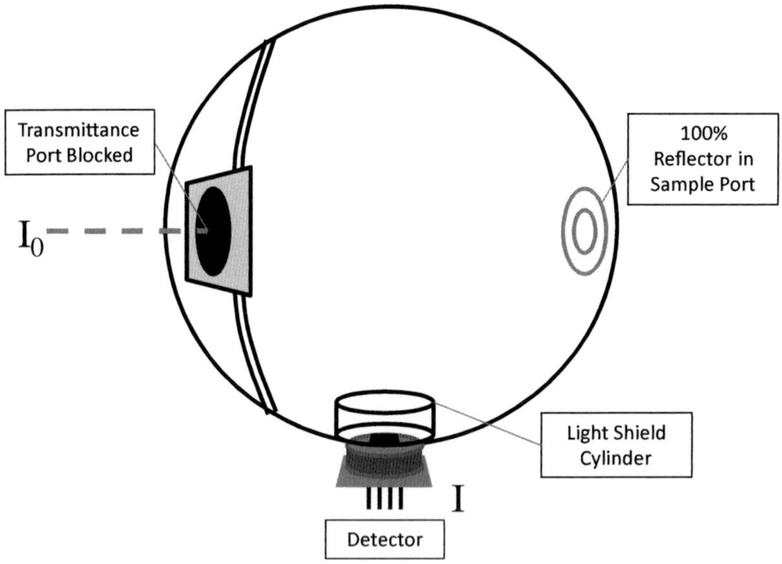

Fig. 7.22 Transmittance measurement set-up for 0% transmittance: Single-beam integrating sphere.

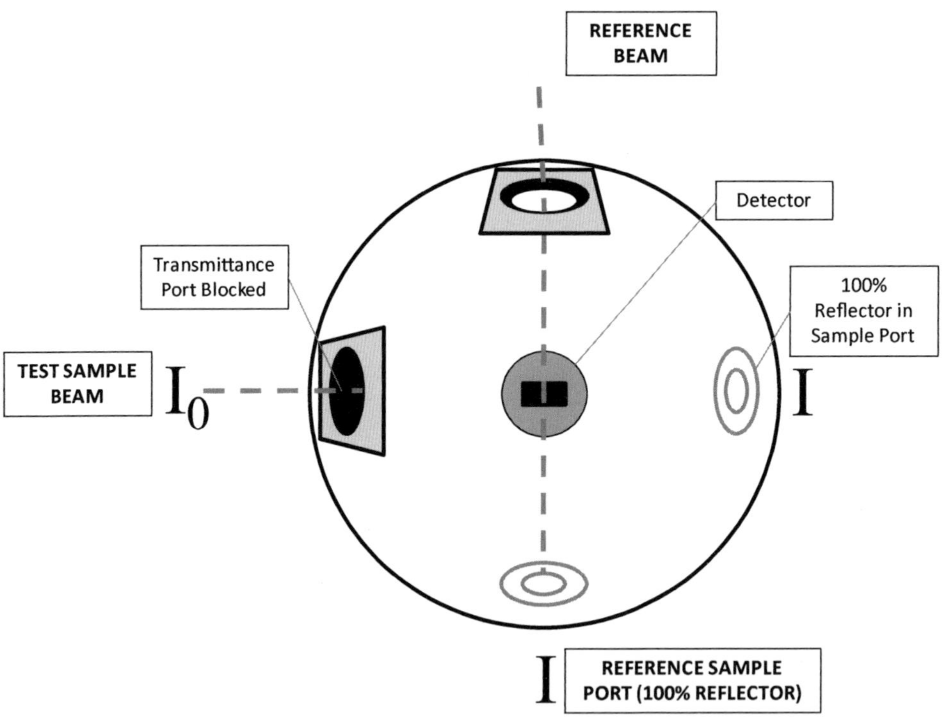

Fig. 7.23 Transmittance measurement set-up for 0% transmittance: Double-beam integrating sphere.

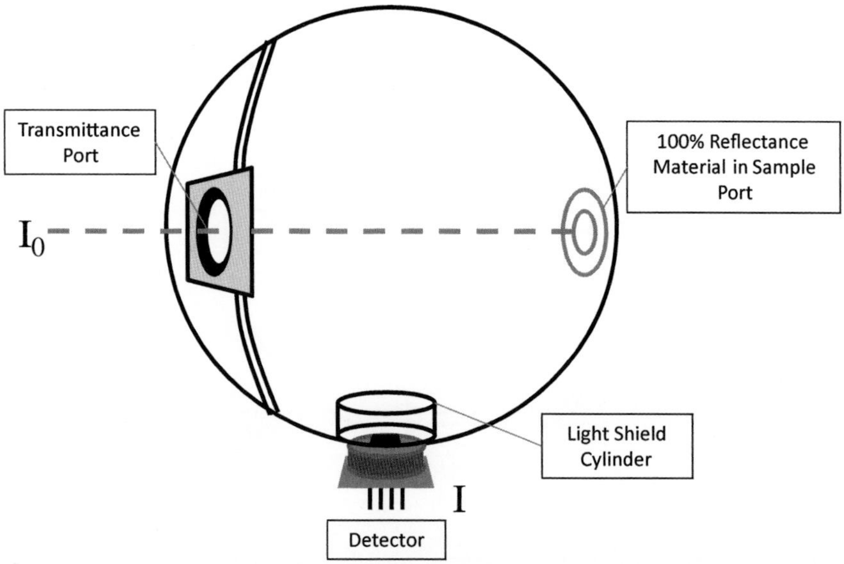

Fig. 7.24 Transmittance measurement set-up for 100% transmittance: Single-beam integrating sphere.

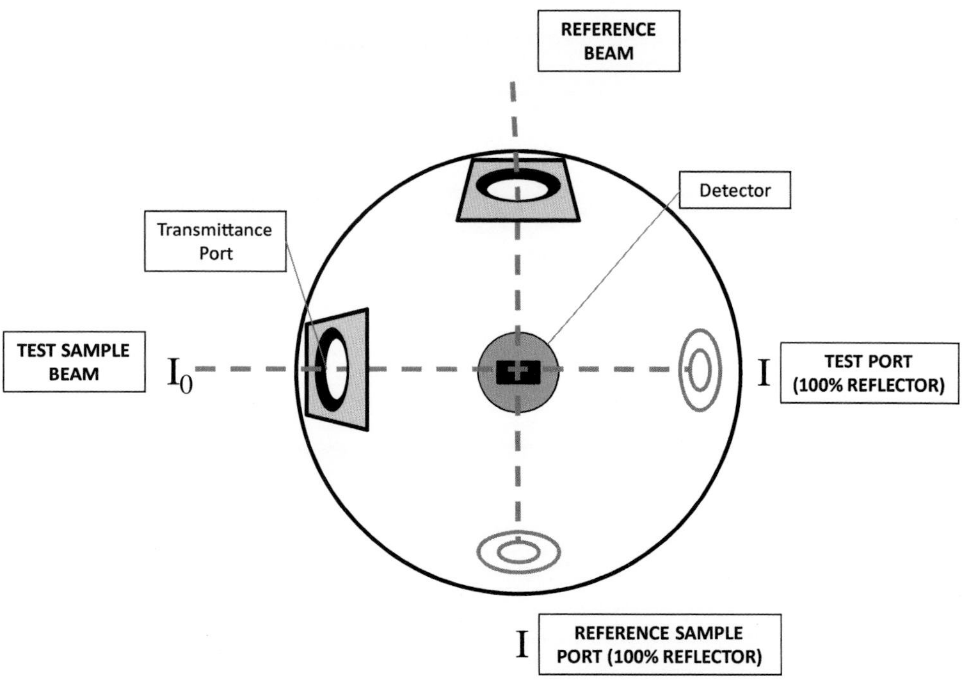

Fig. 7.25 Transmittance measurement set-up for 100% transmittance: Double-beam integrating sphere.

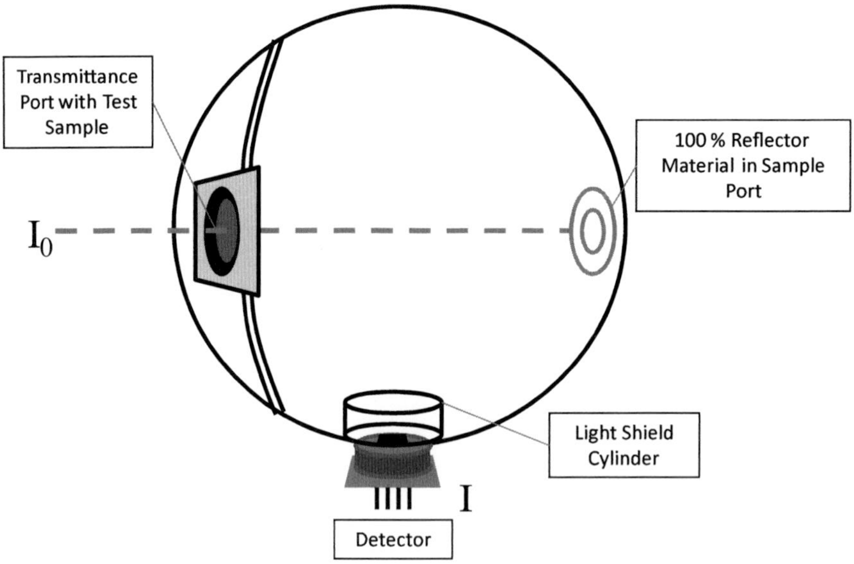

Fig. 7.26 Transmittance measurement set-up for test sample transmittance: Single-beam integrating sphere.

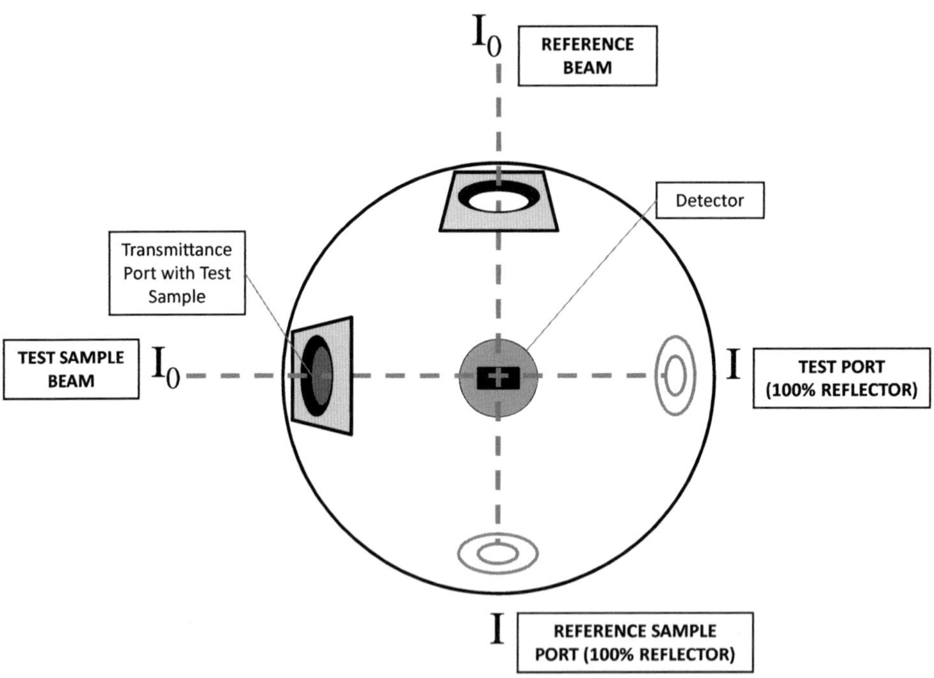

Fig. 7.27 Transmittance measurement set-up for test sample transmittance: Double-beam integrating sphere.

When using an absolute sphere or a single-beam sphere the following equation is used to compute reflectance:[16]

$$\rho(\lambda) = \frac{(S_\lambda - Z_\lambda)}{(100_\lambda - Z_\lambda)} \tag{7.36}$$

where the 100_λ is the 100% correction obtained using the measurement shown in Figures 7.18 and 7.19 (i.e., 100% correction scheme).

Note: For materials that are translucent or of low reflectance the test sample is measured with a light trap or sample of low reflectance ($<0.02R$) behind the sample measured in reflectance.

The above 2 equations may be re-written in a more standard spectroscopy nomenclature as:

$$\%R_\lambda = \frac{\%R_S - \%R_0}{(\%R_{100} - \%R_0)R_{Ref}} \tag{7.37}$$

where $\%R_\lambda$ is the test sample percent reflectance measurement; $\%R_0$ is the 0% reflectance measurement; $\%R_{100}$ is the 100% reflectance measurement; and R_{Ref} is the calibrated standard reference material measurand values per wavelength (λ).

When using an absolute sphere or a single-beam sphere the following equation is re-written from above to compute reflectance:

$$\%R_\lambda = \frac{\%R_S - \%R_0}{(\%R_{100} - \%R_0)} \tag{7.38}$$

7.3.3 *Computing Transmittance of Materials for Solar Measurements*

The spectral transmittance of samples is computed as follows from ASTM E903.[16]

$$\tau(\lambda) = \frac{(S_\lambda - Z_\lambda)}{(100_\lambda - Z_\lambda)} \tag{7.39}$$

where S_λ is the test sample transmittance measurement with the sample over the entrance port; Z_λ is the 0% transmittance measurement with the sample beam blocked; and 100_λ is the 100% transmittance measurement with no test sample in the entrance port.

The above equation may be re-written in a more standard spectroscopy nomenclature as:

$$\%T_\lambda = \frac{\%T_S - \%T_0}{(\%T_{100} - \%T_0)} \tag{7.40}$$

where $\%T_\lambda$ is the test sample percent reflectance measurement; $\%T_0$ is the 0% transmittance measurement; and $\%T_{100}$ is the 100% transmittance measurement.

7.3.4 *Computing the Solar Reflectance of Materials*

The solar reflectance ρ_s of materials is computed by integrating the spectral reflectance over the standard spectral irradiance $E\lambda$ distribution (See Example Tables 7.13–7.14, and Figure 7.28). The formula as given in ASTM E903 is as:

$$\rho_s = \frac{\left(\sum_{i=1}^{n} \rho(\lambda_i) E_{\lambda i}\right) \Delta\lambda_i}{\left(\sum_{i=1}^{n} E_{\lambda i} \Delta\lambda_i\right)} \tag{7.41}$$

This can be re-written as standard integration formulas such as:

$$\rho_{Etr} = \int_{300}^{2500} \rho(\lambda) \cdot E(\lambda n)_{Etr}(\lambda) d\lambda \tag{7.42}$$

$$\rho_{Gt} = \int_{300}^{2500} \rho(\lambda) \cdot E(\lambda n)_{Gt}(\lambda) d\lambda \tag{7.43}$$

$$\rho_{Dc} = \int_{300}^{2500} \rho(\lambda) \cdot E(\lambda n)_{Dc}(\lambda) d\lambda \tag{7.44}$$

where $E(\lambda n)_x$ are the normalized standard spectral irradiance $E\lambda$ distributions (Figures 7.30 and 7.31) such as:

$\mathbf{E(\lambda n)_{Etr}}$ or Extraterrestrial Radiation (solar spectrum at top of atmosphere) at mean Earth-Sun distance;

$\mathbf{E(\lambda n_{Dc})}$ or Direct Normal Irradiance, which is nearly parallel (0.5 deg divergent cone) radiation on the surface with surface normal tracking (pointing to) the sun,

Table 7.14 Showing method of calculation for solar transmittance.

Wavelength (nm)	%T Sample	$E(\lambda n)_{Etr}$	$E(\lambda n)_{Gt}$	$E(\lambda n)D_c$	$t_{(Etr)}$	$t_{(Gt)}$	$t_{(Dc)}$
330	0.40	0.090	0.051	0.033	0.036071	0.02	0.013154
370	62.40	0.105	0.082	0.065	6.557907	5.11	4.047656
450	79.40	0.168	0.169	0.162	13.348387	13.42	12.840570
550	84.00	0.151	0.167	0.171	12.715690	14.02	14.393371
650	73.80	0.124	0.147	0.154	9.150792	10.87	11.395684
750	58.20	0.104	0.134	0.142	6.024766	7.79	8.237145
850	46.90	0.074	0.097	0.104	3.467864	4.54	4.881368
950	41.20	0.067	0.016	0.018	2.774129	0.66	0.721272
1060	39.50	0.053	0.069	0.075	2.080787	2.72	2.979138
1300	43.60	0.034	0.038	0.043	1.471531	1.67	1.853205
1600	60.50	0.021	0.026	0.029	1.241708	1.56	1.757121
2000	63.90	0.009	0.004	0.005	0.606082	0.26	0.300775
Sum		**1.00**	**1.00**	**1.00**	**59.48**	**62.65**	**63.42**

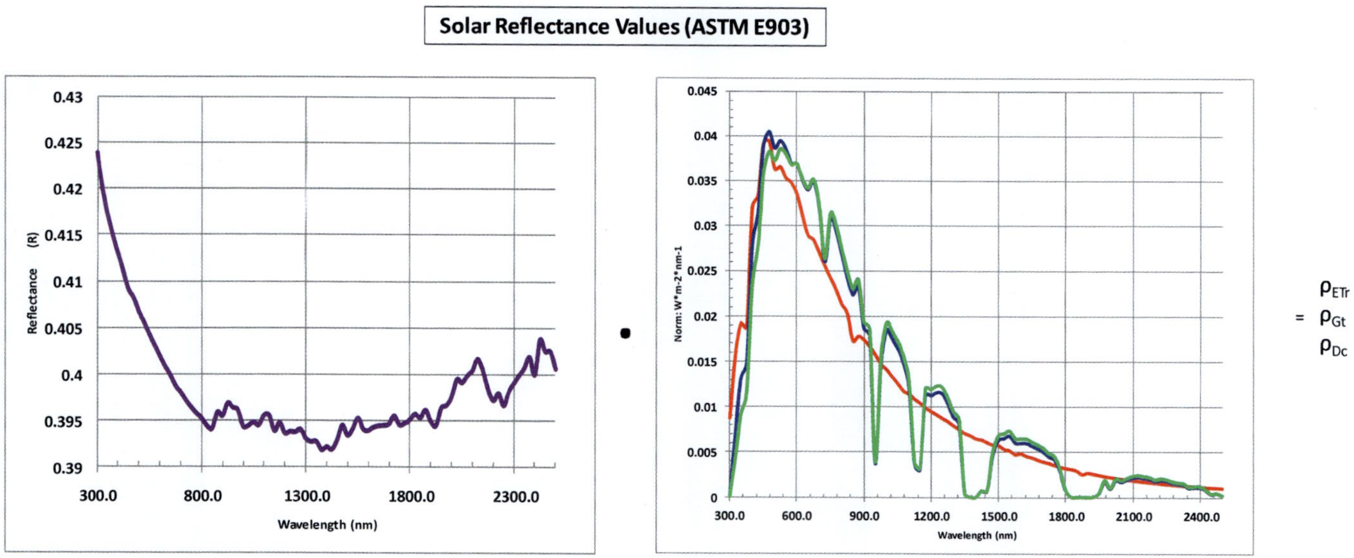

$$\rho(\lambda) \cdot E(\lambda n)_{ETr} = \rho_{ETr}$$
$$\rho(\lambda) \cdot E(\lambda n)_{Gt} = \rho_{Gt}$$
$$\rho(\lambda) \cdot E(\lambda n)_{Dc} = \rho_{Dc}$$

Fig. 7.28 Illustration of calculation of solar reflectance using three normalized standard spectral irradiance $E\lambda$ distributions.

excluding scattered sky and reflected ground radiation. This is combined with Circumsolar or Spectral irradiance within +/−2.5 degree (5 degree diameter) field of view centered on the 0.5 degree diameter solar disk, but excluding the radiation from the disk.

$E(\lambda n)_{Gt}$ or "Global Tilt", which is spectral radiation from solar disk plus sky diffuse and diffuse reflected from ground on south facing surface tilted 37 degrees from horizontal.

7.3.5 *Computing the Solar Transmittance of Materials*

The solar transmittance τ_S of materials is computed by integrating the spectral reflectance over the standard spectral irradiance $E\lambda$ distribution (See Example Tables 7.13–7.14, and Figure 7.29). The formula as given in ASTM E903 is as:

$$\tau_s = \frac{(\sum_{i=1}^{n} \tau(\lambda_i) E_{\lambda i}) \Delta \lambda_i}{(\sum_{i=1}^{n} E_{\lambda i} \Delta \lambda_i)} \tag{7.45}$$

This can be re-written as standard integration formulas such as:

$$\tau_{Etr} = \int_{300}^{2500} \tau(\lambda) \cdot E(\lambda n)_{Etr}(\lambda) d\lambda \tag{7.46}$$

$$\tau_{Gt} = \int_{300}^{2500} \tau(\lambda) \cdot E(\lambda n)_{Gt}(\lambda) d\lambda \tag{7.47}$$

$$\tau_{Dc} = \int_{300}^{2500} \tau(\lambda) \cdot E(\lambda n)_{Dc}(\lambda) d\lambda \tag{7.48}$$

where $E(\lambda n)$ are the normalized standard spectral irradiance $E\lambda$ distributions (Figures 7.30 and 7.31) such as:

$E(\lambda n)_{Etr}$ or Extraterrestrial Radiation (solar spectrum at top of atmosphere) at mean Earth-Sun distance;

$E(\lambda n)_{Dc}$, or Direct Normal Irradiance, which is nearly parallel (0.5 deg divergent cone) radiation on the surface with surface normal tracking (pointing to) the sun, excluding scattered sky and reflected ground radiation. This is combined with Circumsolar or Spectral irradiance within +/−2.5 degree (5 degree diameter) field of view centered on the 0.5 deg diameter solar disk, but excluding the radiation from the disk;

$E(\lambda n)_{Gt}$ or "Global Tilt", which is spectral radiation from solar disk plus sky diffuse and diffuse reflected from ground on south facing surface tilted 37 deg from horizontal.

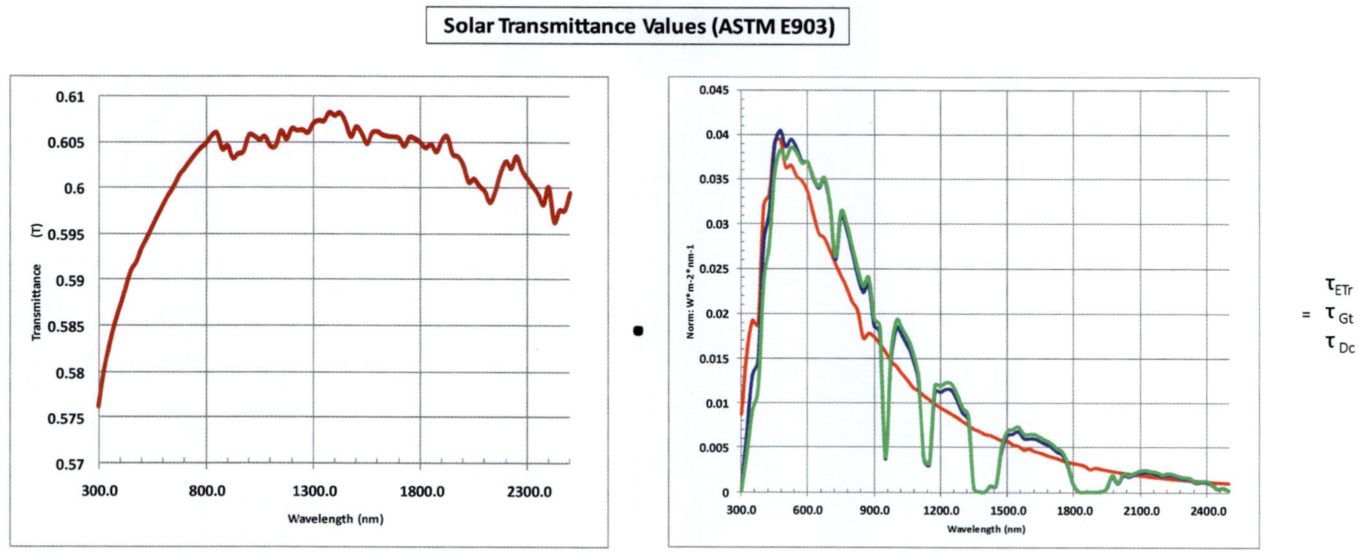

$$\tau(\lambda) \cdot E(\lambda n)_{ETr} = \tau_{ETr}$$
$$\tau(\lambda) \cdot E(\lambda n)_{Gt} = \tau_{Gt}$$
$$\tau(\lambda) \cdot E(\lambda n)_{Dc} = \tau_{Dc}$$

Fig. 7.29 Illustration of calculation of solar transmittance using three normalized standard spectral irradiance $E\lambda$ distributions.

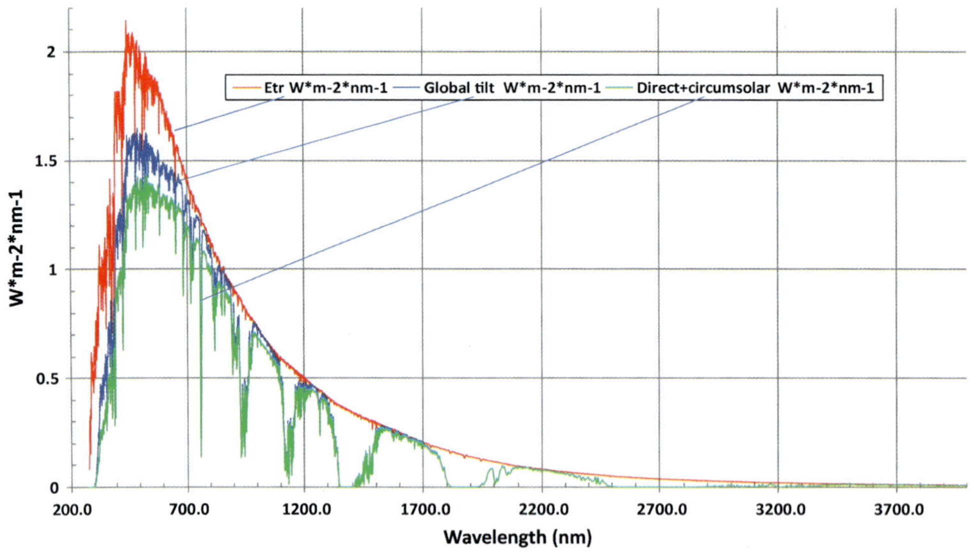

Fig. 7.30 Reference solar spectral irradiance: Air mass 1.5 from ASTM G-173-03 (See reference 32).

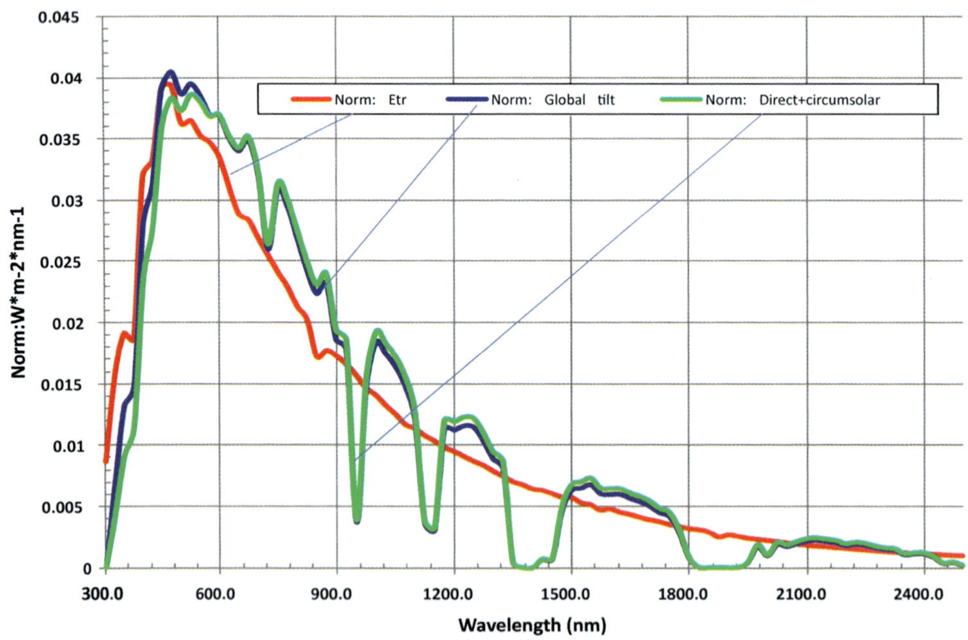

Fig. 7.31 Normalized (all values sum to 1.0) Reference solar spectral irradiance: Air mass 1.5, computed from ASTM G-173-03 (See reference 32).

7.3.6 *Computing Solar Absorptance of Materials*

For opaque materials the solar absorptance α_S is computed as:

$$\alpha_S = 1 - \rho_S \tag{7.49}$$

For non-opaque materials the solar absorptance α_S is computed as:

$$\alpha_S = 1 - \rho_S - \tau_S \tag{7.50}$$

7.3.7 *Computing the Normalized Standard Spectral Irradiance ($E\lambda n$) Distributions*

The normalized standard spectral irradiance distributions (Eλn) are computed as the individual standard spectral irradiance values at each wavelength divided by the sum of all the standard spectral irradiance distribution values. This normalizes all values in the solar spectrum to sum to 1.0 for standard weighting when computing the solar values. This normalizes the spectral irradiance distributions to sum to 1.0, but maintains each wavelength relative weighting. Thus, the normalized Standard Spectral Irradiance (Eλn) Distributions for each type will sum to 1.00. Each data point in the spectral irradiance distributions are computed as:

$$E(\lambda n)_i = \frac{(E_i)\Delta\lambda_i}{\left(\sum_{i=1}^{n} E_{\lambda i}\Delta\lambda_i\right)} \tag{7.51}$$

To illustrate this normalization, the Reference Solar Spectral Irradiance: Air Mass 1.5 from ASTM G-173-03 is given as Figure 7.30 and the normalized version with 89 data points is given in Figure 7.31. Any number of data points may be used for the estimated calculation, although specific standard methods may vary in their specified wavelength ranges, number of data points to use for the computations, and specific methods for measurement. This chapter section presents a generalized method based upon ASTM E903.

7.3.8 *Summary of Solar Calculations using a Basic Example*

The solar calculation data shown in Table 7.14 is for only a few data points and demonstrates the concepts and types of data used to complete the calculations for solar transmittance or reflectance measurements. There is specific wavelength information (column 1); the percent transmittance spectral data at the specified wavelengths (column 2); the three normalized standard spectral irradiance E(λ) distributions as $E(\lambda n)_{Etr}$ (column 3); $E(\lambda n)_{Gt}$ (column 4); and $E(\lambda n)_{Dc}$ (column 5). The solar transmittance values for each standard spectral irradiance distribution are given as $\tau_{(Etr)}$; the sum of column 6, $\tau_{(Gt)}$; the sum of column 7, and $\tau_{(Dc)}$; the sum of column 8. The solar reflectance may be determined using the %Reflectance as $\rho_{(Etr)}$, $\rho_{(Gt)}$, and $\rho_{(Dc)}$. Once these are determined the solar Solar absorptance values for each spectral irradiance distribution may be determined as $\alpha_S = 1 - \rho_S - \tau_S$. The standard and normalized spectral irradiance distributions are given in Table 7.15 at 5 nm intervals. A section discussing solar UV measurements is contained within Volume 1 of this set (Chapter 7, Section 7.4).

7.4 Reflectance Measurements Using Polarized Light

7.4.1 *Introduction*

Reflectance or transmittance measurements at varying angles, with or without linearly polarized light, are critical to the design and quality assurance of optical components, thin films, metal surfaces and semiconductor interfaces.[26] Spectral measurements of percent transmittance or percent reflectance are the most common uses of spectrophotometers in these applications. The angle of illuminance for both reflectance and transmittance is sometimes varied from near normal (approximately 0°) to 85° angles of illumination. Figure 7.32 demonstrates standard specular reflection where the incident and reflection angles are equivalent.

The smaller the angle of incidence of light interacting with a sample, the smaller is the degree of interaction with that surface. The electronic vector of the incident light determines the amount of interaction with a sample surface as will be illustrated in the following figures. When the electronic field vector of the surface is orthogonal (perpendicular) to the field direction vector of the incident energy, there is very little interaction with the surface (Figures 7.33 and 7.34).

When the electronic field vector of the surface is parallel to the field direction vector of the incident energy there is increased interaction with the surface (Figures 7.35 and 7.36).

Light which is s-polarized is polarized in a parallel direction to the surface of a sample, but perpendicular to the surface electronic (E) field. s-polarized light will not interact with the surface and we would expect the relatively featureless spectrum as in Figure 7.34.

Light which is p-polarized is then polarized perpendicularly to the surface of a sample, but is parallel to the surface electronic field. The p-polarized light will interact significantly at the sample surface with the interaction increasing as the angle of incidence. Thus we would expect the greatest amount of detail in an external reflectance spectrum if we use p-polarized light with a large incident angle as in Figure 7.36.

Table 7.15 Standard and normalized reference solar spectral irradiance at 25 nm intervals: Air mass 1.5, computed from ASTM G-173-03. Note normalized irradiance values sum to 1.0. These normalized values are plotted in Figure 7.31.[32]

Wavelength (nm)	Etr $W^*m^{-2}*nm^{-1}$	Global tilt $W^*m^{-2}*nm^{-1}$	Direct + circumsolar $W^*m^{-2}*nm^{-1}$	Norm Etr	Norm Gt	Norm Dc
300.0	4.5794E-01	1.0205E-03	4.5631E-04	8.6757E-03	2.5513E-05	1.2700E-05
325.0	8.2918E-01	2.7894E-01	1.5504E-01	1.5709E-02	6.9735E-03	4.3151E-03
350.0	1.0122E+00	5.2798E-01	3.2913E-01	1.9176E-02	1.3200E-02	9.1603E-03
375.0	9.8500E-01	5.8930E-01	4.1087E-01	1.8661E-02	1.4733E-02	1.1435E-02
400.0	1.6885E+00	1.1141E+00	8.3989E-01	3.1989E-02	2.7853E-02	2.3376E-02
425.0	1.7550E+00	1.2488E+00	9.9312E-01	3.3249E-02	3.1220E-02	2.7640E-02
450.0	2.0690E+00	1.5595E+00	1.2881E+00	3.9197E-02	3.8988E-02	3.5850E-02
475.0	2.0800E+00	1.6185E+00	1.3755E+00	3.9406E-02	4.0463E-02	3.8283E-02
500.0	1.9160E+00	1.5451E+00	1.3391E+00	3.6299E-02	3.8628E-02	3.7270E-02
525.0	1.9280E+00	1.5781E+00	1.3859E+00	3.6526E-02	3.9453E-02	3.8572E-02
550.0	1.8630E+00	1.5399E+00	1.3648E+00	3.5295E-02	3.8498E-02	3.7985E-02
575.0	1.8340E+00	1.4777E+00	1.3225E+00	3.4745E-02	3.6943E-02	3.6808E-02
600.0	1.7700E+00	1.4753E+00	1.3278E+00	3.3533E-02	3.6883E-02	3.6955E-02
625.0	1.6440E+00	1.4026E+00	1.2667E+00	3.1146E-02	3.5065E-02	3.5255E-02
650.0	1.5260E+00	1.3594E+00	1.2299E+00	2.8910E-02	3.3985E-02	3.4230E-02
675.0	1.4990E+00	1.3958E+00	1.2639E+00	2.8399E-02	3.4895E-02	3.5177E-02
700.0	1.4220E+00	1.2823E+00	1.1636E+00	2.6940E-02	3.2058E-02	3.2385E-02
725.0	1.3465E+00	1.0380E+00	9.4741E-01	2.5510E-02	2.5950E-02	2.6368E-02
750.0	1.2740E+00	1.2341E+00	1.1273E+00	2.4136E-02	3.0853E-02	3.1375E-02
775.0	1.2080E+00	1.1771E+00	1.0801E+00	2.2886E-02	2.9428E-02	3.0061E-02
800.0	1.1248E+00	1.0725E+00	9.8859E-01	2.1309E-02	2.6813E-02	2.7514E-02

(Continued)

Table 7.15 (*Continued*)

Wavelength (nm)	Etr $W*m^{-2}*nm^{-1}$	Global tilt $W*m^{-2}*nm^{-1}$	Direct+circumsolar $W*m^{-2}*nm^{-1}$	Norm Etr	Norm Gt	Norm Dc
825.0	1.0699E+00	9.6935E-01	8.9752E-01	2.0269E-02	2.4234E-02	2.4980E-02
850.0	9.1000E-01	8.9372E-01	8.2900E-01	1.7240E-02	2.2343E-02	2.3073E-02
875.0	9.3562E-01	9.2687E-01	8.6204E-01	1.7725E-02	2.3172E-02	2.3992E-02
900.0	9.1378E-01	7.4260E-01	6.9429E-01	1.7312E-02	1.8565E-02	1.9323E-02
925.0	8.7642E-01	7.1110E-01	6.6621E-01	1.6604E-02	1.7778E-02	1.8542E-02
950.0	8.2867E-01	1.4726E-01	1.3944E-01	1.5699E-02	3.6815E-03	3.8809E-03
975.0	7.7348E-01	5.8987E-01	5.5536E-01	1.4654E-02	1.4747E-02	1.5457E-02
1000.0	7.4255E-01	7.3532E-01	6.9159E-01	1.4068E-02	1.8383E-02	1.9248E-02
1025.0	6.9918E-01	6.9753E-01	6.5727E-01	1.3246E-02	1.7438E-02	1.8293E-02
1050.0	6.6117E-01	6.5463E-01	6.1802E-01	1.2526E-02	1.6366E-02	1.7201E-02
1075.0	6.1768E-01	5.9252E-01	5.6054E-01	1.1702E-02	1.4813E-02	1.5601E-02
1100.0	6.0000E-01	4.8577E-01	4.6113E-01	1.1367E-02	1.2144E-02	1.2834E-02
1125.0	5.7012E-01	1.4428E-01	1.3794E-01	1.0801E-02	3.6070E-03	3.8391E-03
1150.0	5.4623E-01	1.2164E-01	1.1648E-01	1.0348E-02	3.0410E-03	3.2419E-03
1175.0	5.1852E-01	4.5240E-01	4.3142E-01	9.8234E-03	1.1310E-02	1.2007E-02
1200.0	5.0005E-01	4.4825E-01	4.2789E-01	9.4735E-03	1.1206E-02	1.1909E-02
1225.0	4.7925E-01	4.6236E-01	4.4141E-01	9.0795E-03	1.1559E-02	1.2285E-02
1250.0	4.5860E-01	4.5705E-01	4.3684E-01	8.6882E-03	1.1426E-02	1.2158E-02
1275.0	4.4072E-01	4.1233E-01	3.9455E-01	8.3495E-03	1.0308E-02	1.0981E-02
1300.0	4.1537E-01	3.5312E-01	3.3855E-01	7.8692E-03	8.8280E-03	9.4225E-03
1325.0	3.9369E-01	3.2224E-01	3.0943E-01	7.4585E-03	8.0560E-03	8.6120E-03
1350.0	3.7081E-01	1.6025E-02	1.5488E-02	7.0250E-03	4.0063E-04	4.3106E-04
1375.0	3.5749E-01	3.2332E-04	3.1309E-04	6.7727E-03	8.0830E-06	8.7139E-06
1400.0	3.3896E-01	3.2466E-09	3.1513E-09	6.4216E-03	8.1165E-11	8.7707E-11
1425.0	3.3256E-01	2.5850E-02	2.5142E-02	6.3004E-03	6.4625E-04	6.9975E-04

(*Continued*)

Table 7.15 (*Continued*)

Wavelength (nm)	Etr $W*m^{-2}*nm^{-1}$	Global tilt $W*m^{-2}*nm^{-1}$	Direct+circumsolar $W*m^{-2}*nm^{-1}$	Norm Etr	Norm Gt	Norm Dc
1450.0	3.1774E-01	2.7412E-02	2.6699E-02	6.0196E-03	6.8530E-04	7.4308E-04
1475.0	3.0349E-01	1.8463E-01	1.7954E-01	5.7497E-03	4.6158E-03	4.9969E-03
1500.0	3.0077E-01	2.5061E-01	2.4339E-01	5.6981E-03	6.2653E-03	6.7740E-03
1525.0	2.7846E-01	2.5884E-01	2.5140E-01	5.2755E-03	6.4710E-03	6.9969E-03
1550.0	2.6961E-01	2.6990E-01	2.6226E-01	5.1078E-03	6.7475E-03	7.2992E-03
1575.0	2.4738E-01	2.3974E-01	2.3294E-01	4.6866E-03	5.9935E-03	6.4832E-03
1600.0	2.5259E-01	2.3810E-01	2.3133E-01	4.7854E-03	5.9525E-03	6.4384E-03
1625.0	2.3746E-01	2.3782E-01	2.3109E-01	4.4987E-03	5.9455E-03	6.4317E-03
1650.0	2.2840E-01	2.2526E-01	2.1902E-01	4.3271E-03	5.6315E-03	6.0957E-03
1675.0	2.1621E-01	2.1360E-01	2.0793E-01	4.0961E-03	5.3400E-03	5.7871E-03
1700.0	2.0539E-01	1.9975E-01	1.9464E-01	3.8911E-03	4.9938E-03	5.4172E-03
1725.0	1.9688E-01	1.7808E-01	1.7367E-01	3.7299E-03	4.4520E-03	4.8336E-03
1750.0	1.8518E-01	1.6566E-01	1.6162E-01	3.5083E-03	4.1415E-03	4.4982E-03
1775.0	1.7600E-01	1.1484E-01	1.1213E-01	3.3343E-03	2.8710E-03	3.1208E-03
1800.0	1.6800E-01	3.1828E-02	3.1112E-02	3.1828E-03	7.9570E-04	8.6591E-04
1825.0	1.6257E-01	1.2744E-03	1.2463E-03	3.0799E-03	3.1860E-05	3.4687E-05
1850.0	1.5337E-01	2.9993E-06	2.9348E-06	2.9056E-03	7.4983E-08	8.1681E-08
1875.0	1.3231E-01	4.5130E-10	4.4296E-10	2.5066E-03	1.1283E-11	1.2328E-11
1900.0	1.4041E-01	8.6221E-07	8.4916E-07	2.6601E-03	2.1555E-08	2.3634E-08
1925.0	1.3447E-01	9.3615E-04	9.2326E-04	2.5476E-03	2.3404E-05	2.5696E-05
1950.0	1.2627E-01	1.6727E-02	1.6482E-02	2.3922E-03	4.1818E-04	4.5873E-04
1975.0	1.2150E-01	6.7857E-02	6.6730E-02	2.3018E-03	1.6964E-03	1.8572E-03

(*Continued*)

Table 7.15 *(Continued)*

Wavelength (nm)	Etr $W*m^{-2}*nm^{-1}$	Global tilt $W*m^{-2}*nm^{-1}$	Direct+circumsolar $W*m^{-2}*nm^{-1}$	Norm Etr	Norm Gt	Norm Dc
2000.0	1.1673E-01	3.8156E-02	3.7491E-02	2.2115E-03	9.5390E-04	1.0434E-03
2025.0	1.1176E-01	7.4010E-02	7.2779E-02	2.1173E-03	1.8503E-03	2.0256E-03
2050.0	1.0592E-01	6.7927E-02	6.6892E-02	2.0067E-03	1.6982E-03	1.8617E-03
2075.0	1.0095E-01	7.7443E-02	7.6305E-02	1.9125E-03	1.9361E-03	2.1237E-03
2100.0	9.6240E-02	8.6133E-02	8.4869E-02	1.8233E-03	2.1533E-03	2.3621E-03
2125.0	9.2180E-02	8.8632E-02	8.7303E-02	1.7464E-03	2.2158E-03	2.4298E-03
2150.0	8.9710E-02	8.4639E-02	8.3369E-02	1.6996E-03	2.1160E-03	2.3203E-03
2175.0	8.5760E-02	8.0448E-02	7.9257E-02	1.6247E-03	2.0112E-03	2.2059E-03
2200.0	8.2790E-02	7.1202E-02	7.0175E-02	1.5685E-03	1.7801E-03	1.9531E-03
2225.0	7.8840E-02	7.5453E-02	7.4400E-02	1.4936E-03	1.8863E-03	2.0707E-03
2250.0	7.5370E-02	7.1937E-02	7.1034E-02	1.4279E-03	1.7984E-03	1.9770E-03
2275.0	7.2630E-02	6.4021E-02	6.3309E-02	1.3760E-03	1.6005E-03	1.7620E-03
2300.0	6.9640E-02	5.8824E-02	5.8193E-02	1.3193E-03	1.4706E-03	1.6196E-03
2325.0	6.5560E-02	5.6215E-02	5.5626E-02	1.2420E-03	1.4054E-03	1.5482E-03
2350.0	6.4340E-02	4.1536E-02	4.1115E-02	1.2189E-03	1.0384E-03	1.1443E-03
2375.0	6.1410E-02	4.4147E-02	4.3704E-02	1.1634E-03	1.1037E-03	1.2164E-03
2400.0	5.9740E-02	4.4150E-02	4.3726E-02	1.1318E-03	1.1038E-03	1.2170E-03
2425.0	5.7330E-02	3.3078E-02	3.2802E-02	1.0861E-03	8.2695E-04	9.1294E-04
2450.0	5.4590E-02	1.3611E-02	1.3523E-02	1.0342E-03	3.4028E-04	3.7637E-04
2475.0	5.3370E-02	1.6455E-02	1.6368E-02	1.0111E-03	4.1138E-04	4.5555E-04
2500.0	5.1380E-02	7.0642E-03	7.0328E-03	9.7340E-04	1.7661E-04	1.9574E-04
SUM	52.78364	39.99639844	35.93099855	1.00E+00	1.00E+00	1.00E+00

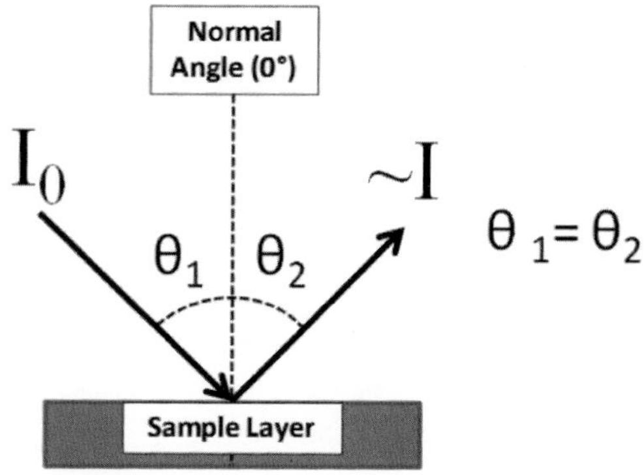

Fig. 7.32 In specular reflectance measurements the angle of incidence is equal to the angle of reflectance.

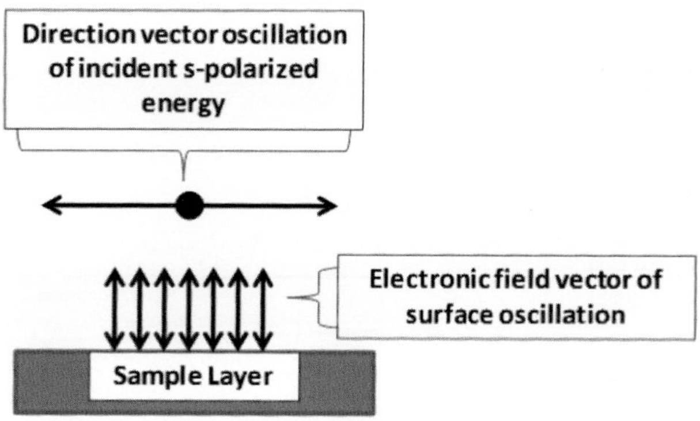

Fig. 7.33 Diagram showing the direction vector of s-polarized light.

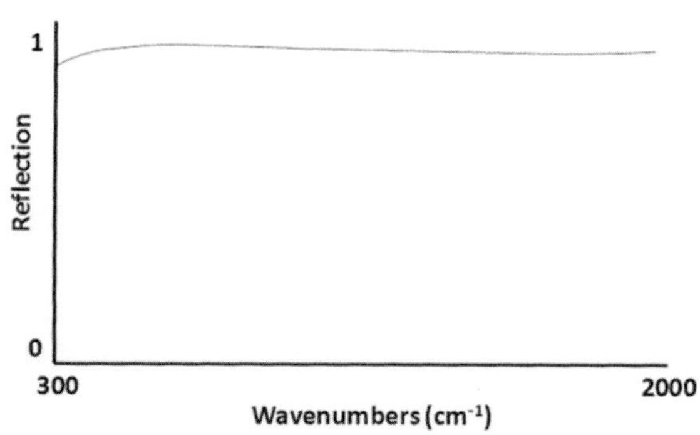

Fig. 7.34 Spectrum of SiO film on aluminum showing minimal interaction of incident energy with sample surface in the IR region; the result is no spectral features.

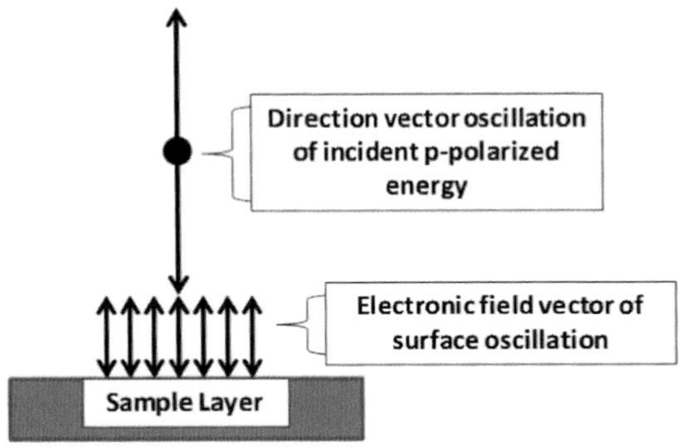

Fig. 7.35 Diagram showing the direction vector of p-polarized light.

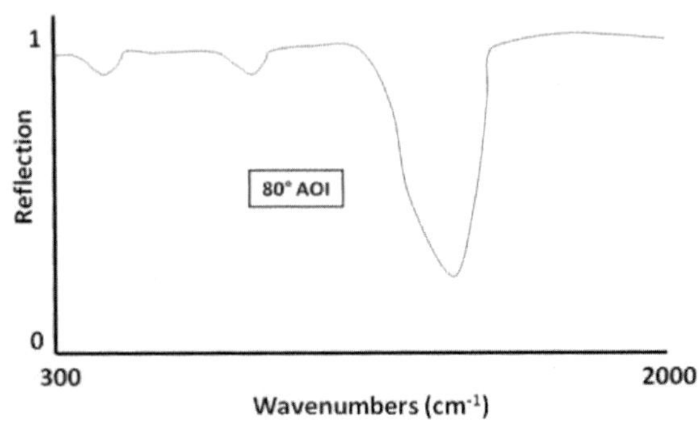

Fig. 7.36 Spectrum of SiO film on aluminum, showing increased interaction of incident energy with sample surface in the IR region; the result is increased spectral features.

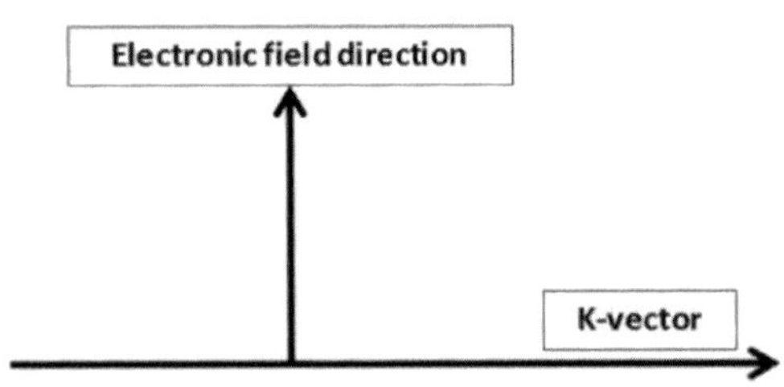

Fig. 7.37 Diagram showing the direction vector and oscillation vector of light.

If we look at a diagram of a "piece" of light such as Figure 7.37, we see that light has a direction of travel, the so-called "k-vector", and an electronic field direction.

The electronic field of light oscillates up and down at a frequency of 10 cycles/sec (Hz). So, if we are looking at p-polarized light coming directly at us we would see the electronic field vector as in Figure 7.38. This is vertically p-polarized light.

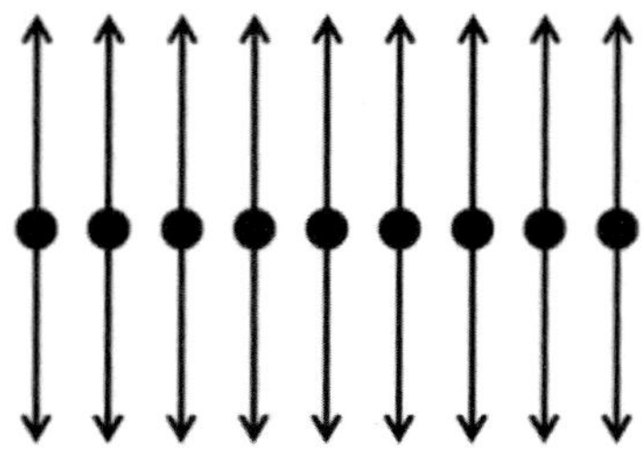

Fig. 7.38 An illustration of p-polarized light coming out of the page toward the reader.

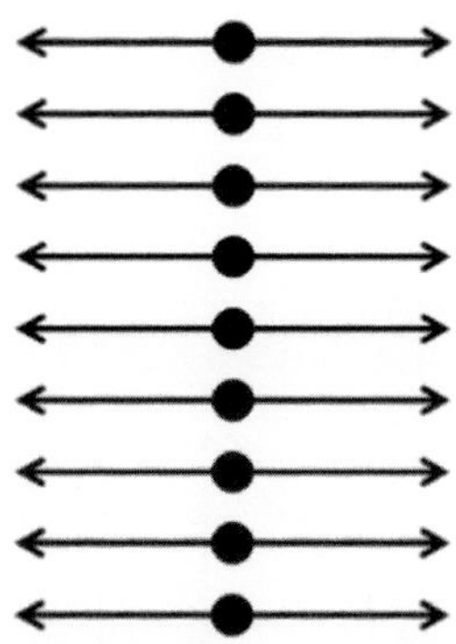

Fig. 7.39 An illustration of s-polarized light coming out of the page toward the reader.

Now if we were looking at s-polarized light coming toward us, we would see Figure 7.39; this is horizontally polarized light.

We do not, however, recognize the different states of polarization with our eyes. We see all light randomly polarized. The light diffracted from the surface of a spectrophotometer grating becomes polarized in the p-direction. Thus all grating instruments suffer from decreased energy in the s-polarized plane.

This can be a problem when using prism polarizing elements to perform measurements using either s- or p-polarized light. If the energy from the spectrophotometer is not random (or depolarized) prior to passing through the polarizer there will be different energy levels for both p- and s-orientations. Also, the p-polarized standard beam will produce different spectral results than a depolarized beam. These types of differences in spectral results can produce an analytical ambiguity, resulting in a enigma for the analyst who must interpret the results.

The elements or crystals generally used to make a prism polarizer are manufactured from optical grade natural calcite selected to be defect free. Figure 7.40 shows a diagram of the two calcite pieces involved in a configuration termed the Glan-Taylor

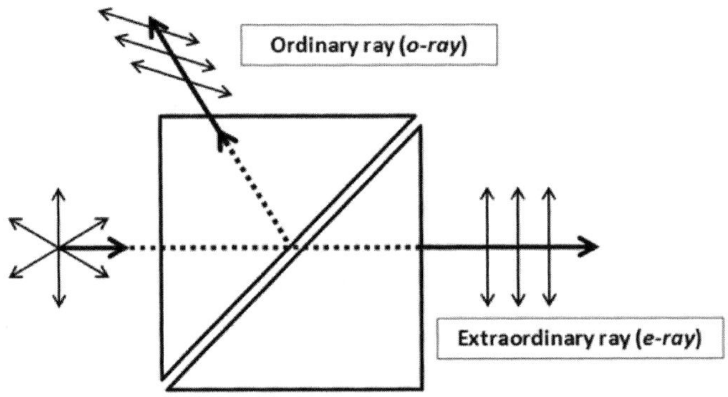

Fig. 7.40 Diagram of light interaction with Glan-Taylor prism polarizer.

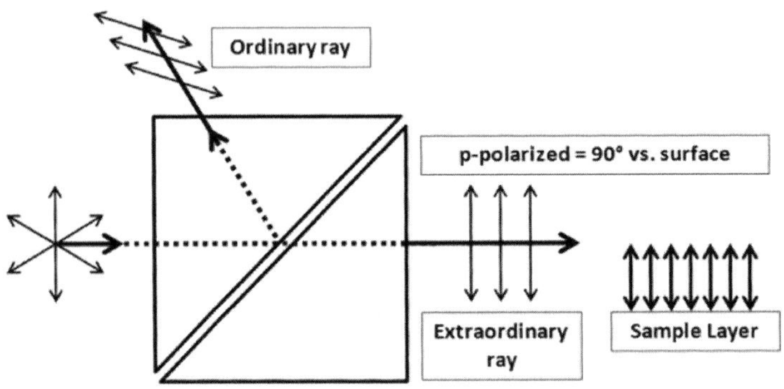

Fig. 7.41 p-polarized orientation of Glan-Taylor prism.

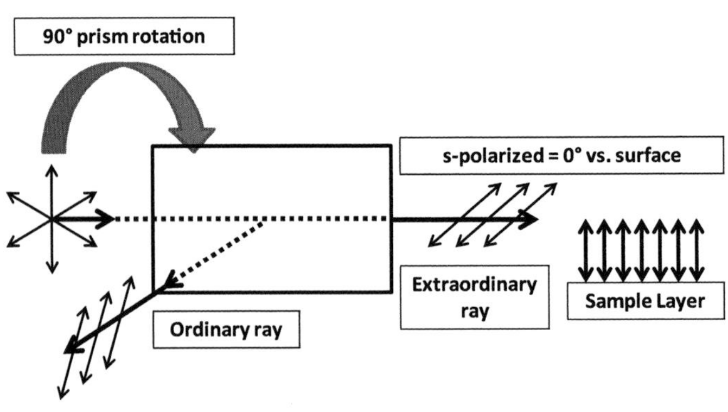

Fig. 7.42 s-polarized orientation of Glan-Taylor prism.

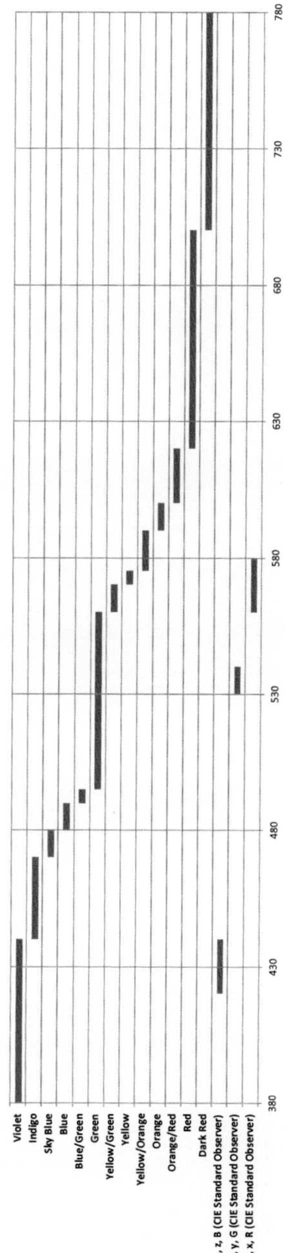

Fig. 7.43 Visible chromophore band positions in nanometers (Color designations and color coordinates).

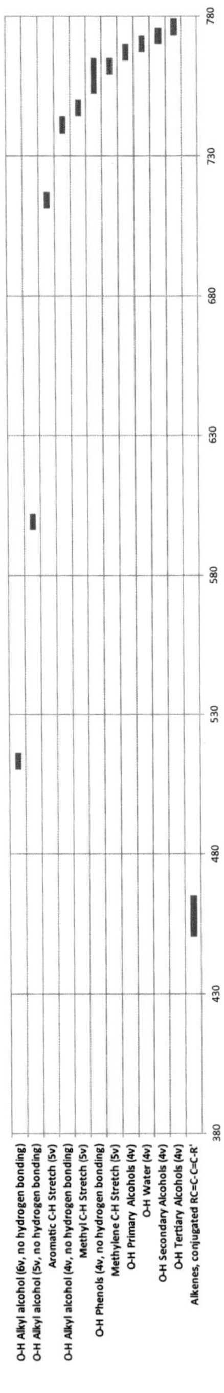

Fig. 7.44 Visible chromophore band positions in nanometers (Chemical functional groups).

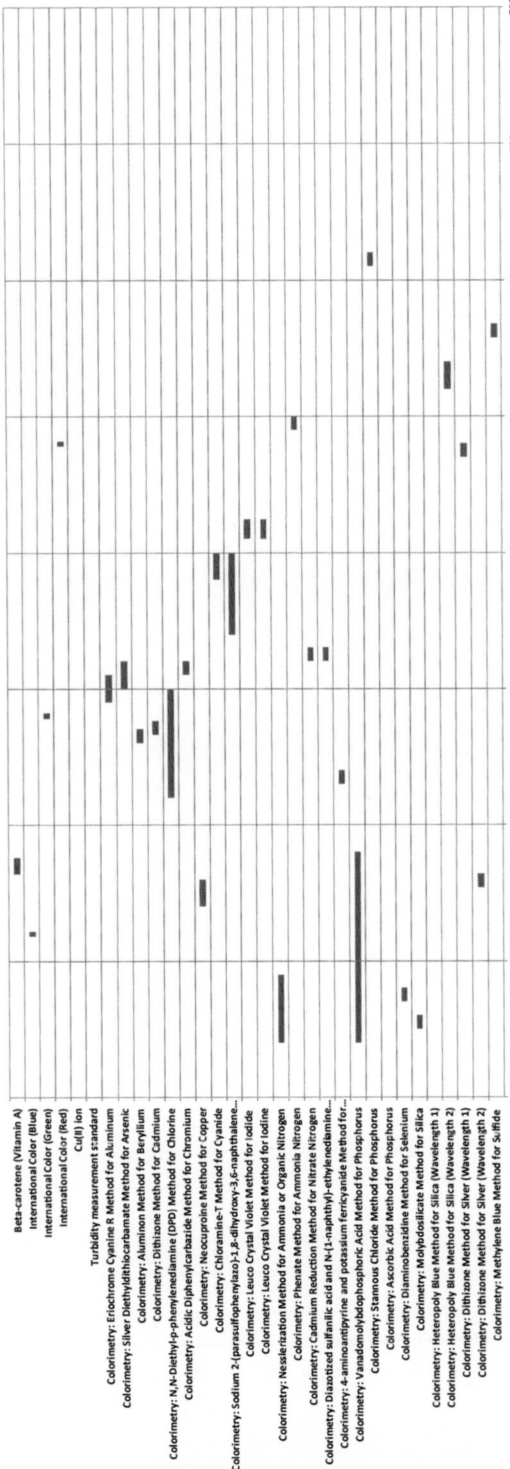

Fig. 7.45 Visible chromophore band positions in nanometers (Colorimetry color reactions, Page 1 of 3).

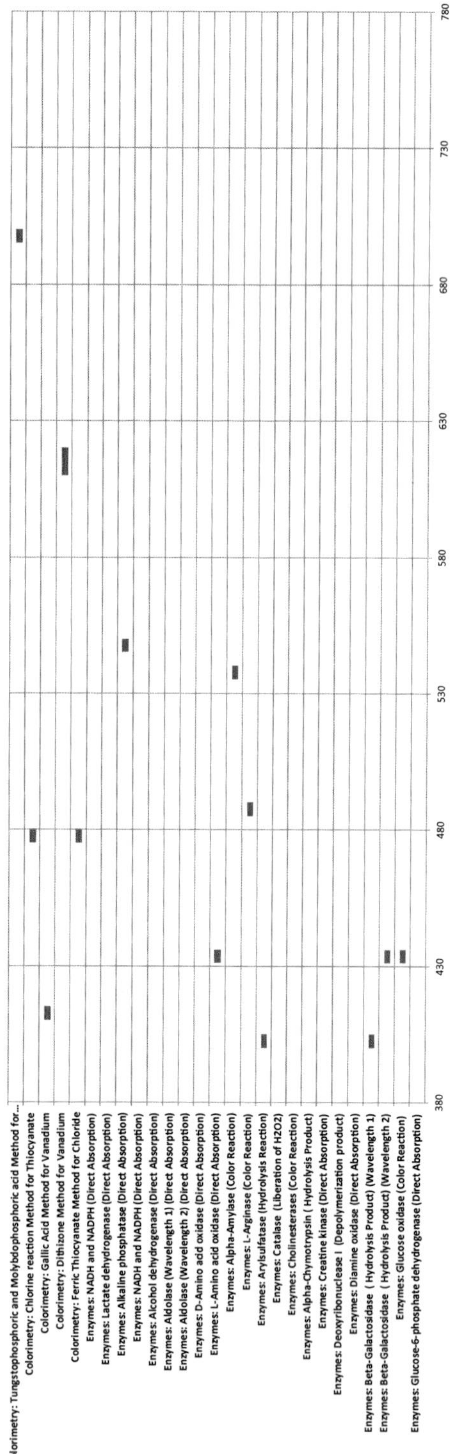

Fig. 7.46 Visible chromophore band positions in nanometers (Colorimetry color reactions, Page 2 of 3).

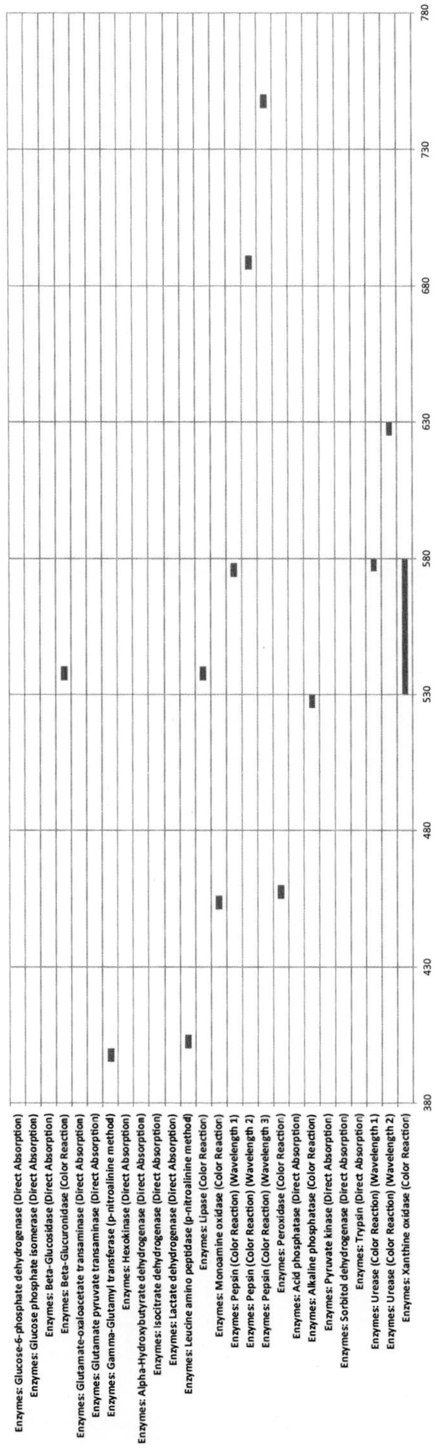

Fig. 7.47 Visible chromophore band positions in nanometers (Colorimetry color reactions, Page 3 of 3).

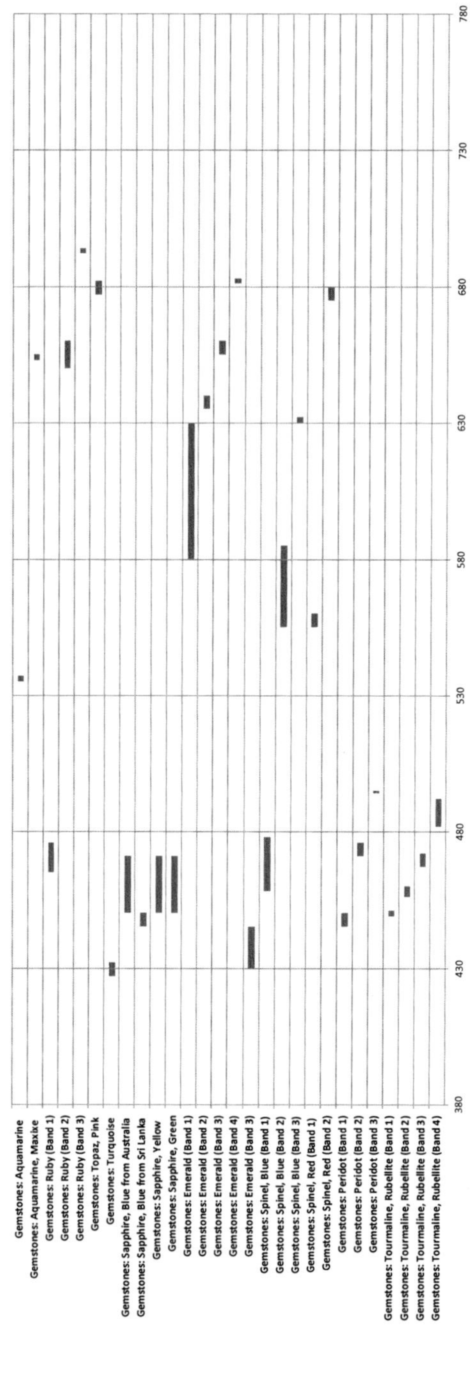

Fig. 7.48 Visible chromophore band positions in nanometers (Colors of gems and minerals, Page 1 of 3).

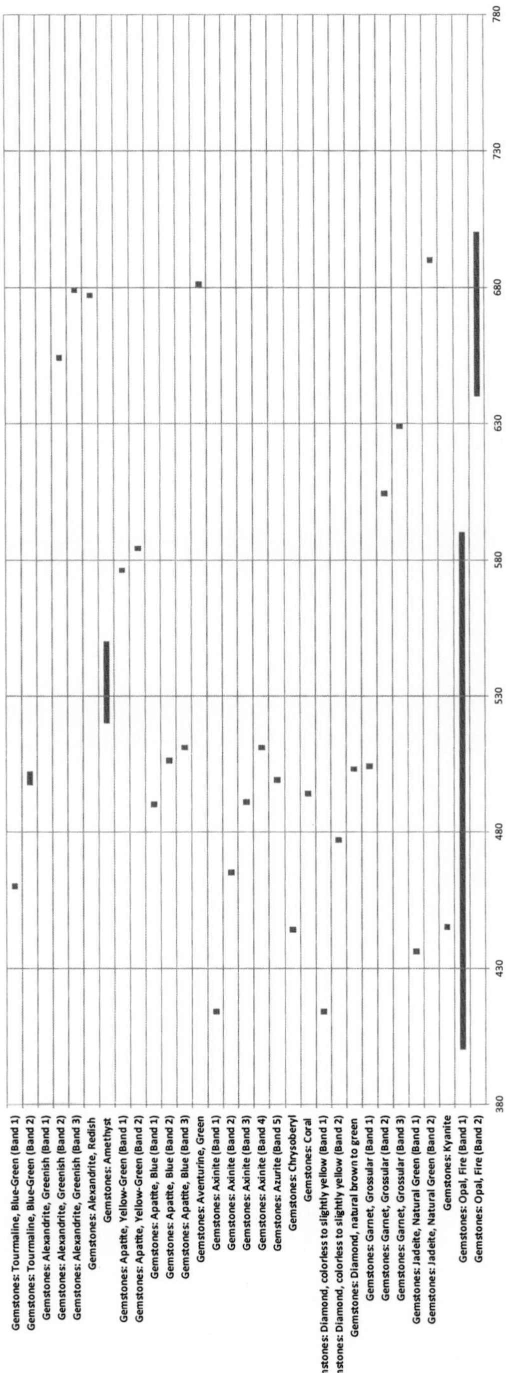

Fig. 7.49 Visible chromophore band positions in nanometers (Colors of gems and minerals, Page 2 of 3).

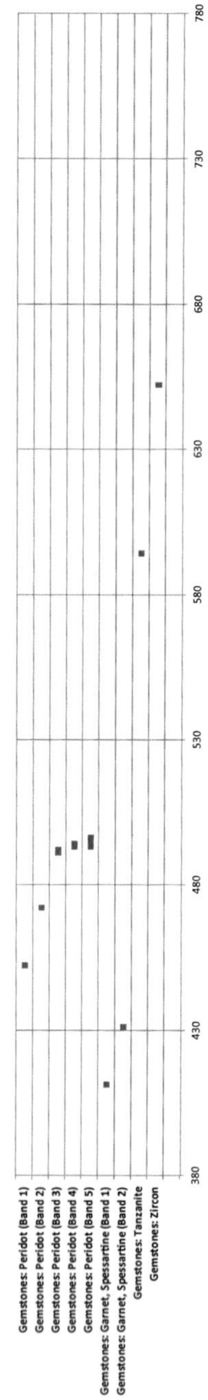

Fig. 7.50 Visible chromophore band positions in nanometers (Colors of gems and minerals, Page 3 of 3).

polarizing prism. In this two-element prism system, the entrance and exit faces are cut and polished to be normal to the incoming light beam. In Figure 7.40 we see that the oscillating direction of the exit beam is oriented according to the rotation of the prism elements. If we are looking from the top at the Glan-Taylor polarizer, then we have s-polarized light. If we are looking at the diagram from the side, our exit beam is p-polarized. Figures 7.41 and 7.42 also illustrate this principle.

Reflective surfaces are often measured with both s- and p-polarized light to determine the specific characteristics of the reflecting surface, the p-polarized light giving more interaction with the surface than the s-polarized. Knowing these relationships allows the analyst to experiment with the Glan-Taylor prism system and various angles of incidence to produce the desired spectral results.

7.5 Other Measurements using Visible Light

Appearance is measured over the visible wavelength range using such standards as ASTM E1767, Standard Practice for Specifying the Geometries of Observation and Measurement to Characterize the Appearance of Materials. References as shown.[27–29]

7.6 Visible Spectra Band Locations

Figures 7.43 through 7.50 demonstrate the locations of various color designations, chromophores (functional group harmonic absorption bands), colorimetry color band positions for various common reactions used for analysis, and spectral colors for natural gems and minerals.

References

1. ASTM (American Society for Testing and Materials) Method ASTM E805-12a, "Standard Practice for Identification of Instrumental Methods of Color or Color-Difference Measurement of Materials", ASTM International, 100 Barr Harbor Drive, PO Box C700, West Conshohocken, PA (2012).
2. ASTM (American Society for Testing and Materials) Method E1164-12, "Standard Practice for Obtaining Spectrometric Data for Object-Color Evaluation", ASTM International, 100 Barr Harbor Drive, PO Box C700, West Conshohocken, PA (2012).
3. ASTM (American Society for Testing and Materials) Method E1247-12, "Standard Practice for Detecting Fluorescence in Object-Color Specimens by Spectrophotometry", ASTM International, 100 Barr Harbor Drive, PO Box C700, West Conshohocken, PA (2012).

4. ASTM (American Society for Testing and Materials) Method E1345-98(2008)e1, "Standard Practice for Reducing the Effect of Variability of Color Measurement by Use of Multiple Measurements", ASTM International, 100 Barr Harbor Drive, PO Box C700, West Conshohocken, PA (2008).
5. ASTM (American Society for Testing and Materials) Method E1347-06(2011), "Standard Test Method for Color and Color-Difference Measurement by Tristimulus Colorimetry", ASTM International, 100 Barr Harbor Drive, PO Box C700, West Conshohocken, PA (2011).
6. ASTM (American Society for Testing and Materials) Method C1510-01(2012), "Standard Test Method for Color and Color Difference of Whitewares by Abriged Spectrophotometry", ASTM International, 100 Barr Harbor Drive, PO Box C700, West Conshohocken, PA (2012).
7. ASTM (American Society for Testing and Materials) Method E2153-01(2011), "Standard Practice for Obtaining Bispectral Photometric Data for Evaluation of Fluorescent Color", ASTM International, 100 Barr Harbor Drive, PO Box C700, West Conshohocken, PA (2011).
8. ASTM (American Society for Testing and Materials) Method D2244-14, "Standard Practice for Calculation of Color Tolerances and Color Differences from Instrumentally Measured Color Coordinates", ASTM International, 100 Barr Harbor Drive, PO Box C700, West Conshohocken, PA (2014).
9. ASTM (American Society for Testing and Materials) Method E2539-12, "Standard Practice for Multiangle Color Measurement of Interference Pigments", ASTM International, 100 Barr Harbor Drive, PO Box C700, West Conshohocken, PA (2012).
10. ASTM (American Society for Testing and Materials) Method D7856-14, "Standard Specification for Color and Appearance Retention of Solid and Variegated Color Plastic Siding Products using CIELab Color Space", ASTM International, 100 Barr Harbor Drive, PO Box C700, West Conshohocken, PA (2014).
11. ASTM (American Society for Testing and Materials) Method E 308-01, "Standard Practice for Computing the Colors of Objects by using the CIE System", ASTM International, 100 Barr Harbor Drive, PO Box C700, West Conshohocken, PA (2001).
12. J. Workman and A. Springsteen (Eds.), Applied Spectroscopy: A Compact Reference for Practitioners (Academic Press, Boston, 1998).
13. Precise Color Guide, Minolta, 101 Williams Drive, Ramsey, New Jersey 07446, 1993.
14. ASTM (American Society for Testing and Materials) Method C1549-09, "Standard Test Method for Determination of Solar Reflectance Near Ambient Temperature Using a Portable Solar Reflectometer", ASTM International, 100 Barr Harbor Drive, PO Box C700, West Conshohocken, PA (2009).
15. ASTM (American Society for Testing and Materials) Method E1175-87(2009), "Standard Test Method for Determining Solar or Photopic Reflectance, Transmittance, and Absorptance of Materials Using a Large Diameter Integrating Sphere", ASTM International, 100 Barr Harbor Drive, PO Box C700, West Conshohocken, PA (2009).
16. ASTM (American Society for Testing and Materials) Method E903-12,"Standard Test Method for Solar Absorptance, Reflectance, and Transmittance of Materials Using Integrating Spheres", ASTM International, 100 Barr Harbor Drive, PO Box C700, West Conshohocken, PA (2012). Reprinted, with permission from ASTM E903-96 (Historical Version) Standard Test Method for Solar Absorptance, Reflectance, and Transmittance of Materials Using Integrating Spheres (Withdrawn 2005), copyright ASTM International, 100 Barr Harbor Drive, West Conshohocken,

PA 19428. Contact ASTM International (HYPERLINK "http://www.astm.org" www.astm.org) for the latest information.'

17. ASTM (American Society for Testing and Materials) Method E1980-11 Practice for Calculating Solar Reflectance Index of Horizontal and Low-Sloped Opaque Surfaces", ASTM International, 100 Barr Harbor Drive, PO Box C700, West Conshohocken, PA (2012).
18. European Standards EN 410:2011, "Glass in building — Determination of luminous and solar characteristics of glazing", European Standard Store, Krimicka 134, 318 13 Pilsen, Czech Republic (2011); http://www.en-standard.eu/
19. European Standards BS EN 14500:2008, "Blinds and shutters. Thermal and visual comfort. Test and calculation methods (British Standard)", European Standard Store, Krimicka 134, 318 13 Pilsen, Czech Republic (2008); http://www.en-standard.eu/
20. ISO 9050, ISO 9050:2003, Glass in building — Determination of light transmittance, solar direct transmittance, total solar energy transmittance, ultraviolet transmittance and related glazing factors", ISO Central Secretariat, 1, ch. de la Voie-Creuse, CP 56- CH-1211 Geneva 20, Switzerland, 2003.
21. NFRC 300 2014 A0E0 "Test Method for Determining the Solar Optical Properties of Glazing Materials and Systems", NFRC Optical Properties Subcommittee, National Fenestration Rating Council, 6305 Ivy Lane, Suite 140, Greenbelt, MD 20770 (2014); www.nfrc.org
22. Refer to this website for compare and contrast statements relative to the solar measurement standard methods: http://windowoptics.lbl.gov/data/standards/solar
23. Japanese Industrial Standard (JIS) R 3106:1998, "Testing method on transmittance, reflectance and emittance of flat glasses and evaluation of solar heat gain coefficient", Japanese Standards Association, 4-1-24, Akasaka, Minato-ku, Tokyo, 107-8440 JAPAN (Reaffirmed 2012-10-22); http://www.webstore.jsa.or.jp/webstore/Top/index En.jsp?lang=en
24. Japanese Industrial Standard (JIS) JIS A 5759:2008, "Adhesive films for glazings", Japanese Standards Association, 4-1-24, Akasaka, Minato-ku, Tokyo, 107-8440 JAPAN (Reaffirmed (2013-10-21); http://www.webstore.jsa.or.jp/webstore/Top/index En.jsp?lang=en
25. JIS K 5602:2008, "Determination Of Reflectance Of Solar Radiation By Paint Film", Japanese Standards Association, 4-1-24, Akasaka, Minato-ku, Tokyo, 107-8440 JAPAN (Reaffirmed2013-10-21); http://www.webstore.jsa.or.jp/webstore/Top/index En.jsp?lang=en
26. J. Harrick, Optical Spectroscopy: Sampling techniques manual (Harrick Scientific, Ossining, New York, 1987).
27. ASTM (American Society for Testing and Materials) Method E1767-11, "Standard Practice for Specifying the Geometries of Observation and Measurement to Characterize the Appearance of Materials", ASTM International, 100 Barr Harbor Drive, PO Box C700, West Conshohocken, PA (2012).
28. ASTM (American Society for Testing and Materials) Method E284-13b, "Standard Terminology of Appearance", ASTM International, 100 Barr Harbor Drive, PO Box C700, West Conshohocken, PA (2012).
29. ASTM (American Society for Testing and Materials) Method E179-12, "Standard Guide for Selection of Geometric Conditions for Measurement of Reflection and Transmission Properties of Materials", ASTM International, 100 Barr Harbor Drive, PO Box C700, West Conshohocken, PA (2012).

30. A. Bartecki and J. Burgess, *The Colour of Metal Compounds*, 1st edn. (Overseas Publishers Association, Netherlands, 2000).
31. W. Schumann, *Gemstones of the World*, Revised Edition, 2nd edn. (NAG press, 2001).
32. Reprinted, with permission from ASTM G173-03 (Historical Version) Standard Tables for Reference Solar Spectral Irradiances: Direct Normal and Hemispherical on 37° Tilted Surface, copyright ASTM International, 100 Barr Harbor Drive, West Conshohocken, PA 19428. Contact ASTM International (HYPERLINK "http://www.astm.org" www.astm.org) for the latest information.

Chapter 8

Visible Reference Material Spectra and Tables

Contents

8.1 Introduction to Standard Reference Materials (SRMs) for Photometric Accuracy Measurements

The National Institute for Standards and Technology (NIST) previously known as the National Bureau of Standards (NBS) provides materials designed as reference sources to verify the transmittance and absorbance scale accuracy of spectrophotometers. The materials are termed SRMs or Standard Reference Materials. In the case of SRM 930D, a set of three individual glass filters are provided in cuvette-like black metal holders. In addition, one empty filter holder is provided for use as a reference sample.[1]

8.1.1 *The Meaning of Photometric Accuracy*

Definition:
Photometric accuracy is a formal term used to describe how well a measuring device (spectrophotometer or illuminance meter) is able to determine the total energy flux

transmitted through (or reflected from) a Standard Reference Material (SRM). As stated in volume 14.01 of the American Society for Testing and Materials (ASTM) International.[2,3] The measurement of the photometric accuracy for an instrument is obtained as follows:

20.1 "Select the appropriate Standard Reference Material and obtain ten successive readings of the apparent absorbance or transmittance at the specified wavelength. Average the ten readings. The photometric accuracy is the difference between the true absorbance or transmittance value and the average observed value."

It is further stated that the following apply to the reporting of photometric accuracy (20.3).

20.3 "Report the photometric accuracy in the following order: reference material, wavelength, true absorbance or transmittance, observed absorbance or transmittance plus or minus the standard deviation."

8.1.2 *Example of Reporting Photometric Accuracy*

As an example the stated specifications for photometric accuracy for a test instrument might be written as:

Photometric Accuracy

±0.002 Au (for range of 0.0 to 0.5 Absorbance units)

±0.004 Au (for range of 0.5 to 1.0 Absorbance units)

±0.3%T

Measured with NIST 930D filters

Here is an evaluation of these specifications in greater detail. A photometric accuracy of "0.002 Au at 0 to 0.5 Au" indicates that after the instrument has been set to zero, a standard sample which transmits between 30.1%T (i.e., 0.5 Au) and 100%T (i.e., 0.0 Au) measures within ±0.002 Au as compared to the specified value for that reference standard material at any wavelength position. Tables 8.1 and 8.2 are used to convert from transmittance or reflectance scale to absorbance scale. This issue of how to explain a specification such as ±0.004 at 0.5 to 1.0 Au, when using the NIST 930D filter set has been brought forward in competitive sales situations between instrument manufacturers. The tolerance for each of the 930d (or 930D) filters is stated by NIST as ±0.5 percent relative. Thus, a 10%T filter (which corresponds to 0.1 T or 1.0 Au) neutral density 930D-type reference standard would be expected to be within the range of 9.95 to 10.05%T. These values are equivalent to 1.0022 Au to 0.9978 Au. The difference in Au is 1.0022 Au minus 0.9978 Au equals 0.0044 Au. The standard tolerance in Au is 1.0000 ±0.0022 Au, rounded to 1.000 ± 0.002 Au. Conservatively for transmittance we state 10.00 ± 0.03%T; and related to 0.0 Au or 100%T, we specify 100.0 ± 0.3%T.

If the stated tolerance for the NIST 930D filter is ±0.002 Au at 1.0 Au, we are stating that our maximum deviation in photometric accuracy for our instrument at 1.0 Au is also ±0.002 Au. For the worst case measurement for the NIST filter, we would have the filter error of ±0.002 added to the instrument error of ±0.002, to result in a total maximum variation ±0.004 Au error (This is our stated specification for the example given).

Table 8.1 Relationship of %T and absorbance unit (Au) values.

T (as ppm)	%T	T	1/T	Au
10000000	1000	10	$0.1 = 10^{-1}$	−1.0
1000000	100	1	$1.0 = 10^{0}$	0.0
316230	31.6	0.316	3.16	0.5
100000	10.0	0.1	$10 = 10^{1}$	1.0
10000	1	0.01	$100 = 10^{2}$	2.0
1000	0.1	0.001	$1000 = 10^{3}$	3.0
100	0.01	0.0001	$10000 = 10^{4}$	4.0
10	0.001	0.00001	$100000 = 10^{5}$	5.0
1	0.0001	0.000001	$1000000 = 10^{6}$	6.0

And one can readily calculate the reflectance or transmittance of any measurement given the absorbance of that measurement as follows. For conversion of Absorbance to Transmittance we use:

$$A = -\log_{10}\left(\frac{I}{I_0}\right) = \log_{10}\left(\frac{I_0}{I}\right) \tag{8.1}$$

$$\frac{I}{I_0} = 10^{-A} \Rightarrow \frac{I_0}{I} = \frac{1}{10^{-A}} \tag{8.2}$$

$$\frac{I}{I_0} = 10^{-A} = T \tag{8.3}$$

$$\%\mathrm{T} = \mathrm{T} \times 100. \tag{8.4}$$

To convert Absorbance to Reflectance we use:

$$A = -\log_{10}\left(\frac{I}{I_0}\right) = \log_{10}\left(\frac{I_0}{I}\right) \tag{8.5}$$

$$\frac{I}{I_0} = 10^{-A} \Rightarrow \frac{I_0}{I} = \frac{1}{10^{-A}} \tag{8.6}$$

$$\frac{I}{I_0} = 10^{-A} = R \tag{8.7}$$

$$\%\mathrm{R} = \mathrm{R} \times 100. \tag{8.8}$$

Table 8.2 Expanded table showing the relationship of %T and %R to absorbance unit (Au) values.

Transmittance or Reflectance	Percent T or R	Absorbance (Au)
1.000	100.0	0.000000
0.995	99.5	0.002177
0.990	99.0	0.004365
0.985	98.5	0.006564
0.980	98.0	0.008774
0.975	97.5	0.010995
0.970	97.0	0.013228
0.965	96.5	0.015473
0.960	96.0	0.017729
0.955	95.5	0.019997
0.950	95.0	0.022276
0.945	94.5	0.024568
0.940	94.0	0.026872
0.935	93.5	0.029188
0.930	93.0	0.031517
0.925	92.5	0.033858
0.920	92.0	0.036212
0.915	91.5	0.038579
0.910	91.0	0.040959
0.905	90.5	0.043351
0.900	90.0	0.045757
0.895	89.5	0.048177
0.890	89.0	0.050610
0.885	88.5	0.053057
0.880	88.0	0.055517
0.875	87.5	0.057992
0.870	87.0	0.060481
0.865	86.5	0.062984
0.860	86.0	0.065502
0.855	85.5	0.068034
0.850	85.0	0.070581
0.845	84.5	0.073143
0.840	84.0	0.075721
0.835	83.5	0.078314

(*Continued*)

Table 8.2 (*Continued*)

Transmittance or Reflectance	Percent T or R	Absorbance (Au)
0.830	83.0	0.080922
0.825	82.5	0.083546
0.820	82.0	0.086186
0.815	81.5	0.088842
0.810	81.0	0.091515
0.805	80.5	0.094204
0.800	80.0	0.096910
0.795	79.5	0.099633
0.790	79.0	0.102373
0.785	78.5	0.105130
0.780	78.0	0.107905
0.775	77.5	0.110698
0.770	77.0	0.113509
0.765	76.5	0.116339
0.760	76.0	0.119186
0.755	75.5	0.122053
0.750	75.0	0.124939
0.745	74.5	0.127844
0.740	74.0	0.130768
0.735	73.5	0.133713
0.730	73.0	0.136677
0.725	72.5	0.139662
0.720	72.0	0.142668
0.715	71.5	0.145694
0.710	71.0	0.148742
0.705	70.5	0.151811
0.700	70.0	0.154902
0.695	69.5	0.158015
0.690	69.0	0.161151
0.685	68.5	0.164309
0.680	68.0	0.167491
0.675	67.5	0.170696
0.670	67.0	0.173925
0.665	66.5	0.177178
0.660	66.0	0.180456
0.655	65.5	0.183759
0.650	65.0	0.187087
0.645	64.5	0.190440
0.640	64.0	0.193820
0.635	63.5	0.197226
0.630	63.0	0.200659
0.625	62.5	0.204120
0.620	62.0	0.207608

(*Continued*)

Table 8.2 (*Continued*)

Transmittance or Reflectance	Percent T or R	Absorbance (Au)
0.615	61.5	0.211125
0.610	61.0	0.214670
0.605	60.5	0.218245
0.600	60.0	0.221849
0.595	59.5	0.225483
0.590	59.0	0.229148
0.585	58.5	0.232844
0.580	58.0	0.236572
0.575	57.5	0.240332
0.570	57.0	0.244125
0.565	56.5	0.247952
0.560	56.0	0.251812
0.555	55.5	0.255707
0.550	55.0	0.259637
0.545	54.5	0.263603
0.540	54.0	0.267606
0.535	53.5	0.271646
0.530	53.0	0.275724
0.525	52.5	0.279841
0.520	52.0	0.283997
0.515	51.5	0.288193
0.510	51.0	0.292430
0.505	50.5	0.296709
0.500	50.0	0.301030
0.495	49.5	0.305395
0.490	49.0	0.309804
0.485	48.5	0.314258
0.480	48.0	0.318759
0.475	47.5	0.323306
0.470	47.0	0.327902
0.465	46.5	0.332547
0.460	46.0	0.337242
0.455	45.5	0.341989
0.450	45.0	0.346787
0.445	44.5	0.351640
0.440	44.0	0.356547
0.435	43.5	0.361511
0.430	43.0	0.366532
0.425	42.5	0.371611
0.420	42.0	0.376751
0.415	41.5	0.381952
0.410	41.0	0.387216
0.405	40.5	0.392545
0.400	40.0	0.397940

(*Continued*)

Table 8.2 (*Continued*)

Transmittance or Reflectance	Percent T or R	Absorbance (Au)
0.395	39.5	0.403403
0.390	39.0	0.408935
0.385	38.5	0.414539
0.380	38.0	0.420216
0.375	37.5	0.425969
0.370	37.0	0.431798
0.365	36.5	0.437707
0.360	36.0	0.443697
0.355	35.5	0.449772
0.350	35.0	0.455932
0.345	34.5	0.462181
0.340	34.0	0.468521
0.335	33.5	0.474955
0.330	33.0	0.481486
0.325	32.5	0.488117
0.320	32.0	0.494850
0.315	31.5	0.501689
0.310	31.0	0.508638
0.305	30.5	0.515700
0.300	30.0	0.522879
0.295	29.5	0.530178
0.290	29.0	0.537602
0.285	28.5	0.545155
0.280	28.0	0.552842
0.275	27.5	0.560667
0.270	27.0	0.568636
0.265	26.5	0.576754
0.260	26.0	0.585027
0.255	25.5	0.593460
0.250	25.0	0.602060
0.245	24.5	0.610834
0.240	24.0	0.619789
0.235	23.5	0.628932
0.230	23.0	0.638272
0.225	22.5	0.647817
0.220	22.0	0.657577
0.215	21.5	0.667562
0.210	21.0	0.677781
0.205	20.5	0.688246
0.200	20.0	0.698970
0.195	19.5	0.709965
0.190	19.0	0.721246
0.185	18.5	0.732828
0.180	18.0	0.744727
0.175	17.5	0.756962

(*Continued*)

Table 8.2 (*Continued*)

Transmittance or Reflectance	Percent T or R	Absorbance (Au)
0.170	17.0	0.769551
0.165	16.5	0.782516
0.160	16.0	0.795880
0.155	15.5	0.809668
0.150	15.0	0.823909
0.145	14.5	0.838632
0.140	14.0	0.853872
0.135	13.5	0.869666
0.130	13.0	0.886057
0.125	12.5	0.903090
0.120	12.0	0.920819
0.115	11.5	0.939302
0.110	11.0	0.958607
0.105	10.5	0.978811
0.100	10.0	1.000000
0.095	9.50	1.022276
0.090	9.00	1.045757
0.085	8.50	1.070581
0.080	8.00	1.096910
0.075	7.50	1.124939
0.070	7.00	1.154902
0.065	6.50	1.187087
0.060	6.00	1.221849
0.055	5.50	1.259637
0.050	5.00	1.301030
0.045	4.50	1.346787
0.040	4.00	1.397940
0.035	3.50	1.455932
0.030	3.00	1.522879
0.025	2.50	1.602060
0.020	2.00	1.698970
0.015	1.50	1.823909
0.010	1.00	2.000000
0.009	0.90	2.045757
0.008	0.80	2.096910
0.007	0.70	2.154902
0.006	0.60	2.221849
0.005	0.50	2.301030
0.004	0.40	2.397940
0.003	0.30	2.522879
0.002000	0.2000	2.698970
0.001500	0.1500	2.823909
0.001000	0.1000	3.000000
0.000100	0.0100	4.000000
0.000010	0.0010	5.000000
0.000001	0.0001	6.000000

8.2 Reference Standards for Visible Spectroscopy

The following Text, Tables, and Figures demonstrate the variety of reference standards available for visible spectroscopic measurements. The list of figures following is shown below.

Fig. 8.1. NIST SRM-2036 reflectance wavelength SRM (standard reference material) measured using 8°/Hemispherical Spectral Reflectance Factor geometry and a calibrated double-monochromator instrument from 250 nm to 850 nm. Peak designations marked.

Fig. 8.2. NIST SRM-2036 reflectance wavelength SRM (standard reference material) measured using 8°/Hemispherical Spectral Reflectance Factor geometry (reported as Absorbance or $\log_{10}$ (1/R)) and a calibrated double-monochromator instrument from 300 nm to 800 nm.

Fig. 8.3. Matte White, Grey, and Black photometric standards 0°/45° Spectral Reflectance Factor geometry with a calibrated double-monochromator instrument.

Fig. 8.4. Ceramics as Matte Red, Deep Pink, Orange, and Yellow photometric color standards measured using 0°/45° Spectral Reflectance Factor geometry with a calibrated double-monochromator instrument.

Fig. 8.5. Ceramics as Cyan, Diff. Green, Deep Blue, and Green photometric color standards measured using 0°/45° Spectral Reflectance Factor geometry with a calibrated double-monochromator instrument. (Data and spectrum used with permission from Avian Technologies, New London, NH).

Fig. 8.6. Matte Russian Opal Glass photometric standard measured using 8°/Hemispherical Spectral Reflectance Factor geometry with a calibrated double-monochromator instrument.

Fig. 8.7. Transmittance of SRM-930d standard set photometric standards; Filter 10–1225, Filter 20-1255, and Filter 30–1255.

Fig. 8.8. Russian Opal Glass Glossy reflectance standard measured using 8°/Hemispherical Spectral Reflectance Factor geometry. Mean Reflectance over the spectral region shown is 0.967. Measured photometric data is given in the Table below the figure.

Fig. 8.9. MBR *(minimum blue reflectance)* reflectance wavelength reference standards measured using 8°/Hemispherical Spectral Reflectance Factor geometry and a calibrated double-monochromator instrument from 360 nm to 820 nm.

Fig. 8.10. Basic Blue Green color standards measured using 8°/ Hemispherical Spectral Reflectance Factor geometry and a calibrated double-monochromator instrument from 360 nm to 820 nm.

Fig. 8.11. Basic Red Orange color standards measured using 8°/ Hemispherical Spectral Reflectance Factor geometry and a calibrated double-monochromator instrument from 360 nm to 820 nm.

Fig. 8.12. Basic CERAM/BCRA (British Ceramic Research series II) Chromatic Tiles measured using 8°/Hemispherical Spectral Reflectance Factor geometry and a calibrated double-monochromator instrument from 360 nm to 820 nm.

Fig. 8.13. Basic BCRA (British Ceramic Research Series II) Achromatic Tiles measured using 8°/Hemispherical Spectral Reflectance Factor geometry and a calibrated double-monochromator instrument from 360 nm to 820 nm.

Fig. 8.14. BCRA (British Ceramic Research) G-GS9-02c Standards measured using 8°/Hemispherical Spectral Reflectance Factor geometry and a calibrated double-monochromator instrument from 360 nm to 820 nm.

Fig. 8.15. BCRA (British Ceramic Research) G-GS9-02c Standards measured using 8°/Hemispherical Spectral Reflectance Factor geometry and a calibrated double-monochromator instrument from 360 nm to 820 nm.

Fig. 8.16. IPAC GmbH Color Standards measured using Transmittance measurement geometry and a calibrated double-monochromator instrument from 350 nm to 830 nm.

Fig. 8.17. IPAC GmbH Color Standards measured using Transmittance measurement geometry and a calibrated double-monochromator instrument from 350 nm to 830 nm.

Fig. 8.18. Color Filter Set CFS-12-02c measured using Transmittance measurement geometry and a calibrated double-monochromator instrument from 300 nm to 830 nm.

Fig. 8.19. Basic Set of RGB (Red-Green-Blue) Color Standards measured using 8°/Hemispherical Spectral Reflectance Factor geometry and a calibrated double-monochromator instrument from 350 nm to 830 nm.

Fig. 8.20. Basic Set of optical glass materials measured using Transmittance geometry from 300 nm to 800 nm.

Fig. 8.21. Basic Set of optical glass materials measured using Absorbance as $\log_{10}$ (1/T) geometry from 300 nm to 800 nm.

Fig. 8.22. Basic Set of metal surfaces measured using Absorbance as $\log_{10}$ (1/R) geometry from 680 nm to 800 nm.

Fig. 8.23. Delrin (Black polymer), Fluorilon 10% Reflectance (R10), and Fluorilon 99% Reflectance (R99) measured using Absorbance as $\log_{10}$ (1/R) geometry from 680 nm to 800 nm.

Fig. 8.24. Ceramic comparison: White ceramic polished, White ceramic diffuse, and Fluorilon 99% Reflectance measured using Absorbance as $\log_{10}$ (1/R) geometry from 680 nm to 800 nm.

Fig. 8.25. Visible Region: Optical Materials comparison measured in Transmittance from 350 nm to 800 nm.

Fig. 8.26. Visible Region: Close-up of Figure 8.24 showing Optical Materials comparison measured in Transmittance from 350 nm to 800 nm.

Fig. 8.27. Visible Region: Close-up of Figure 8.25 showing Optical Materials comparison measured in Transmittance from 350 nm to 800 nm.

Fig. 8.28. Detector Sensitivity Ranges from 0 microns (0 nm) to 15 microns (15000 nm).

Fig. 8.29. Source Emissivity Ranges (in microns).

Fig. 8.30. Optical Materials Transmittance Ranges (in microns).

Fig. 8.31. d/8° Sample Measurement geometry (8°/Hemispherical Spectral Reflectance Factor geometry). An integrating sphere is used for diffuse illumination and collection of light.

Fig. 8.32. 0°/45° Sample Measurement geometry for Reflectance/Reflection Measurements. The Reflectance spectrum may be converted to absorbance using Beer's law as absorbance $= \log_{10}(1/R)$.

Fig. 8.33. 0°/180° Specular Transmission Sample Measurement geometry. The measurement may also be made slightly off-axis by 2–5 degrees. The Transmittance/Transmission spectrum may be converted to absorbance using Beer's law as absorbance $= \log_{10}(1/T)$.

8.3 Visible Wavelength Measurement Standards

Materials noted when provided by courtesy of Avian Technologies, New London, NH.

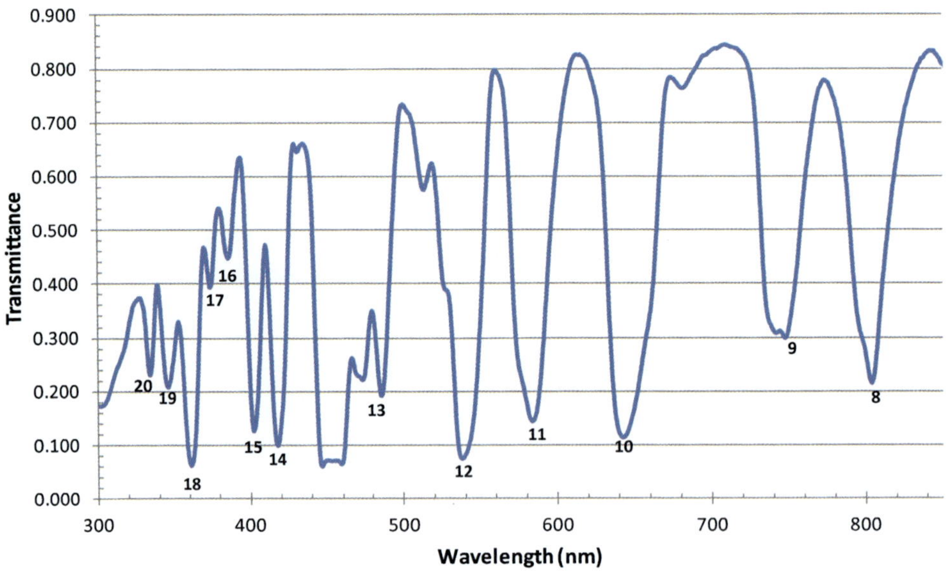

Fig. 8.1 NIST SRM-2036 reflectance wavelength SRM (standard reference material) measured using 8°/Hemispherical Spectral Reflectance Factor geometry and a calibrated double-monochromator instrument from 250 nm to 850 nm. Peak designations marked. (Data and spectrum used with permission from Avian Technologies, New London, NH).

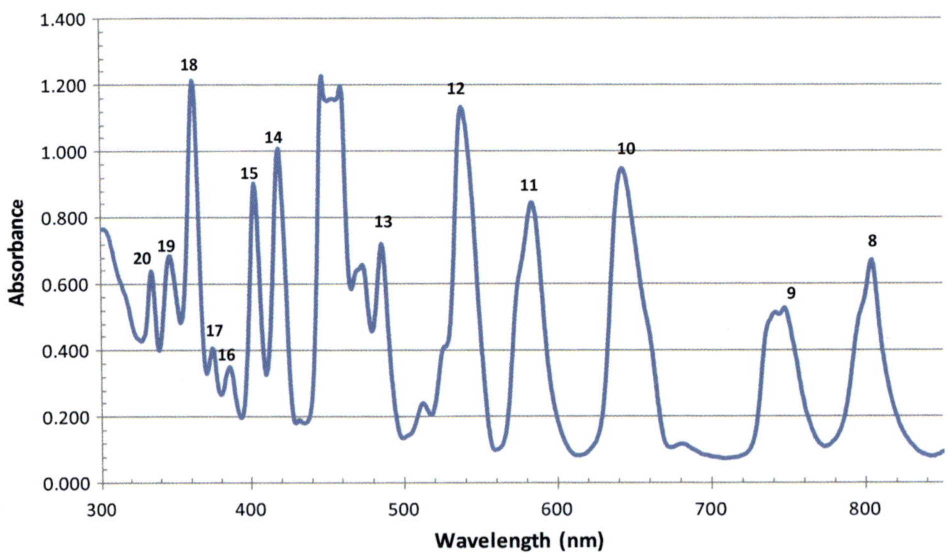

Fig. 8.2 NIST SRM-2036 reflectance wavelength SRM (standard reference material) measured using 8°/Hemispherical Spectral Reflectance Factor geometry (reported as Absorbance or $\log_{10}$ (1/R)) and a calibrated double-monochromator instrument from 300 nm to 800 nm. Peak designations marked. (Data and spectrum used with permission from Avian Technologies, New London, NH).

Table 8.3 Absorbance peak values for NIST SRM 2036 for Visible Spectral Region.

Band designation #	Literature SRM-2036	Uncertainty (nm)	Measured NIST SRM2036
8	804.3	0.7	803.8
9	747.7	0.7	747.7
10	642.4	0.7	642.3
11	583.4	0.7	583.3
12	537.7	0.7	537.8
13	485.4	0.7	485.3
14	417.9	0.7	417.6
15	402.5	0.7	402.5
16	386.1	0.7	386.4
17	374.5	0.7	374.2
18	360.8	0.7	360.9
19	345.4	0.7	345.3
20	334.6	0.7	334.4

8.4 Visible Photometric and Color Measurement Standards

Materials noted when provided by courtesy of Avian Technologies, New London, NH.

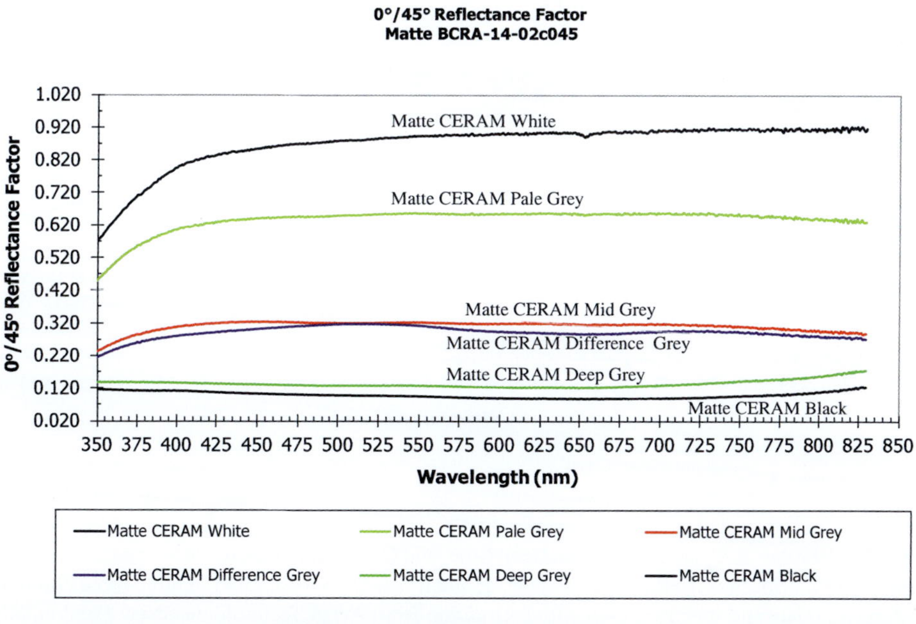

Fig. 8.3 Matte White, Grey, and Black photometric standards measured using 0°/45° Spectral Reflectance Factor geometry with a calibrated double-monochromator instrument. (Data and spectrum used with permission from Avian Technologies, New London, NH).

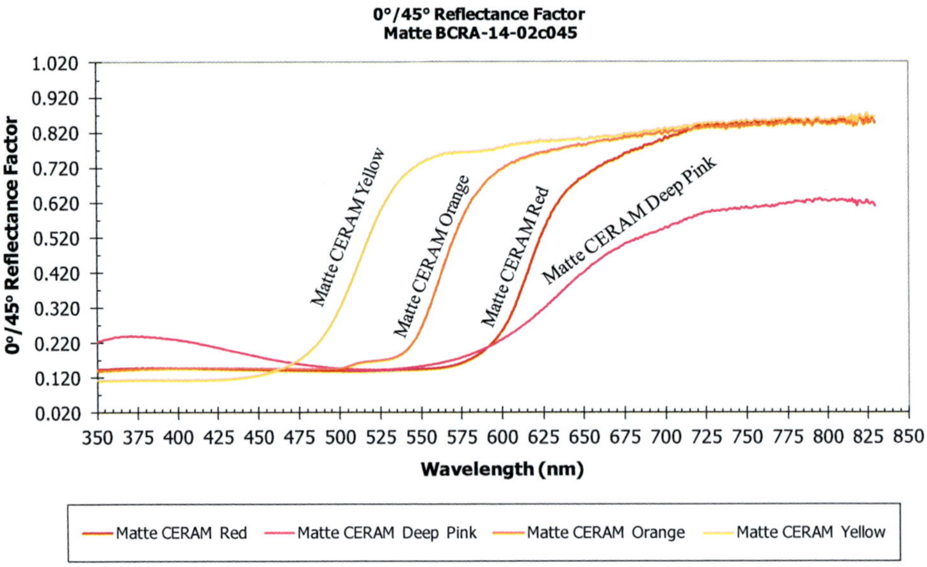

Fig. 8.4 Ceramics as Matte Red, Deep Pink, Orange, and Yellow photometric color standards measured using 0°/45° Spectral Reflectance Factor geometry with a calibrated double-monochromator instrument. (Data and spectrum used with permission from Avian Technologies, New London, NH).

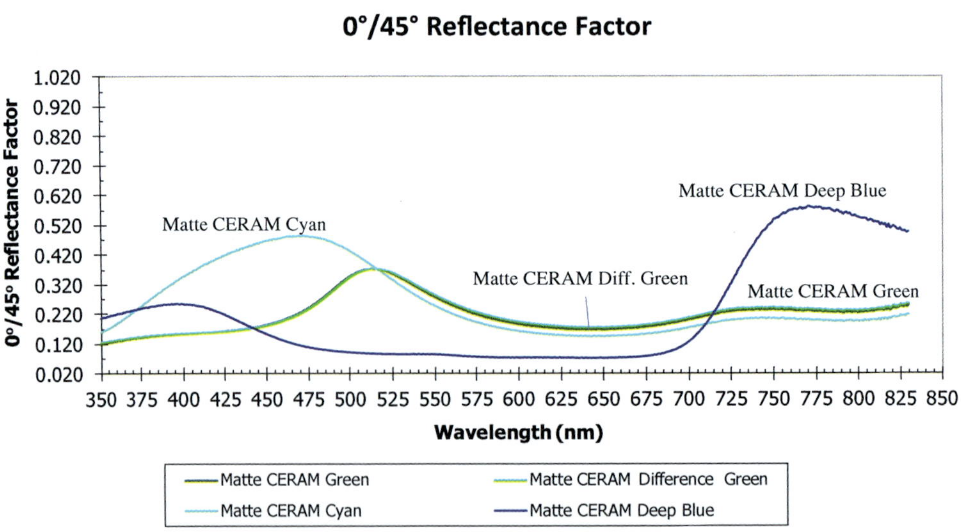

Fig. 8.5 Ceramics as Cyan, Diff. Green, Deep Blue, and Green photometric color standards measured using 0°/45° Spectral Reflectance Factor geometry with a calibrated double-monochromator instrument. (Data and spectrum used with permission from Avian Technologies, New London, NH).

Table 8.4 Reference Spectral Values for Matte Ceramic Color Standards.

Wavelength (nm)	White	Pale Grey	Mid Grey	Difference Grey	Deep Grey	Black	Red	Deep Pink	Orange	Yellow	Green	Difference Green	Cyan	Deep Blue
350	0.568	0.448	0.231	0.213	0.136	0.115	0.143	0.223	0.141	0.115	0.123	0.127	0.162	0.208
360	0.631	0.499	0.256	0.235	0.137	0.113	0.145	0.236	0.144	0.116	0.132	0.135	0.192	0.222
370	0.688	0.540	0.276	0.252	0.137	0.112	0.146	0.241	0.146	0.117	0.141	0.143	0.229	0.234
380	0.729	0.567	0.289	0.264	0.137	0.111	0.147	0.239	0.147	0.116	0.148	0.149	0.271	0.246
390	0.767	0.590	0.300	0.272	0.136	0.111	0.147	0.235	0.148	0.117	0.152	0.153	0.313	0.254
400	0.797	0.605	0.308	0.280	0.135	0.111	0.147	0.230	0.149	0.116	0.156	0.156	0.351	0.255
410	0.816	0.616	0.313	0.284	0.134	0.109	0.146	0.222	0.149	0.116	0.159	0.159	0.383	0.248
420	0.830	0.625	0.318	0.289	0.133	0.107	0.145	0.212	0.149	0.117	0.162	0.162	0.410	0.230
430	0.842	0.632	0.321	0.294	0.132	0.106	0.144	0.202	0.149	0.119	0.167	0.166	0.433	0.206
440	0.848	0.637	0.324	0.298	0.131	0.104	0.143	0.191	0.148	0.123	0.175	0.173	0.454	0.179
450	0.855	0.640	0.325	0.301	0.130	0.102	0.143	0.181	0.147	0.130	0.185	0.184	0.470	0.154
460	0.862	0.643	0.324	0.305	0.129	0.101	0.141	0.172	0.147	0.141	0.203	0.200	0.481	0.132
470	0.869	0.644	0.323	0.308	0.128	0.100	0.140	0.164	0.147	0.160	0.227	0.223	0.486	0.116
480	0.870	0.643	0.321	0.311	0.127	0.099	0.140	0.157	0.146	0.192	0.262	0.257	0.481	0.105
490	0.874	0.646	0.321	0.314	0.126	0.098	0.139	0.152	0.146	0.243	0.306	0.301	0.464	0.098
500	0.879	0.649	0.320	0.316	0.126	0.097	0.139	0.148	0.148	0.324	0.350	0.346	0.436	0.093
510	0.881	0.650	0.320	0.317	0.126	0.097	0.138	0.145	0.162	0.431	0.373	0.373	0.398	0.090
520	0.884	0.651	0.320	0.317	0.126	0.096	0.139	0.144	0.169	0.546	0.368	0.370	0.357	0.087
530	0.889	0.654	0.321	0.316	0.126	0.096	0.141	0.145	0.175	0.639	0.342	0.347	0.317	0.087
540	0.890	0.654	0.322	0.315	0.126	0.095	0.143	0.149	0.197	0.701	0.310	0.316	0.281	0.087
550	0.894	0.655	0.322	0.312	0.126	0.094	0.144	0.154	0.264	0.736	0.279	0.286	0.250	0.086
560	0.896	0.655	0.321	0.308	0.125	0.093	0.147	0.161	0.386	0.756	0.252	0.259	0.224	0.083
570	0.896	0.654	0.320	0.304	0.124	0.092	0.154	0.172	0.515	0.764	0.229	0.236	0.203	0.079
580	0.897	0.652	0.318	0.299	0.123	0.090	0.171	0.187	0.617	0.768	0.213	0.220	0.187	0.077
590	0.897	0.653	0.318	0.296	0.122	0.089	0.202	0.206	0.680	0.772	0.198	0.206	0.174	0.075

(*Continued*)

Table 8.4 (*Continued*)

Wavelength (nm)	White	Pale Grey	Mid Grey	Difference Grey	Deep Grey	Black	Red	Deep Pink	Orange	Yellow	Green	Difference Green	Cyan	Deep Blue
600	0.900	0.653	0.318	0.293	0.121	0.089	0.255	0.231	0.719	0.782	0.188	0.196	0.165	0.075
610	0.903	0.655	0.319	0.292	0.121	0.088	0.351	0.262	0.743	0.790	0.180	0.187	0.158	0.075
620	0.902	0.655	0.319	0.291	0.121	0.088	0.480	0.299	0.759	0.795	0.175	0.182	0.153	0.075
630	0.904	0.656	0.319	0.289	0.122	0.088	0.589	0.339	0.773	0.801	0.172	0.179	0.150	0.074
640	0.906	0.656	0.319	0.288	0.122	0.087	0.656	0.383	0.782	0.804	0.170	0.177	0.148	0.074
650	0.898	0.652	0.316	0.286	0.121	0.087	0.694	0.422	0.789	0.803	0.170	0.177	0.148	0.074
660	0.903	0.654	0.317	0.287	0.122	0.087	0.724	0.459	0.798	0.810	0.172	0.179	0.150	0.075
670	0.907	0.654	0.316	0.287	0.122	0.088	0.745	0.487	0.801	0.812	0.175	0.183	0.152	0.077
680	0.907	0.656	0.316	0.290	0.125	0.088	0.770	0.512	0.812	0.822	0.182	0.190	0.159	0.085
690	0.906	0.654	0.317	0.291	0.126	0.089	0.786	0.531	0.817	0.826	0.192	0.199	0.167	0.098
700	0.911	0.655	0.317	0.294	0.128	0.090	0.807	0.550	0.827	0.837	0.203	0.210	0.178	0.129
710	0.915	0.656	0.317	0.296	0.130	0.090	0.818	0.564	0.826	0.835	0.216	0.222	0.187	0.186
720	0.911	0.653	0.315	0.296	0.132	0.092	0.838	0.584	0.835	0.848	0.228	0.235	0.199	0.276
730	0.919	0.668	0.315	0.298	0.136	0.093	0.844	0.595	0.838	0.848	0.234	0.240	0.204	0.377
740	0.916	0.652	0.313	0.294	0.138	0.095	0.846	0.602	0.838	0.850	0.237	0.243	0.208	0.472
750	0.915	0.649	0.310	0.292	0.142	0.096	0.853	0.607	0.845	0.859	0.238	0.245	0.207	0.540
760	0.916	0.648	0.307	0.290	0.144	0.098	0.852	0.609	0.846	0.858	0.236	0.242	0.205	0.571
770	0.921	0.650	0.306	0.288	0.147	0.100	0.853	0.615	0.848	0.859	0.234	0.240	0.204	0.583
780	0.913	0.643	0.302	0.284	0.149	0.102	0.857	0.623	0.848	0.861	0.230	0.237	0.200	0.576
790	0.912	0.641	0.298	0.280	0.154	0.104	0.855	0.624	0.849	0.857	0.228	0.234	0.199	0.564
800	0.916	0.637	0.298	0.280	0.158	0.108	0.848	0.625	0.846	0.859	0.226	0.234	0.198	0.548
810	0.921	0.641	0.295	0.278	0.165	0.114	0.855	0.628	0.851	0.863	0.233	0.239	0.203	0.533
820	0.925	0.636	0.293	0.277	0.172	0.119	0.860	0.623	0.858	0.871	0.242	0.247	0.211	0.516
830	0.918	0.630	0.288	0.271	0.177	0.123	0.848	0.610	0.853	0.867	0.252	0.257	0.221	0.500

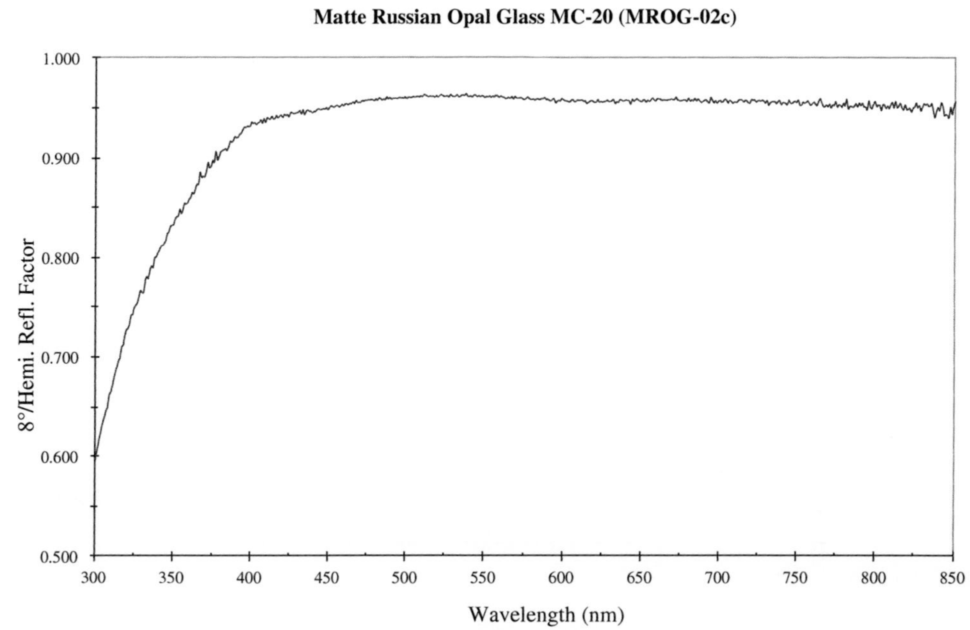

Fig. 8.6 Matte Russian Opal Glass photometric standard measured using 8°/Hemispherical Spectral Reflectance Factor geometry with a calibrated double-monochromator instrument. (Data and spectrum used with permission from Avian Technologies, New London, NH).

Table 8.5 Opal glass reflectance factor values.

Wavelength (nm)	Reflectance factor	Wavelength (nm)	Reflectance factor
300	0.596	600	0.958
310	0.665	610	0.957
320	0.727	620	0.955
330	0.765	630	0.956
340	0.805	640	0.957
350	0.833	650	0.956
360	0.858	660	0.958
370	0.880	670	0.958
380	0.906	680	0.959
390	0.920	690	0.957
400	0.935	700	0.957
410	0.940	710	0.955
420	0.940	720	0.958
430	0.945	730	0.957
440	0.946	740	0.954
450	0.950	750	0.957

(*Continued*)

Table 8.5 (*Continued*)

Wavelength (nm)	Reflectance factor	Wavelength (nm)	Reflectance factor
460	0.953	760	0.955
470	0.955	770	0.953
480	0.958	780	0.952
490	0.959	790	0.952
500	0.959	800	0.951
510	0.961	810	0.955
520	0.961	820	0.948
530	0.961	830	0.954
540	0.961	840	0.947
550	0.960	850	0.956
560	0.961		
570	0.959		
580	0.958		
590	0.958		

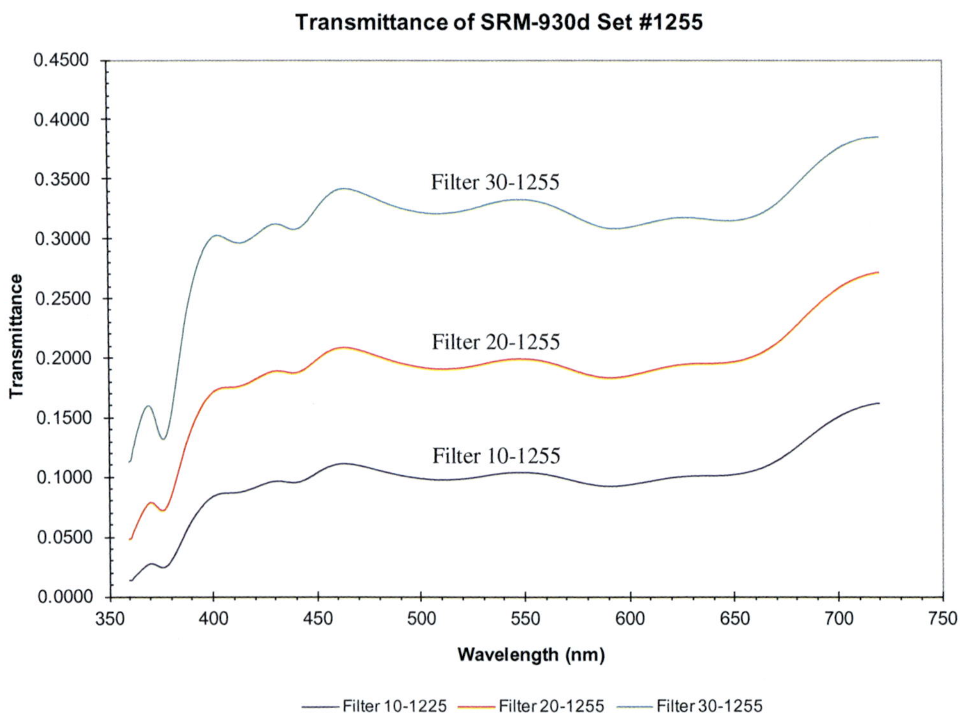

Fig. 8.7 Transmittance of SRM-930d standard set photometric standards; Filter 10-1225, Filter 20-1255, and Filter 30-1255. (Data and spectrum used with permission from Avian Technologies, New London, NH).

Table 8.6 Sit and Dwell Measurements for SRM930d at Different Concentrations (1 nm bandpass).

Sit and Dwell Measurements					
1 nm bandpass					
Transmittance at Wavelength					
Sample	440.0 nm	465.0 nm	546.1 nm	590.0 nm	635.0 nm
10-1225	0.0948	0.1106	0.1034	0.0920	0.1007
20-1225	0.1871	0.2084	0.1989	0.1833	0.1953
30-1225	0.3070	0.3411	0.3319	0.3085	0.3166
Absorbance at Wavelength					
Sample	440.0 nm	465.0 nm	546.1 nm	590.0 nm	635.0 nm
10-1225	1.0232	0.9562	0.9855	1.0362	0.9970
20-1225	0.7279	0.6811	0.7014	0.7368	0.7093
30-1225	0.5129	0.4671	0.4790	0.5107	0.4996

Averages of 16 Measurements: all nominally ±0.0002 T.

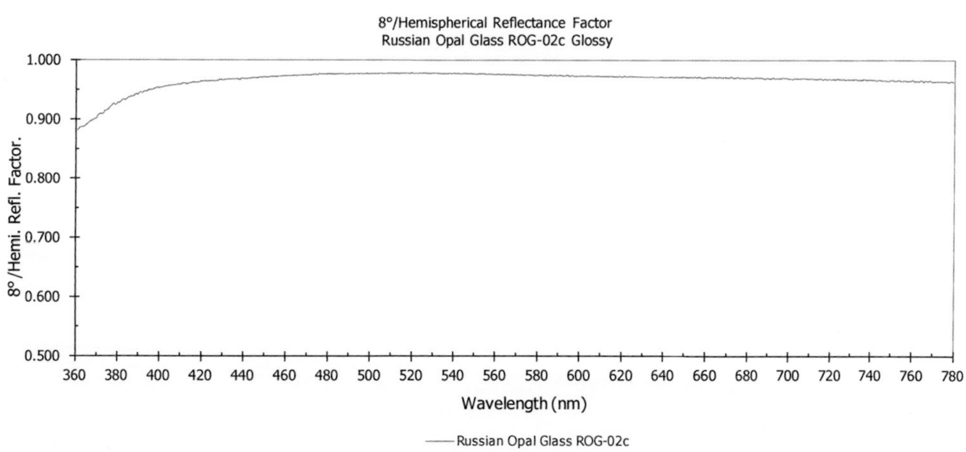

Fig. 8.8 Russian Opal Glass Glossy reflectance standard measured using 8°/Hemispherical Spectral Reflectance Factor geometry. Mean Reflectance over the spectral region shown is 0.967. Measured photometric data is given in the Table below. (Data and spectrum used with permission from Avian Technologies, New London, NH).

Table 8.7. Russian Opal Glass Glossy Reflectance Values.

Wavelength	Glossy reflectance	Wavelength	Glossy reflectance
(nm)	Factor	580	0.975
360	0.882	590	0.975
370	0.903	600	0.974
380	0.929	610	0.974
390	0.943	620	0.972
400	0.954	630	0.973
410	0.960	640	0.972
420	0.966	650	0.973
430	0.968	660	0.972
440	0.970	670	0.972
450	0.973	680	0.972
460	0.975	690	0.971
470	0.976	700	0.970
480	0.978	710	0.970
490	0.978	720	0.969
500	0.978	730	0.969
510	0.979	740	0.968
520	0.979	750	0.968
530	0.979	760	0.968
540	0.979	770	0.965
550	0.978	780	0.964
560	0.977		
570	0.976		

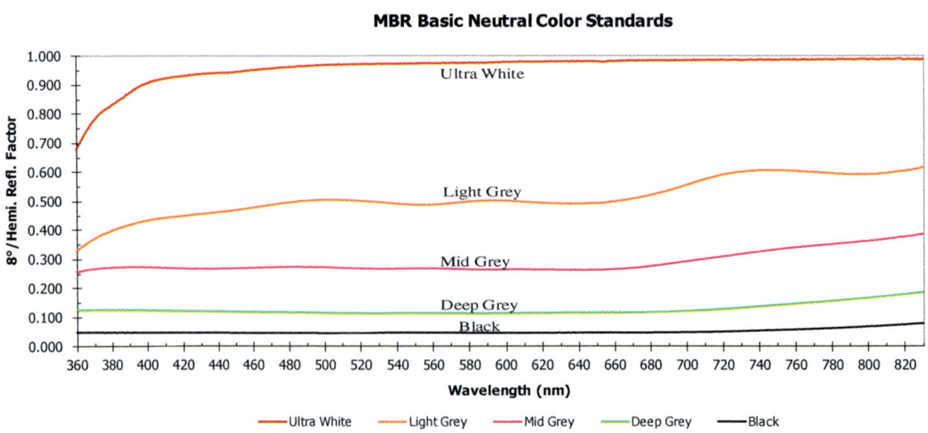

Fig. 8.9 MBR (minimum blue reflectance) reflectance wavelength reference standards measured using 8°/Hemispherical Spectral Reflectance Factor geometry and a calibrated double-monochromator instrument from 360 nm to 820 nm. (Data and spectrum used with permission from Avian Technologies, New London, NH).

Table 8.8 MBR neutral color standards reflectance data.

Wavelength (nm)	B21 Ultra White	B22 Light Grey	B23 Mid Grey	B24 Deep Grey	B25 Black
360	0.680	0.332	0.259	0.125	0.051
370	0.779	0.373	0.268	0.126	0.051
380	0.830	0.401	0.273	0.126	0.051
390	0.871	0.421	0.275	0.126	0.050
400	0.907	0.436	0.274	0.125	0.050
410	0.923	0.445	0.272	0.124	0.050
420	0.932	0.452	0.270	0.123	0.050
430	0.938	0.458	0.269	0.122	0.050
440	0.943	0.465	0.270	0.121	0.050
450	0.946	0.472	0.271	0.121	0.050
460	0.953	0.481	0.273	0.120	0.049
470	0.958	0.490	0.275	0.119	0.049
480	0.963	0.499	0.276	0.119	0.049
490	0.967	0.505	0.275	0.118	0.049
500	0.970	0.508	0.274	0.117	0.049
510	0.972	0.507	0.273	0.116	0.049
520	0.973	0.504	0.271	0.115	0.049
530	0.975	0.499	0.270	0.115	0.049
540	0.975	0.494	0.270	0.115	0.049
550	0.976	0.491	0.271	0.116	0.049
560	0.977	0.491	0.271	0.116	0.049
570	0.978	0.496	0.270	0.115	0.049
580	0.979	0.502	0.268	0.115	0.049
590	0.979	0.505	0.267	0.115	0.049
600	0.981	0.504	0.267	0.116	0.049
610	0.982	0.501	0.268	0.116	0.049
620	0.982	0.497	0.267	0.116	0.049
630	0.983	0.495	0.266	0.117	0.049
640	0.984	0.495	0.266	0.117	0.049
650	0.982	0.497	0.266	0.117	0.049
660	0.983	0.502	0.268	0.118	0.049
670	0.986	0.512	0.272	0.118	0.049
680	0.987	0.525	0.279	0.119	0.050
690	0.985	0.539	0.286	0.120	0.050
700	0.987	0.559	0.295	0.122	0.051
710	0.988	0.579	0.304	0.125	0.052
720	0.989	0.595	0.312	0.129	0.053
730	0.988	0.604	0.320	0.133	0.054
740	0.989	0.609	0.329	0.138	0.056

(*Continued*)

Table 8.8 (*Continued*)

Wavelength (nm)	B21 Ultra White	B22 Light Grey	B23 Mid Grey	B24 Deep Grey	B25 Black
750	0.988	0.608	0.336	0.143	0.058
760	0.989	0.607	0.343	0.148	0.059
770	0.988	0.603	0.349	0.153	0.061
780	0.990	0.600	0.354	0.158	0.064
790	0.990	0.596	0.360	0.164	0.066
800	0.989	0.596	0.365	0.169	0.069
810	0.991	0.600	0.372	0.176	0.072
820	0.990	0.607	0.379	0.182	0.076
830	0.991	0.619	0.389	0.190	0.080

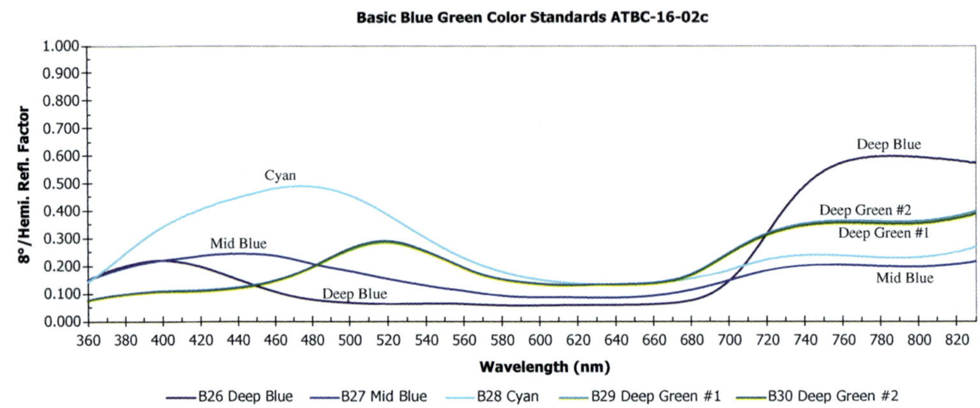

Fig. 8.10 Basic Blue Green color standards measured using 8°/Hemispherical Spectral Reflectance Factor geometry and a calibrated double-monochromator instrument from 360 nm to 820 nm. (Data and spectrum used with permission from Avian Technologies, New London, NH).

Table 8.9 MBR blue-green color standards reflectance data.

Wavelength (nm)	B26 Deep Blue	B27 Mid Blue	B28 Cyan	B29 Deep Green #1	B30 Deep Green #2
360	0.148	0.150	0.142	0.078	0.077
370	0.176	0.173	0.190	0.089	0.089
380	0.198	0.194	0.243	0.098	0.097
390	0.213	0.209	0.294	0.106	0.104
400	0.219	0.220	0.340	0.110	0.108
410	0.212	0.229	0.376	0.112	0.109
420	0.197	0.237	0.404	0.114	0.111

(*Continued*)

Table 8.9 (*Continued*)

Wavelength (nm)	B26 Deep Blue	B27 Mid Blue	B28 Cyan	B29 Deep Green #1	B30 Deep Green #2
430	0.175	0.244	0.428	0.119	0.115
440	0.151	0.246	0.448	0.125	0.122
450	0.127	0.245	0.465	0.135	0.132
460	0.106	0.238	0.480	0.150	0.148
470	0.089	0.225	0.488	0.170	0.169
480	0.077	0.209	0.487	0.197	0.198
490	0.070	0.195	0.477	0.230	0.232
500	0.066	0.183	0.456	0.259	0.263
510	0.063	0.168	0.424	0.280	0.285
520	0.061	0.154	0.384	0.287	0.292
530	0.060	0.141	0.342	0.275	0.279
540	0.061	0.130	0.301	0.253	0.255
550	0.062	0.119	0.263	0.226	0.226
560	0.060	0.110	0.230	0.196	0.195
570	0.057	0.100	0.202	0.170	0.169
580	0.055	0.092	0.180	0.155	0.153
590	0.055	0.087	0.164	0.145	0.143
600	0.055	0.086	0.152	0.138	0.136
610	0.056	0.086	0.143	0.135	0.132
620	0.056	0.085	0.138	0.135	0.132
630	0.056	0.084	0.134	0.136	0.133
640	0.057	0.084	0.133	0.136	0.133
650	0.057	0.087	0.135	0.137	0.134
660	0.059	0.092	0.138	0.140	0.137
670	0.063	0.100	0.145	0.151	0.148
680	0.073	0.113	0.155	0.173	0.169
690	0.096	0.129	0.169	0.208	0.205
700	0.144	0.148	0.187	0.250	0.246
710	0.221	0.167	0.207	0.289	0.284
720	0.318	0.184	0.224	0.319	0.315
730	0.413	0.195	0.235	0.341	0.336
740	0.492	0.202	0.240	0.355	0.349
750	0.546	0.205	0.241	0.363	0.357
760	0.577	0.204	0.238	0.365	0.359
770	0.593	0.202	0.235	0.364	0.357
780	0.599	0.200	0.231	0.363	0.356
790	0.600	0.198	0.230	0.362	0.355
800	0.596	0.198	0.231	0.364	0.356
810	0.590	0.201	0.238	0.370	0.363
820	0.584	0.206	0.251	0.382	0.375
830	0.574	0.216	0.269	0.398	0.391

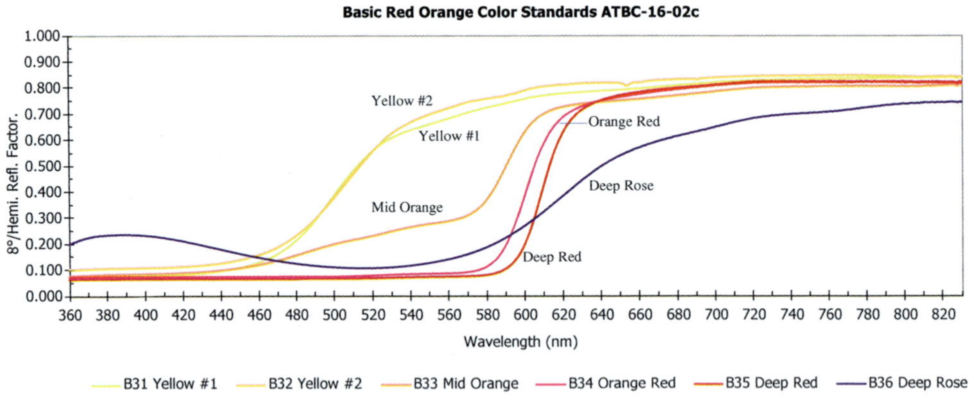

Fig. 8.11 Basic Red Orange color standards measured using 8°/Hemispherical Spectral Reflectance Factor geometry and a calibrated double-monochromator instrument from 360 nm to 820 nm. (Data and spectrum used with permission from Avian Technologies, New London, NH).

Table 8.10 MBR red-orange color standards reflectance data.

Wavelength (nm)	B31 Yellow #1	B32 Yellow #2	B33 Mid Orange	B34 Orange Red	B35 Deep Red	B36 Deep Rose
360	0.071	0.103	0.079	0.073	0.064	0.196
370	0.074	0.106	0.082	0.074	0.064	0.221
380	0.076	0.108	0.085	0.074	0.065	0.231
390	0.078	0.110	0.086	0.074	0.065	0.234
400	0.079	0.111	0.088	0.075	0.065	0.231
410	0.081	0.112	0.089	0.075	0.065	0.222
420	0.084	0.115	0.092	0.075	0.065	0.209
430	0.089	0.120	0.096	0.075	0.065	0.193
440	0.097	0.128	0.102	0.075	0.065	0.177
450	0.110	0.141	0.110	0.075	0.065	0.160
460	0.130	0.160	0.122	0.075	0.065	0.145
470	0.162	0.189	0.139	0.075	0.065	0.132
480	0.213	0.233	0.159	0.075	0.066	0.122
490	0.288	0.296	0.181	0.076	0.066	0.114
500	0.385	0.377	0.202	0.076	0.066	0.108
510	0.481	0.469	0.218	0.076	0.066	0.105
520	0.558	0.556	0.234	0.078	0.067	0.105

(*Continued*)

Table 8.10 (*Continued*)

Wavelength (nm)	B31 Yellow #1	B32 Yellow #2	B33 Mid Orange	B34 Orange Red	B35 Deep Red	B36 Deep Rose
530	0.607	0.625	0.251	0.081	0.069	0.108
540	0.638	0.670	0.267	0.083	0.071	0.114
550	0.662	0.700	0.279	0.085	0.072	0.125
560	0.684	0.724	0.290	0.086	0.073	0.139
570	0.708	0.747	0.312	0.091	0.075	0.159
580	0.726	0.761	0.373	0.112	0.080	0.186
590	0.743	0.772	0.498	0.195	0.103	0.222
600	0.759	0.792	0.631	0.386	0.198	0.268
610	0.772	0.807	0.702	0.587	0.428	0.323
620	0.780	0.814	0.729	0.687	0.628	0.384
630	0.786	0.819	0.741	0.730	0.714	0.444
640	0.790	0.821	0.747	0.751	0.751	0.497
650	0.794	0.820	0.753	0.765	0.770	0.539
660	0.799	0.822	0.759	0.776	0.782	0.570
670	0.806	0.832	0.766	0.786	0.791	0.595
680	0.811	0.835	0.773	0.794	0.798	0.614
690	0.817	0.834	0.780	0.802	0.804	0.631
700	0.823	0.842	0.788	0.810	0.811	0.649
710	0.827	0.845	0.795	0.815	0.817	0.667
720	0.830	0.847	0.802	0.819	0.822	0.683
730	0.832	0.848	0.804	0.820	0.823	0.693
740	0.833	0.848	0.806	0.821	0.823	0.698
750	0.835	0.848	0.807	0.821	0.823	0.703
760	0.837	0.850	0.807	0.821	0.823	0.708
770	0.837	0.849	0.806	0.820	0.822	0.715
780	0.838	0.850	0.807	0.821	0.823	0.724
790	0.839	0.848	0.807	0.820	0.822	0.732
800	0.838	0.845	0.805	0.818	0.820	0.738
810	0.837	0.843	0.807	0.818	0.819	0.742
820	0.839	0.844	0.809	0.818	0.819	0.744
830	0.838	0.842	0.810	0.816	0.818	0.744

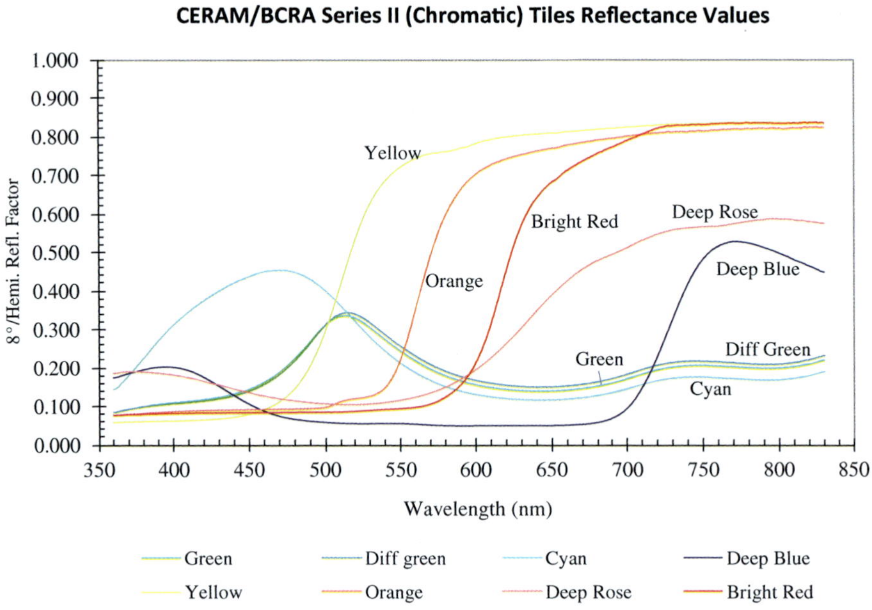

Fig. 8.12 Basic CERAM/BCRA (British Ceramic Research series II) Chromatic Tiles measured using 8°/Hemispherical Spectral Reflectance Factor geometry and a calibrated double-monochromator instrument from 360 nm to 820 nm. (Data and spectrum used with permission from Avian Technologies, New London, NH).

Table 8.11 CERAM/BCRA Series II (Chromatic) tiles reflectance values.

Wavelength (nm)	Green	Diff green	Cyan	Deep Blue	Yellow	Orange	Deep Rose	Bright Red
360	0.085	0.085	0.144	0.175	0.061	0.076	0.186	0.075
370	0.093	0.093	0.181	0.185	0.063	0.079	0.190	0.077
380	0.100	0.099	0.226	0.195	0.064	0.081	0.189	0.078
390	0.106	0.103	0.271	0.202	0.065	0.084	0.187	0.079
400	0.110	0.107	0.312	0.201	0.066	0.086	0.182	0.080
410	0.113	0.110	0.345	0.193	0.067	0.087	0.175	0.081
420	0.118	0.114	0.374	0.176	0.068	0.089	0.165	0.081
430	0.124	0.120	0.399	0.153	0.071	0.089	0.155	0.081
440	0.132	0.127	0.421	0.129	0.075	0.090	0.145	0.082
450	0.144	0.139	0.437	0.107	0.082	0.091	0.136	0.082
460	0.162	0.156	0.450	0.089	0.094	0.091	0.127	0.082
470	0.188	0.181	0.454	0.076	0.113	0.092	0.120	0.082

(*Continued*)

Table 8.11 (*Continued*)

Wavelength (nm)	Green	Diff green	Cyan	Deep Blue	Yellow	Orange	Deep Rose	Bright Red
480	0.224	0.216	0.449	0.067	0.147	0.092	0.115	0.083
490	0.268	0.262	0.431	0.062	0.204	0.094	0.110	0.083
500	0.312	0.310	0.402	0.059	0.295	0.096	0.107	0.083
510	0.335	0.338	0.363	0.057	0.413	0.111	0.105	0.084
520	0.330	0.338	0.321	0.056	0.534	0.119	0.105	0.085
530	0.305	0.315	0.279	0.056	0.630	0.126	0.106	0.088
540	0.274	0.285	0.242	0.056	0.690	0.149	0.110	0.090
550	0.244	0.255	0.211	0.056	0.725	0.222	0.116	0.092
560	0.218	0.229	0.186	0.055	0.747	0.352	0.124	0.096
570	0.196	0.207	0.166	0.052	0.760	0.490	0.135	0.104
580	0.179	0.190	0.150	0.051	0.766	0.594	0.150	0.122
590	0.166	0.177	0.139	0.050	0.774	0.660	0.170	0.154
600	0.156	0.167	0.130	0.051	0.786	0.701	0.195	0.211
610	0.149	0.159	0.123	0.051	0.797	0.725	0.227	0.314
620	0.144	0.154	0.119	0.051	0.803	0.740	0.264	0.452
630	0.141	0.151	0.116	0.051	0.808	0.752	0.306	0.568
640	0.140	0.150	0.115	0.051	0.811	0.761	0.349	0.640
650	0.140	0.150	0.116	0.051	0.814	0.768	0.391	0.681
660	0.142	0.153	0.118	0.052	0.818	0.776	0.427	0.711
670	0.146	0.157	0.122	0.054	0.820	0.783	0.457	0.735
680	0.153	0.163	0.127	0.059	0.824	0.790	0.480	0.756
690	0.162	0.172	0.135	0.071	0.826	0.794	0.496	0.772
700	0.173	0.183	0.145	0.099	0.830	0.800	0.514	0.790
710	0.185	0.196	0.157	0.153	0.832	0.804	0.533	0.806
720	0.196	0.206	0.166	0.235	0.834	0.808	0.549	0.821
730	0.203	0.213	0.173	0.332	0.836	0.810	0.560	0.827
740	0.206	0.216	0.175	0.421	0.838	0.811	0.565	0.829
750	0.207	0.216	0.175	0.483	0.838	0.813	0.568	0.830
760	0.205	0.215	0.173	0.515	0.840	0.815	0.569	0.833
770	0.203	0.212	0.171	0.526	0.842	0.818	0.576	0.834
780	0.200	0.209	0.169	0.522	0.842	0.819	0.582	0.834
790	0.199	0.208	0.167	0.510	0.841	0.820	0.586	0.835
800	0.200	0.209	0.168	0.496	0.842	0.820	0.588	0.834
810	0.204	0.213	0.172	0.479	0.840	0.821	0.585	0.835
820	0.211	0.220	0.179	0.463	0.842	0.823	0.581	0.835
830	0.220	0.230	0.189	0.448	0.841	0.823	0.576	0.835

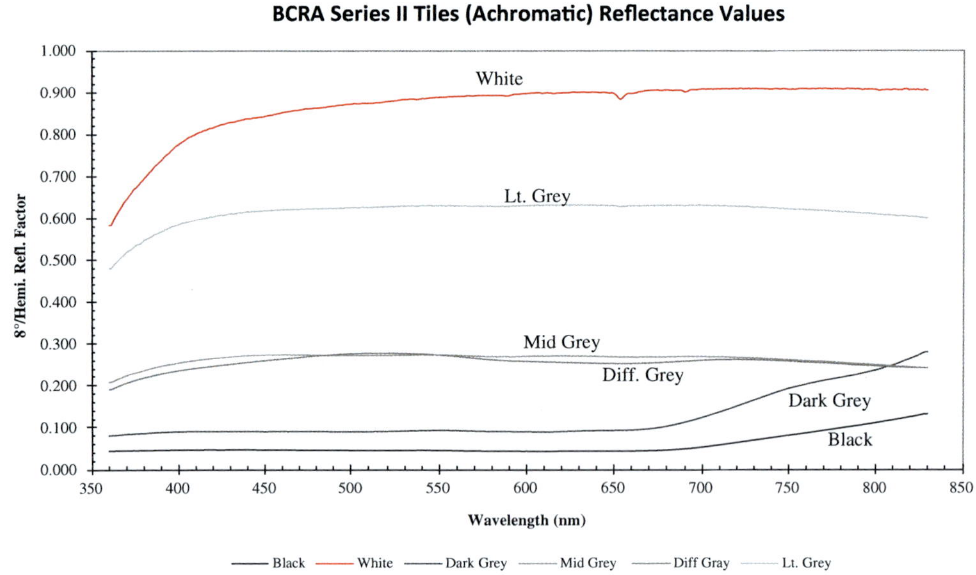

Fig. 8.13 Basic BCRA (British Ceramic Research Series II) Achromatic Tiles measured using 8°/Hemispherical Spectral Reflectance Factor geometry and a calibrated double-monochromator instrument from 360 nm to 820 nm. (Data and spectrum used with permission from Avian Technologies, New London, NH).

Table 8.12 BCRA Series II tiles (Achromatic) reflectance values.

Wavelength (nm)	Black	White	Dark Grey	Mid Grey	Diff Gray	Lt. Grey
360	0.046	0.584	0.080	0.206	0.480	0.478
370	0.046	0.647	0.083	0.222	0.519	0.515
380	0.047	0.696	0.085	0.235	0.547	0.543
390	0.047	0.740	0.088	0.246	0.568	0.566
400	0.048	0.776	0.089	0.254	0.585	0.582
410	0.048	0.801	0.089	0.260	0.596	0.593
420	0.048	0.816	0.090	0.265	0.604	0.601
430	0.048	0.828	0.089	0.269	0.611	0.607
440	0.048	0.837	0.089	0.272	0.615	0.612
450	0.048	0.843	0.089	0.273	0.618	0.615
460	0.048	0.851	0.089	0.274	0.621	0.617
470	0.048	0.857	0.089	0.273	0.622	0.619
480	0.047	0.862	0.089	0.272	0.623	0.620

(*Continued*)

Table 8.12 (*Continued*)

Wavelength (nm)	Black	White	Dark Grey	Mid Grey	Diff Gray	Lt. Grey
490	0.047	0.867	0.089	0.272	0.624	0.621
500	0.047	0.872	0.089	0.272	0.626	0.622
510	0.047	0.873	0.089	0.272	0.626	0.623
520	0.047	0.877	0.090	0.272	0.628	0.625
530	0.047	0.882	0.091	0.273	0.630	0.626
540	0.047	0.884	0.092	0.273	0.631	0.627
550	0.047	0.888	0.092	0.273	0.631	0.627
560	0.046	0.890	0.092	0.272	0.630	0.627
570	0.046	0.891	0.090	0.270	0.629	0.626
580	0.045	0.892	0.090	0.269	0.628	0.625
590	0.045	0.892	0.089	0.269	0.628	0.625
600	0.045	0.897	0.089	0.270	0.629	0.627
610	0.045	0.897	0.089	0.270	0.631	0.627
620	0.045	0.898	0.089	0.270	0.631	0.628
630	0.045	0.899	0.091	0.270	0.631	0.627
640	0.045	0.899	0.092	0.269	0.630	0.627
650	0.045	0.895	0.092	0.268	0.629	0.626
660	0.045	0.896	0.093	0.268	0.629	0.625
670	0.046	0.904	0.096	0.268	0.629	0.626
680	0.047	0.905	0.102	0.268	0.630	0.626
690	0.050	0.900	0.111	0.269	0.629	0.627
700	0.054	0.907	0.122	0.269	0.630	0.627
710	0.060	0.907	0.135	0.268	0.629	0.626
720	0.065	0.907	0.149	0.267	0.628	0.625
730	0.071	0.908	0.164	0.266	0.626	0.624
740	0.077	0.907	0.178	0.264	0.624	0.621
750	0.083	0.907	0.192	0.262	0.622	0.620
760	0.088	0.908	0.202	0.259	0.620	0.616
770	0.094	0.909	0.211	0.257	0.618	0.616
780	0.100	0.908	0.218	0.255	0.615	0.614
790	0.106	0.908	0.226	0.252	0.613	0.610
800	0.113	0.906	0.235	0.249	0.610	0.607
810	0.120	0.906	0.247	0.246	0.607	0.604
820	0.127	0.906	0.263	0.244	0.604	0.601
830	0.134	0.904	0.279	0.241	0.600	0.599

Table 8.13 Standards: BCRA-G-GS9-02c (8°/Hemi. Reflectance).

Wavelength (nm)	BCRA (1)	BCRA (2)	BCRA (3)	BCRA (4)	BCRA (5)	BCRA (6)	BCRA (7)	BCRA (8)	BCRA (9)	BCRA (10)	BG-02c
(nm)	White	80%	70%	Pale Grey	50%	40%	33%	Mid Grey	Deep Grey	Black	Black Glass
360	0.595	0.597	0.555	0.479	0.437	0.355	0.280	0.195	0.090	0.056	0.056
370	0.663	0.659	0.607	0.522	0.461	0.372	0.309	0.214	0.091	0.055	0.055
380	0.713	0.706	0.644	0.550	0.477	0.383	0.328	0.228	0.091	0.054	0.054
390	0.758	0.744	0.672	0.572	0.490	0.393	0.342	0.240	0.092	0.054	0.054
400	0.794	0.771	0.691	0.589	0.500	0.401	0.352	0.249	0.092	0.055	0.055
410	0.819	0.787	0.704	0.600	0.509	0.409	0.360	0.255	0.092	0.054	0.054
420	0.834	0.796	0.711	0.608	0.515	0.415	0.364	0.260	0.091	0.053	0.053
430	0.846	0.802	0.717	0.615	0.521	0.421	0.368	0.265	0.091	0.052	0.052
440	0.851	0.804	0.719	0.619	0.525	0.424	0.370	0.268	0.091	0.051	0.051
450	0.858	0.806	0.720	0.622	0.528	0.428	0.371	0.270	0.090	0.051	0.051
460	0.865	0.809	0.722	0.624	0.530	0.429	0.370	0.270	0.090	0.050	0.050
470	0.872	0.810	0.722	0.626	0.529	0.429	0.369	0.270	0.089	0.050	0.050
480	0.875	0.812	0.723	0.627	0.530	0.429	0.367	0.269	0.089	0.050	0.050
490	0.880	0.813	0.723	0.628	0.529	0.428	0.366	0.269	0.089	0.050	0.050
500	0.884	0.814	0.723	0.629	0.528	0.428	0.365	0.269	0.089	0.049	0.049
510	0.886	0.814	0.723	0.630	0.528	0.428	0.365	0.269	0.090	0.050	0.050
520	0.889	0.815	0.724	0.632	0.527	0.428	0.365	0.270	0.091	0.050	0.050

(Continued)

Table 8.13 (*Continued*)

Wavelength (nm)	BCRA (1)	BCRA (2)	BCRA (3)	BCRA (4)	BCRA (5)	BCRA (6)	BCRA (7)	BCRA (8)	BCRA (9)	BCRA (10)	BG-02c
(nm)	White	80%	70%	Pale Grey	50%	40%	33%	Mid Grey	Deep Grey	Black	Black Glass
530	0.893	0.816	0.724	0.633	0.527	0.428	0.367	0.270	0.091	0.050	0.050
540	0.895	0.816	0.724	0.634	0.527	0.428	0.368	0.271	0.092	0.050	0.050
550	0.897	0.817	0.724	0.635	0.526	0.427	0.370	0.271	0.092	0.050	0.050
560	0.899	0.816	0.722	0.634	0.524	0.425	0.370	0.270	0.092	0.049	0.049
570	0.901	0.816	0.721	0.633	0.522	0.423	0.368	0.268	0.091	0.048	0.048
580	0.901	0.814	0.719	0.632	0.520	0.421	0.367	0.267	0.091	0.048	0.048
590	0.900	0.815	0.719	0.632	0.520	0.421	0.368	0.267	0.091	0.048	0.048
600	0.904	0.817	0.720	0.633	0.523	0.422	0.369	0.268	0.090	0.048	0.048
610	0.906	0.817	0.720	0.634	0.524	0.424	0.370	0.269	0.091	0.048	0.048
620	0.906	0.816	0.719	0.634	0.525	0.424	0.371	0.270	0.091	0.048	0.048
630	0.908	0.817	0.719	0.635	0.525	0.424	0.371	0.270	0.092	0.048	0.048
640	0.907	0.817	0.718	0.633	0.525	0.423	0.370	0.269	0.092	0.048	0.048
650	0.904	0.816	0.716	0.633	0.524	0.422	0.370	0.269	0.092	0.048	0.048
660	0.904	0.816	0.716	0.632	0.524	0.422	0.370	0.269	0.093	0.048	0.048
670	0.911	0.817	0.716	0.633	0.524	0.422	0.371	0.269	0.094	0.049	0.049
680	0.913	0.817	0.716	0.633	0.526	0.422	0.372	0.270	0.096	0.049	0.049
690	0.909	0.816	0.716	0.632	0.527	0.422	0.373	0.271	0.097	0.050	0.050

(*Continued*)

Table 8.13 (*Continued*)

Wavelength (nm)	BCRA (1)	BCRA (2)	BCRA (3)	BCRA (4)	BCRA (5)	BCRA (6)	BCRA (7)	BCRA (8)	BCRA (9)	BCRA (10)	BG-02c
700	0.914	0.817	0.715	0.633	0.527	0.422	0.375	0.272	0.099	0.050	0.050
710	0.916	0.816	0.713	0.633	0.526	0.421	0.375	0.272	0.101	0.051	0.051
720	0.916	0.817	0.713	0.631	0.525	0.419	0.373	0.271	0.103	0.052	0.052
730	0.916	0.816	0.712	0.629	0.523	0.416	0.372	0.269	0.106	0.053	0.053
740	0.914	0.814	0.709	0.626	0.520	0.413	0.370	0.267	0.109	0.055	0.055
750	0.916	0.813	0.706	0.625	0.517	0.411	0.368	0.266	0.112	0.057	0.057
760	0.915	0.814	0.705	0.622	0.515	0.408	0.365	0.264	0.115	0.059	0.059
770	0.916	0.811	0.703	0.620	0.512	0.404	0.363	0.262	0.117	0.060	0.060
780	0.915	0.811	0.701	0.618	0.509	0.401	0.360	0.259	0.120	0.062	0.062
790	0.915	0.811	0.699	0.615	0.505	0.398	0.357	0.257	0.123	0.065	0.065
800	0.914	0.809	0.696	0.612	0.502	0.394	0.355	0.254	0.128	0.069	0.069
810	0.913	0.808	0.694	0.609	0.498	0.390	0.352	0.252	0.133	0.073	0.073
820	0.914	0.807	0.691	0.606	0.494	0.386	0.349	0.249	0.140	0.078	0.078
830	0.912	0.807	0.689	0.603	0.490	0.382	0.346	0.246	0.147	0.085	0.085

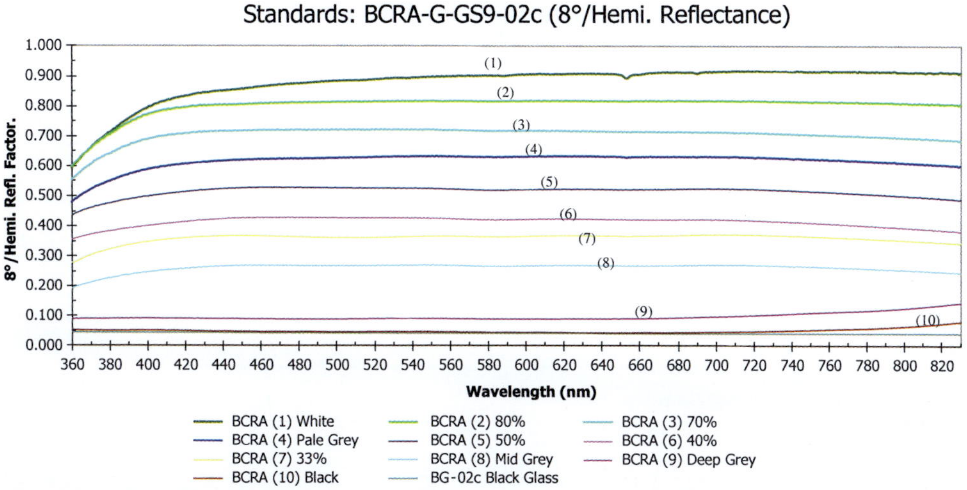

Fig. 8.14 BCRA (British Ceramic Research) G-GS9-02c Standards measured using 8°/ Hemispherical Spectral Reflectance Factor geometry and a calibrated double-monochromator instrument from 360 nm to 820 nm. (Data and spectrum used with permission from Avian Technologies, New London, NH).

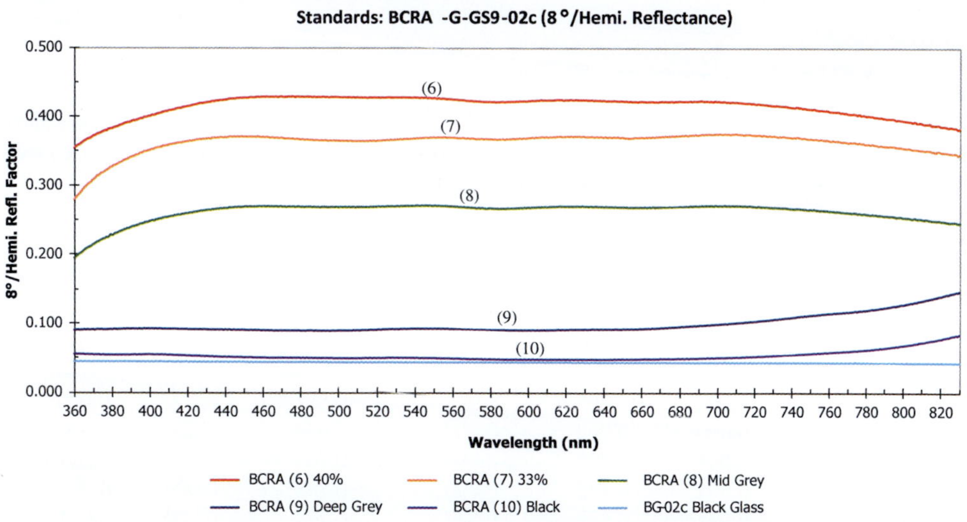

Fig. 8.15 BCRA (British Ceramic Research) G-GS9-02c Standards measured using 8°/ Hemispherical Spectral Reflectance Factor geometry and a calibrated double-monochromator instrument from 360 nm to 820 nm. (Data and spectrum used with permission from Avian Technologies, New London, NH).

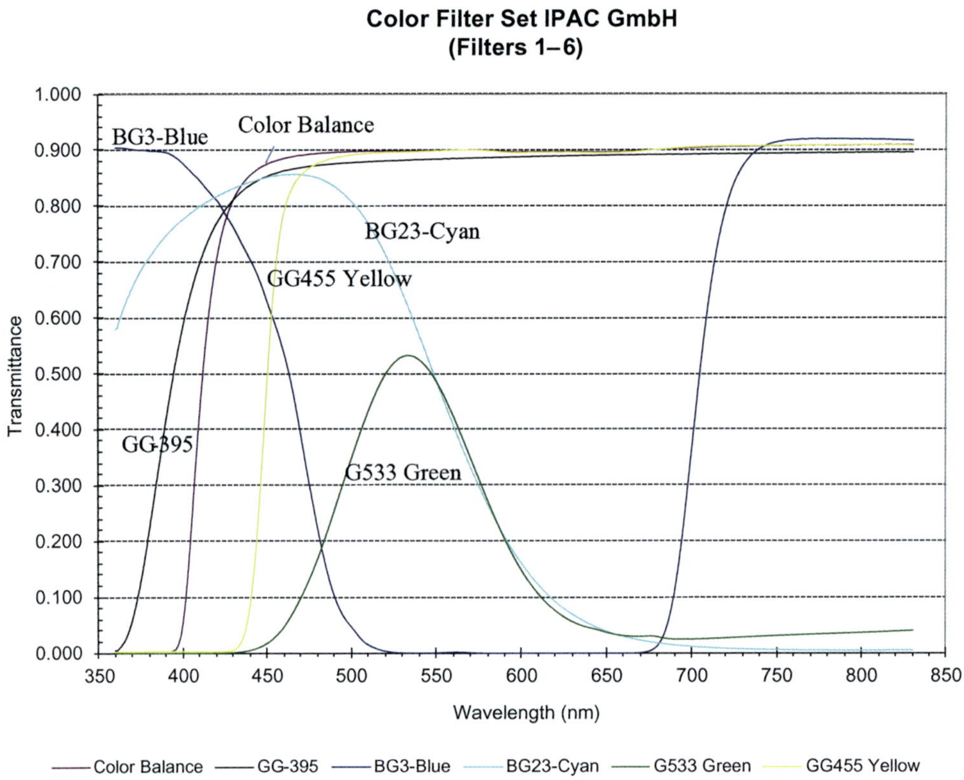

Fig. 8.16 IPAC GmbH Color Standards measured using Transmittance measurement geometry and a calibrated double-monochromator instrument from 350 nm to 830 nm. (Data and spectrum used with permission from Avian Technologies, New London, NH).

Table 8.14 Color filter set from IPAC GmbH (Filters 1–6).

Wavelength (nm)	Color Balance	GG-395	BG3-Blue	BG23-Cyan	G533 Green	GG455 Yellow
360	0.000	0.005	0.904	0.581	0.000	0.000
370	0.000	0.062	0.902	0.656	0.000	0.000
380	0.001	0.225	0.899	0.708	0.000	0.001
390	0.001	0.422	0.896	0.748	0.000	0.001
400	0.055	0.585	0.877	0.777	0.000	0.001
410	0.430	0.698	0.846	0.800	0.000	0.001
420	0.702	0.768	0.811	0.818	0.000	0.001
430	0.811	0.812	0.762	0.832	0.001	0.003
440	0.855	0.837	0.704	0.844	0.005	0.084

(*Continued*)

Table 8.14 (*Continued*)

Wavelength (nm)	Color Balance	GG-395	BG3-Blue	BG23-Cyan	G533 Green	GG455 Yellow
450	0.874	0.853	0.629	0.852	0.018	0.487
460	0.884	0.863	0.537	0.857	0.048	0.786
470	0.889	0.868	0.390	0.857	0.100	0.854
480	0.893	0.873	0.225	0.851	0.169	0.875
490	0.895	0.876	0.103	0.835	0.256	0.885
500	0.896	0.877	0.048	0.807	0.351	0.890
510	0.897	0.879	0.015	0.767	0.436	0.893
520	0.897	0.881	0.004	0.712	0.500	0.895
530	0.897	0.881	0.001	0.643	0.531	0.895
540	0.897	0.883	0.000	0.566	0.524	0.896
550	0.898	0.883	0.001	0.485	0.484	0.897
560	0.898	0.885	0.002	0.405	0.422	0.899
570	0.899	0.885	0.001	0.330	0.347	0.899
580	0.898	0.886	0.000	0.263	0.271	0.897
590	0.896	0.887	0.000	0.207	0.203	0.895
600	0.895	0.888	0.000	0.159	0.147	0.894
610	0.896	0.888	0.000	0.121	0.105	0.895
620	0.896	0.889	0.000	0.092	0.076	0.895
630	0.896	0.889	0.000	0.069	0.056	0.895
640	0.895	0.890	0.000	0.052	0.045	0.894
650	0.895	0.890	0.000	0.039	0.037	0.894
660	0.896	0.891	0.000	0.030	0.031	0.895
670	0.898	0.891	0.001	0.023	0.030	0.897
680	0.900	0.892	0.015	0.018	0.029	0.900
690	0.902	0.892	0.121	0.014	0.025	0.903
700	0.903	0.892	0.384	0.012	0.025	0.905
710	0.904	0.893	0.646	0.010	0.026	0.906
720	0.905	0.893	0.803	0.009	0.027	0.906
730	0.905	0.893	0.875	0.007	0.029	0.906
740	0.906	0.894	0.904	0.007	0.030	0.907
750	0.906	0.894	0.915	0.006	0.032	0.907
760	0.906	0.894	0.918	0.006	0.033	0.907
770	0.907	0.894	0.920	0.005	0.034	0.908
780	0.908	0.895	0.920	0.005	0.035	0.908
790	0.908	0.895	0.920	0.005	0.036	0.908
800	0.908	0.895	0.919	0.005	0.037	0.908
810	0.908	0.896	0.919	0.005	0.038	0.908
820	0.908	0.896	0.918	0.005	0.039	0.908
830	0.908	0.896	0.917	0.005	0.041	0.907

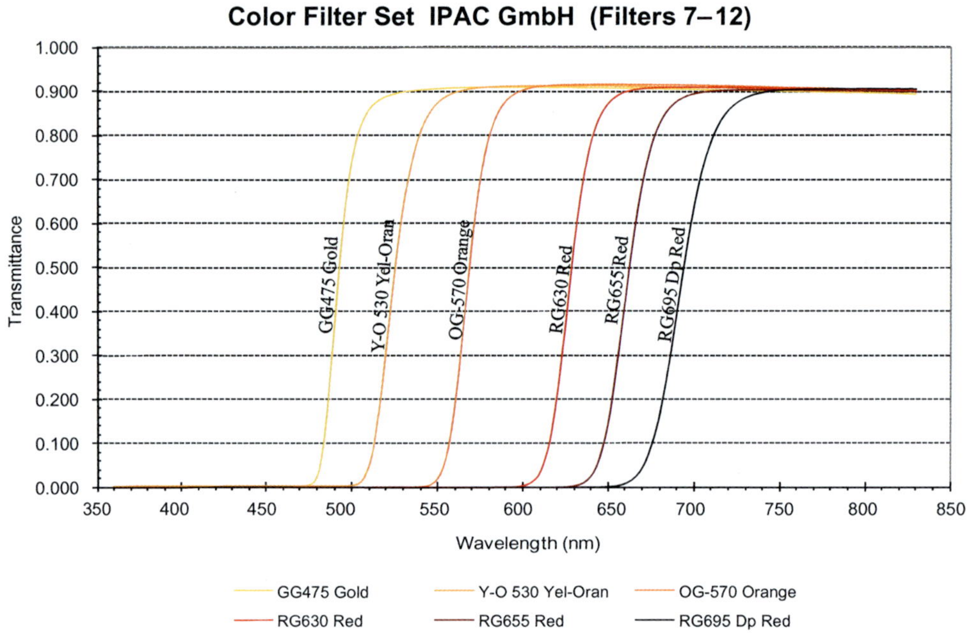

Fig. 8.17 IPAC GmbH Color Standards measured using Transmittance measurement geometry and a calibrated double-monochromator instrument from 350 nm to 830 nm. (Data and spectrum used with permission from Avian Technologies, New London, NH).

Table 8.15 Color filter set IPAC GmbH (Filters 7–12).

Wavelength (nm)	GG475 Gold	Y-O530 Yel-Oran	OG-570 Orange	RG630 Red	RG655 Red	RG695 Dp Red
360	0.000	0.000	0.000	0.000	0.000	0.000
370	0.000	0.000	0.000	0.000	0.000	0.000
380	0.001	0.001	0.001	0.000	0.000	0.000
390	0.001	0.001	0.000	0.000	0.000	0.000
400	0.001	0.001	0.000	0.000	0.000	0.000
410	0.001	0.001	0.000	0.000	0.000	0.000
420	0.001	0.001	0.000	0.000	0.000	0.000
430	0.001	0.000	0.000	0.000	0.000	0.000
440	0.000	0.000	0.000	0.000	0.000	0.000
450	0.001	0.000	0.000	0.000	0.000	0.000
460	0.000	0.000	0.000	0.000	0.000	0.000
470	0.000	0.000	0.000	0.000	0.000	0.000

(*Continued*)

Table 8.15 (*Continued*)

Wavelength (nm)	GG475 Gold	Y-O530 Yel-Oran	OG-570 Orange	RG630 Red	RG655 Red	RG695 Dp Red
480	0.019	0.000	0.000	0.000	0.000	0.000
490	0.371	0.000	0.000	0.000	0.000	0.000
500	0.750	0.001	0.000	0.000	0.000	0.000
510	0.861	0.043	0.000	0.000	0.000	0.000
520	0.889	0.307	0.000	0.000	0.000	0.000
530	0.899	0.643	0.000	0.000	0.000	0.000
540	0.904	0.814	0.001	0.000	0.000	0.000
550	0.907	0.875	0.018	0.000	0.000	0.000
560	0.908	0.896	0.185	0.000	0.000	0.000
570	0.909	0.905	0.563	0.000	0.000	0.000
580	0.910	0.908	0.802	0.000	0.000	0.000
590	0.910	0.910	0.881	0.001	0.000	0.000
600	0.910	0.910	0.904	0.003	0.000	0.000
610	0.910	0.911	0.912	0.032	0.000	0.000
620	0.909	0.911	0.915	0.206	0.001	0.000
630	0.909	0.911	0.916	0.558	0.003	0.000
640	0.908	0.911	0.917	0.791	0.025	0.000
650	0.908	0.910	0.917	0.873	0.144	0.002
660	0.907	0.910	0.916	0.898	0.430	0.008
670	0.907	0.910	0.916	0.905	0.702	0.043
680	0.906	0.909	0.916	0.907	0.832	0.163
690	0.906	0.909	0.916	0.908	0.879	0.401
700	0.905	0.908	0.915	0.908	0.895	0.644
710	0.904	0.907	0.914	0.907	0.901	0.791
720	0.903	0.907	0.914	0.907	0.903	0.858
730	0.902	0.906	0.912	0.906	0.904	0.886
740	0.902	0.905	0.911	0.906	0.903	0.897
750	0.901	0.905	0.910	0.905	0.903	0.902
760	0.900	0.904	0.909	0.904	0.903	0.904
770	0.900	0.903	0.908	0.904	0.902	0.905
780	0.899	0.903	0.907	0.903	0.902	0.905
790	0.898	0.902	0.907	0.903	0.902	0.906
800	0.898	0.901	0.905	0.902	0.901	0.905
810	0.897	0.900	0.904	0.901	0.901	0.906
820	0.895	0.899	0.902	0.900	0.900	0.905
830	0.894	0.898	0.901	0.899	0.899	0.904

Table 8.16 Color filter set CFS-12-02c (Cut-off Filters) total transmittance (5 nm increments).

Wavelength (nm)	GG395	GG455	GG475	OG515	OG530	OG550	OG570	OG590	RG610	RG630	RG665	RG695
360	0.004	0.000	0.000	0.000	0.000	0.000	0.000	0.000	0.000	0.000	0.000	0.000
365	0.019	0.000	0.000	0.000	0.000	0.000	0.000	0.000	0.000	0.000	0.000	0.000
370	0.060	0.000	0.000	0.000	0.000	0.000	0.000	0.000	0.000	0.000	0.000	0.000
375	0.130	0.000	0.000	0.000	0.000	0.000	0.000	0.000	0.000	0.000	0.000	0.000
380	0.224	0.001	0.000	0.001	0.000	0.000	0.000	0.000	0.000	0.000	0.000	0.000
385	0.324	0.001	0.001	0.001	0.001	0.000	0.000	0.000	0.000	0.000	0.000	0.000
390	0.421	0.001	0.001	0.001	0.001	0.000	0.000	0.000	0.000	0.000	0.000	0.000
395	0.510	0.001	0.001	0.001	0.001	0.000	0.000	0.000	0.000	0.000	0.000	0.000
400	0.586	0.001	0.001	0.001	0.001	0.000	0.000	0.000	0.000	0.000	0.000	0.000
405	0.649	0.001	0.001	0.000	0.000	0.000	0.000	0.000	0.000	0.000	0.000	0.000
410	0.700	0.001	0.000	0.000	0.000	0.000	0.000	0.000	0.000	0.000	0.000	0.000
415	0.740	0.000	0.000	0.000	0.000	0.000	0.000	0.000	0.000	0.000	0.000	0.000
420	0.771	0.000	0.000	0.000	0.000	0.000	0.000	0.000	0.000	0.000	0.000	0.000
425	0.796	0.001	0.000	0.000	0.000	0.000	0.000	0.000	0.000	0.000	0.000	0.000
430	0.815	0.003	0.000	0.000	0.000	0.000	0.000	0.000	0.000	0.000	0.000	0.000
435	0.830	0.020	0.000	0.000	0.000	0.000	0.000	0.000	0.000	0.000	0.000	0.000
440	0.841	0.088	0.000	0.000	0.000	0.000	0.000	0.000	0.000	0.000	0.000	0.000
445	0.850	0.257	0.000	0.000	0.000	0.000	0.000	0.000	0.000	0.000	0.000	0.000
450	0.856	0.497	0.000	0.000	0.000	0.000	0.000	0.000	0.000	0.000	0.000	0.000
455	0.862	0.690	0.000	0.000	0.000	0.000	0.000	0.000	0.000	0.000	0.000	0.000
460	0.866	0.790	0.000	0.000	0.000	0.000	0.000	0.000	0.000	0.000	0.000	0.000
465	0.869	0.834	0.000	0.000	0.000	0.000	0.000	0.000	0.000	0.000	0.000	0.000
470	0.872	0.856	0.000	0.000	0.000	0.000	0.000	0.000	0.000	0.000	0.000	0.000
475	0.874	0.869	0.002	0.000	0.000	0.000	0.000	0.000	0.000	0.000	0.000	0.000

(Continued)

Table 8.16 (*Continued*)

Wavelength (nm)	GG395	GG455	GG475	OG515	OG530	OG550	OG570	OG590	RG610	RG630	RG665	RG695
480	0.876	0.877	0.019	0.000	0.000	0.000	0.000	0.000	0.000	0.000	0.000	0.000
485	0.878	0.883	0.133	0.001	0.000	0.000	0.000	0.000	0.000	0.000	0.000	0.000
490	0.879	0.887	0.379	0.006	0.000	0.000	0.000	0.000	0.000	0.000	0.000	0.000
495	0.880	0.890	0.613	0.031	0.000	0.000	0.000	0.000	0.000	0.000	0.000	0.000
500	0.881	0.892	0.755	0.105	0.001	0.000	0.000	0.000	0.000	0.000	0.000	0.000
505	0.882	0.894	0.828	0.241	0.006	0.000	0.000	0.000	0.000	0.000	0.000	0.000
510	0.883	0.895	0.865	0.415	0.036	0.000	0.000	0.000	0.000	0.000	0.000	0.000
515	0.883	0.896	0.883	0.579	0.128	0.000	0.000	0.000	0.000	0.000	0.000	0.000
520	0.884	0.897	0.893	0.705	0.289	0.000	0.000	0.000	0.000	0.000	0.000	0.000
525	0.885	0.898	0.899	0.788	0.475	0.001	0.000	0.000	0.000	0.000	0.000	0.000
530	0.885	0.898	0.902	0.838	0.633	0.006	0.000	0.000	0.000	0.000	0.000	0.000
535	0.886	0.898	0.905	0.867	0.744	0.052	0.001	0.000	0.000	0.000	0.000	0.000
540	0.886	0.899	0.907	0.885	0.813	0.210	0.006	0.000	0.000	0.000	0.000	0.000
545	0.887	0.899	0.909	0.895	0.853	0.444	0.024	0.000	0.000	0.000	0.000	0.000
550	0.887	0.900	0.910	0.902	0.877	0.638	0.077	0.000	0.000	0.000	0.000	0.000
555	0.888	0.901	0.911	0.906	0.891	0.756	0.186	0.000	0.000	0.000	0.000	0.000
560	0.888	0.901	0.911	0.908	0.899	0.820	0.350	0.001	0.000	0.000	0.000	0.000
565	0.888	0.902	0.912	0.910	0.904	0.854	0.529	0.004	0.000	0.000	0.000	0.000
570	0.888	0.902	0.912	0.911	0.907	0.872	0.678	0.018	0.000	0.000	0.000	0.000
575	0.889	0.901	0.913	0.912	0.909	0.882	0.779	0.072	0.000	0.000	0.000	0.000
580	0.889	0.900	0.913	0.912	0.911	0.888	0.839	0.204	0.000	0.000	0.000	0.000
585	0.890	0.899	0.913	0.913	0.912	0.892	0.872	0.400	0.000	0.000	0.000	0.000
590	0.890	0.898	0.913	0.913	0.912	0.894	0.890	0.591	0.004	0.001	0.000	0.000
595	0.890	0.897	0.913	0.913	0.913	0.896	0.899	0.728	0.032	0.001	0.000	0.000
600	0.890	0.898	0.913	0.913	0.913	0.897	0.905	0.811	0.145	0.003	0.000	0.000
605	0.891	0.898	0.913	0.913	0.914	0.898	0.908	0.857	0.354	0.010	0.000	0.000

(*Continued*)

Table 8.16 (*Continued*)

Wavelength (nm)	GG395	GG455	GG475	OG515	OG530	OG550	OG570	OG590	RG610	RG630	RG665	RG695
610	0.891	0.898	0.913	0.914	0.914	0.899	0.910	0.881	0.567	0.031	0.000	0.000
615	0.891	0.898	0.913	0.914	0.914	0.900	0.911	0.895	0.716	0.088	0.000	0.000
620	0.892	0.898	0.912	0.913	0.914	0.901	0.912	0.902	0.804	0.206	0.001	0.000
625	0.892	0.898	0.912	0.913	0.914	0.901	0.912	0.905	0.852	0.379	0.001	0.000
630	0.892	0.898	0.912	0.913	0.914	0.901	0.912	0.908	0.878	0.560	0.003	0.000
635	0.892	0.898	0.912	0.913	0.914	0.901	0.912	0.909	0.893	0.702	0.010	0.000
640	0.893	0.897	0.912	0.913	0.913	0.902	0.912	0.910	0.901	0.794	0.027	0.000
645	0.893	0.897	0.911	0.913	0.913	0.901	0.912	0.910	0.906	0.848	0.069	0.001
650	0.893	0.897	0.911	0.912	0.913	0.902	0.912	0.911	0.909	0.877	0.154	0.002
655	0.893	0.898	0.911	0.912	0.913	0.902	0.912	0.911	0.911	0.893	0.288	0.004
660	0.893	0.898	0.910	0.912	0.913	0.902	0.912	0.911	0.912	0.901	0.448	0.009
665	0.894	0.899	0.910	0.912	0.913	0.903	0.912	0.911	0.913	0.906	0.599	0.022
670	0.894	0.901	0.910	0.912	0.912	0.903	0.911	0.911	0.913	0.909	0.715	0.047
675	0.894	0.902	0.910	0.912	0.912	0.904	0.911	0.911	0.914	0.910	0.792	0.097
680	0.894	0.903	0.909	0.911	0.912	0.904	0.911	0.911	0.914	0.911	0.839	0.178
685	0.894	0.905	0.909	0.911	0.911	0.905	0.910	0.911	0.915	0.911	0.867	0.291
690	0.895	0.906	0.909	0.911	0.911	0.906	0.910	0.910	0.914	0.911	0.883	0.424
695	0.895	0.907	0.908	0.911	0.911	0.906	0.910	0.910	0.915	0.912	0.892	0.553
700	0.895	0.908	0.908	0.910	0.910	0.907	0.909	0.910	0.915	0.912	0.898	0.664
705	0.895	0.909	0.907	0.910	0.910	0.907	0.909	0.910	0.915	0.912	0.902	0.746
710	0.896	0.909	0.907	0.910	0.910	0.908	0.909	0.909	0.915	0.911	0.904	0.803
715	0.895	0.909	0.906	0.909	0.909	0.908	0.908	0.909	0.915	0.911	0.905	0.841
720	0.896	0.910	0.906	0.909	0.909	0.908	0.908	0.909	0.915	0.911	0.906	0.866

(*Continued*)

Table 8.16 (*Continued*)

Wavelength (nm)	GG395	GG455	GG475	OG515	OG530	OG550	OG570	OG590	RG610	RG630	RG665	RG695
725	0.896	0.910	0.906	0.909	0.908	0.908	0.907	0.909	0.915	0.910	0.906	0.881
730	0.896	0.910	0.905	0.908	0.908	0.908	0.907	0.908	0.915	0.910	0.906	0.890
735	0.896	0.910	0.905	0.908	0.908	0.908	0.906	0.908	0.915	0.910	0.906	0.897
740	0.896	0.910	0.904	0.908	0.907	0.908	0.906	0.908	0.915	0.910	0.906	0.901
745	0.896	0.910	0.904	0.907	0.907	0.909	0.905	0.908	0.915	0.909	0.906	0.903
750	0.896	0.910	0.903	0.907	0.906	0.909	0.905	0.907	0.915	0.909	0.906	0.905
755	0.896	0.911	0.903	0.906	0.906	0.909	0.905	0.907	0.915	0.909	0.906	0.906
760	0.896	0.911	0.903	0.906	0.906	0.909	0.904	0.906	0.915	0.908	0.905	0.907
765	0.896	0.911	0.902	0.906	0.905	0.909	0.904	0.906	0.915	0.908	0.906	0.908
770	0.897	0.910	0.901	0.905	0.904	0.909	0.903	0.906	0.915	0.908	0.905	0.908
775	0.897	0.911	0.901	0.905	0.904	0.909	0.903	0.906	0.915	0.907	0.905	0.908
780	0.897	0.911	0.901	0.904	0.904	0.909	0.902	0.905	0.915	0.907	0.904	0.908
785	0.897	0.911	0.900	0.904	0.904	0.910	0.902	0.905	0.916	0.907	0.904	0.908
790	0.897	0.911	0.900	0.904	0.903	0.909	0.902	0.905	0.916	0.907	0.904	0.908
795	0.897	0.911	0.899	0.903	0.903	0.909	0.901	0.905	0.915	0.906	0.904	0.909
800	0.897	0.911	0.899	0.903	0.902	0.909	0.901	0.904	0.915	0.906	0.904	0.908
805	0.898	0.911	0.898	0.902	0.902	0.909	0.900	0.904	0.915	0.905	0.903	0.908
810	0.898	0.910	0.897	0.902	0.901	0.910	0.900	0.903	0.915	0.905	0.903	0.908
815	0.898	0.911	0.897	0.901	0.901	0.909	0.899	0.903	0.915	0.905	0.903	0.908
820	0.898	0.910	0.897	0.901	0.900	0.909	0.898	0.903	0.915	0.904	0.902	0.907
825	0.898	0.910	0.896	0.901	0.900	0.909	0.898	0.902	0.915	0.904	0.902	0.907
830	0.898	0.910	0.896	0.900	0.899	0.909	0.898	0.902	0.915	0.904	0.902	0.907

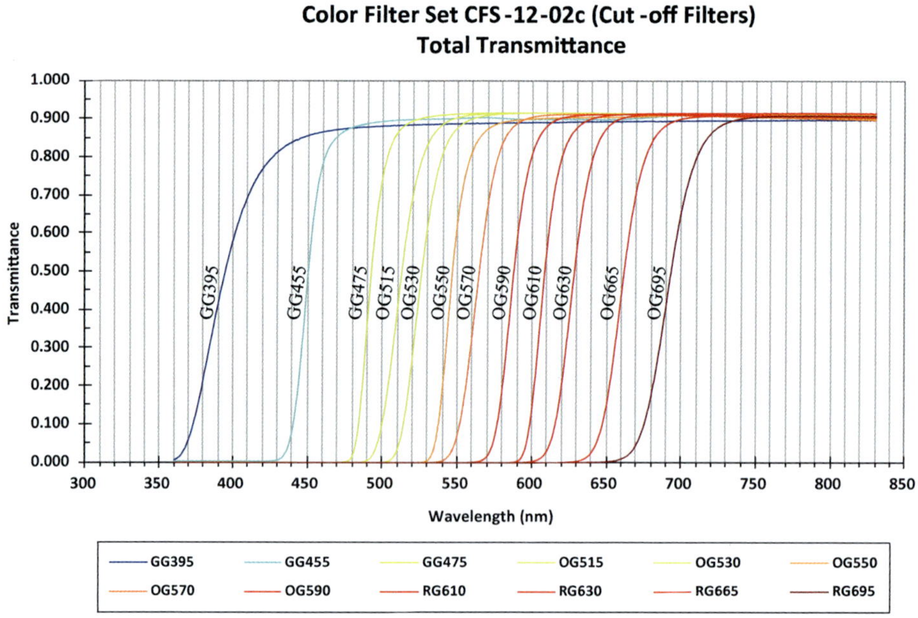

Fig. 8.18 Color Filter Set CFS-12-02c measured using Transmittance measurement geometry and a calibrated double-monochromator instrument from 300 nm to 830 nm. (Data and spectrum used with permission from Avian Technologies, New London, NH).

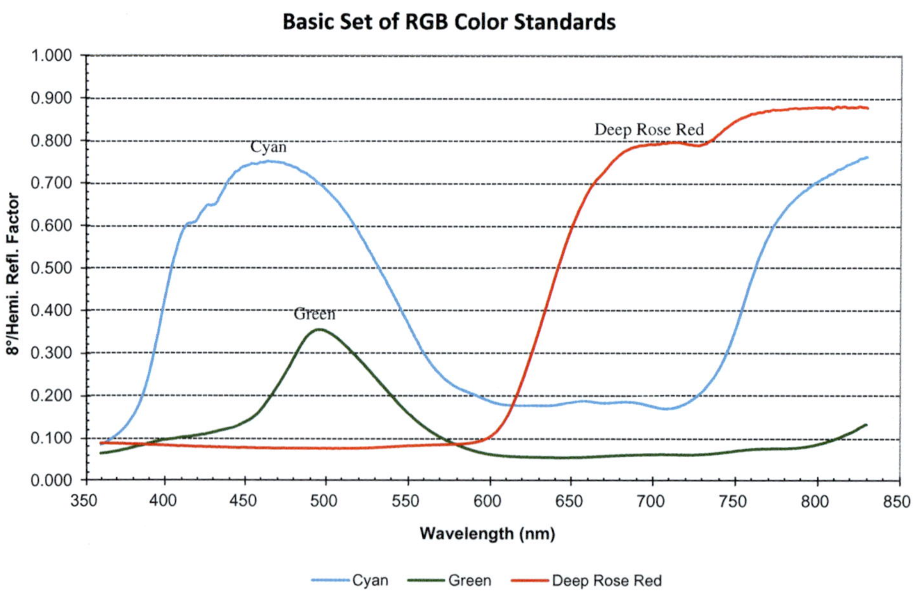

Fig. 8.19 Basic Set of RGB (Red-Green-Blue) Color Standards measured using measured using 8°/Hemispherical Spectral Reflectance Factor geometry and a calibrated double-monochromator instrument from 350 nm to 830 nm. (Data and spectrum used with permission from Avian Technologies, New London, NH).

Table 8.17 Color standards reflectance values at 10 nm increments 2 nm bandpass/360–830 nm 8°/Hemi. Refl. Factor.

Wavelength (nm)	Cyan (Blue)	Green	Deep rose red (Red)
360	0.085	0.064	0.088
370	0.107	0.069	0.087
380	0.149	0.077	0.086
390	0.245	0.087	0.084
400	0.427	0.096	0.083
410	0.580	0.101	0.081
420	0.614	0.106	0.079
430	0.649	0.113	0.078
440	0.708	0.123	0.078
450	0.739	0.139	0.077
460	0.749	0.168	0.077
470	0.749	0.222	0.076
480	0.737	0.289	0.076
490	0.716	0.346	0.076
500	0.685	0.354	0.076
510	0.641	0.327	0.076
520	0.582	0.288	0.076
530	0.514	0.246	0.077
540	0.444	0.203	0.080
550	0.370	0.162	0.082
560	0.301	0.129	0.083
570	0.250	0.105	0.084
580	0.220	0.086	0.086
590	0.204	0.072	0.089
600	0.188	0.063	0.102
610	0.178	0.059	0.145
620	0.177	0.057	0.235
630	0.176	0.056	0.353
640	0.177	0.055	0.481
650	0.184	0.055	0.596
660	0.187	0.056	0.680
670	0.182	0.058	0.728
680	0.184	0.060	0.768
690	0.183	0.062	0.786
700	0.174	0.062	0.790
710	0.169	0.062	0.795
720	0.181	0.062	0.791
730	0.210	0.063	0.790

(*Continued*)

Table 8.17 (*Continued*)

Wavelength (nm)	Cyan (Blue)	Green	Deep rose red (Red)
740	0.262	0.066	0.817
750	0.354	0.071	0.847
760	0.477	0.075	0.865
770	0.577	0.076	0.871
780	0.638	0.077	0.876
790	0.678	0.080	0.879
800	0.705	0.086	0.880
810	0.727	0.098	0.880
820	0.746	0.114	0.881
830	0.762	0.133	0.881

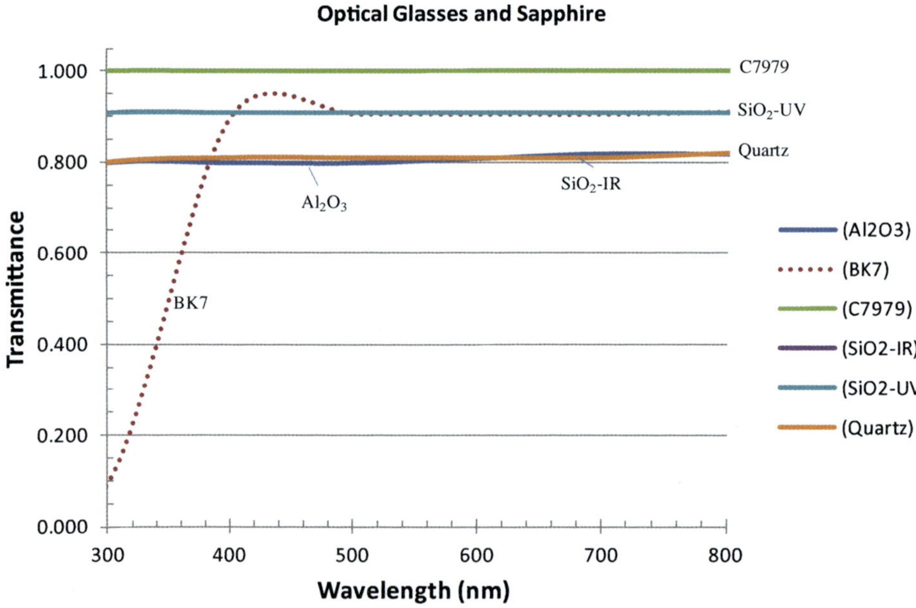

Fig. 8.20 Basic set of optical glass materials measured using transmittance geometry from 300 nm to 800 nm.

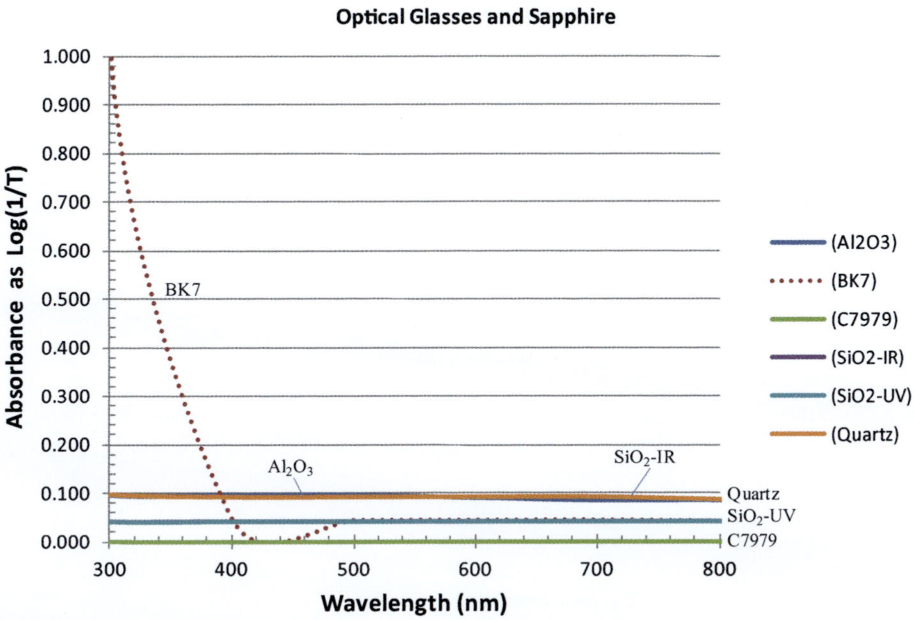

Fig. 8.21 Basic set of optical glass materials measured using absorbance as $\log_{10}$ (1/T) geometry from 300 nm to 800 nm.

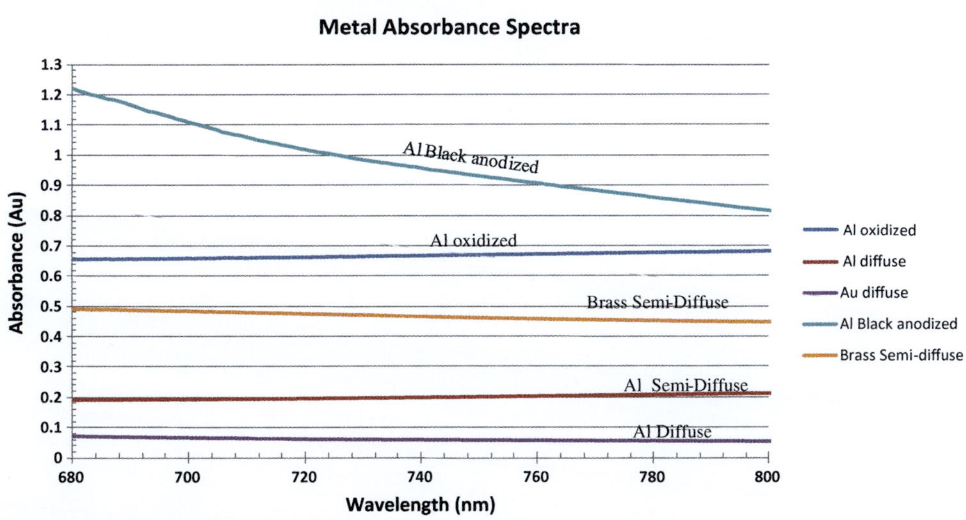

Fig. 8.22 Basic set of metal surfaces measured using absorbance as $\log_{10}$ (1/R) geometry from 680 nm to 800 nm.

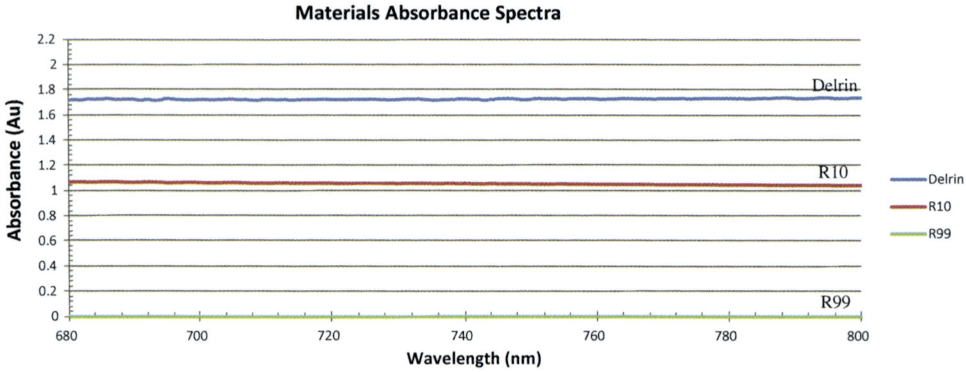

Fig. 8.23 Delrin (Black polymer), Fluorilon 10% Reflectance (R10), and Fluorilon 99% Reflectance (R99) measured using Absorbance as $\log_{10}$ (1/R) geometry from 680 nm to 800 nm.

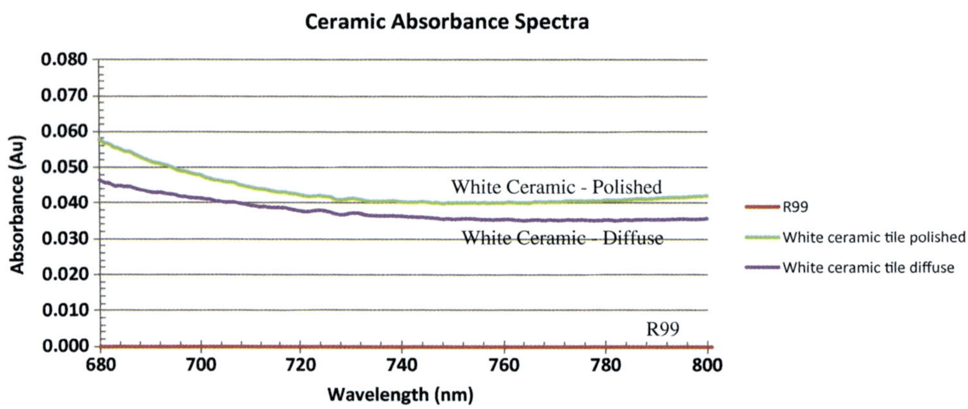

Fig. 8.24 Ceramic comparison: White ceramic polished, White ceramic diffuse, and Fluorilon 99% Reflectance measured using Absorbance as $\log_{10}$ (1/R) geometry from 680 nm to 800 nm.

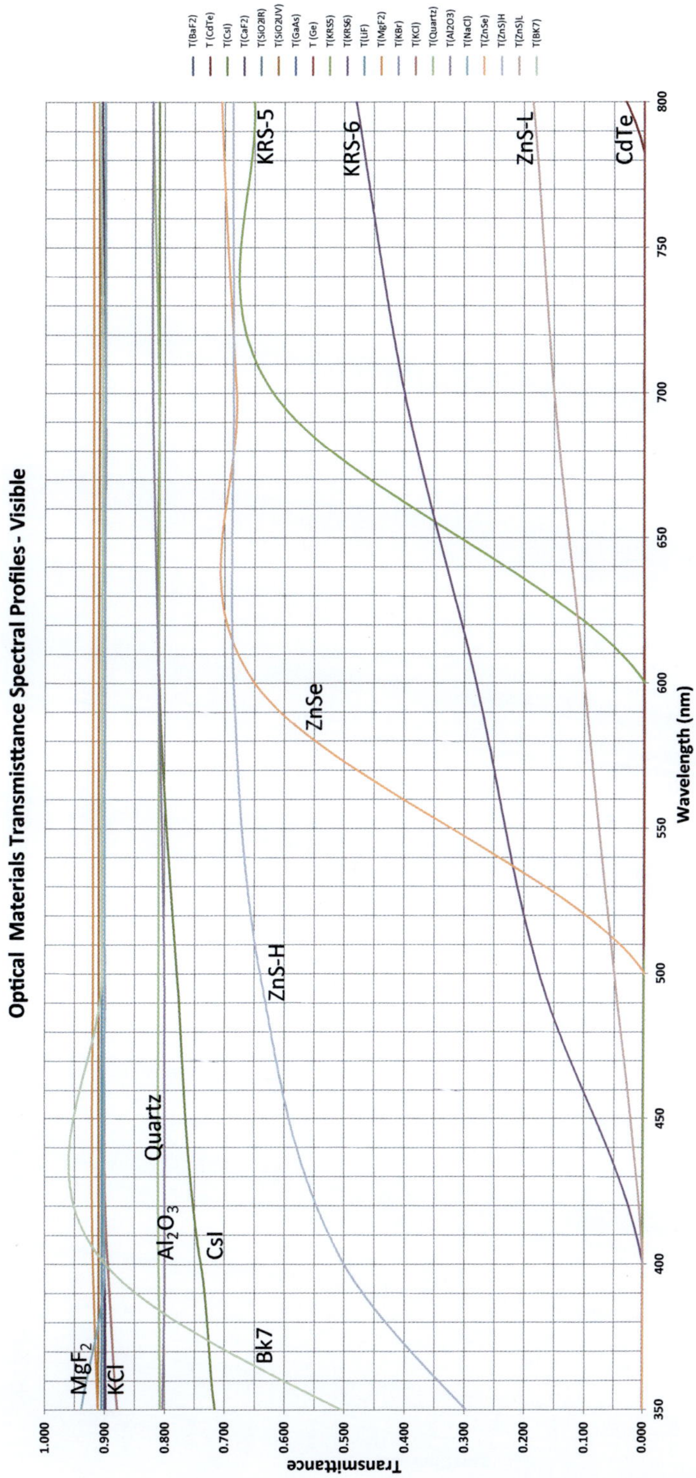

Fig. 8.25 Visible region: Optical materials comparison measured in transmittance from 350 nm to 800 nm.

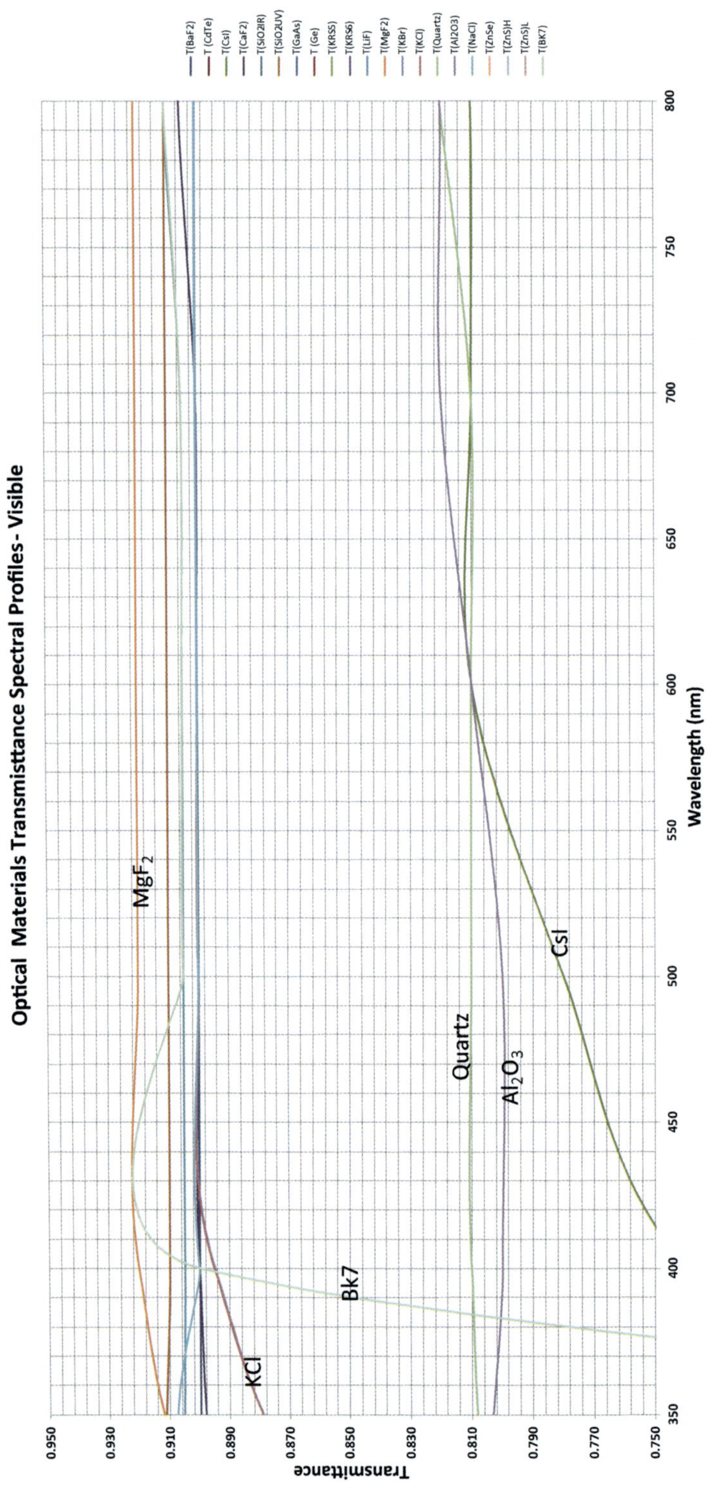

Fig. 8.26 Visible region: Close-up of Figure 8.25 showing optical materials comparison measured in transmittance from 350 nm to 800 nm.

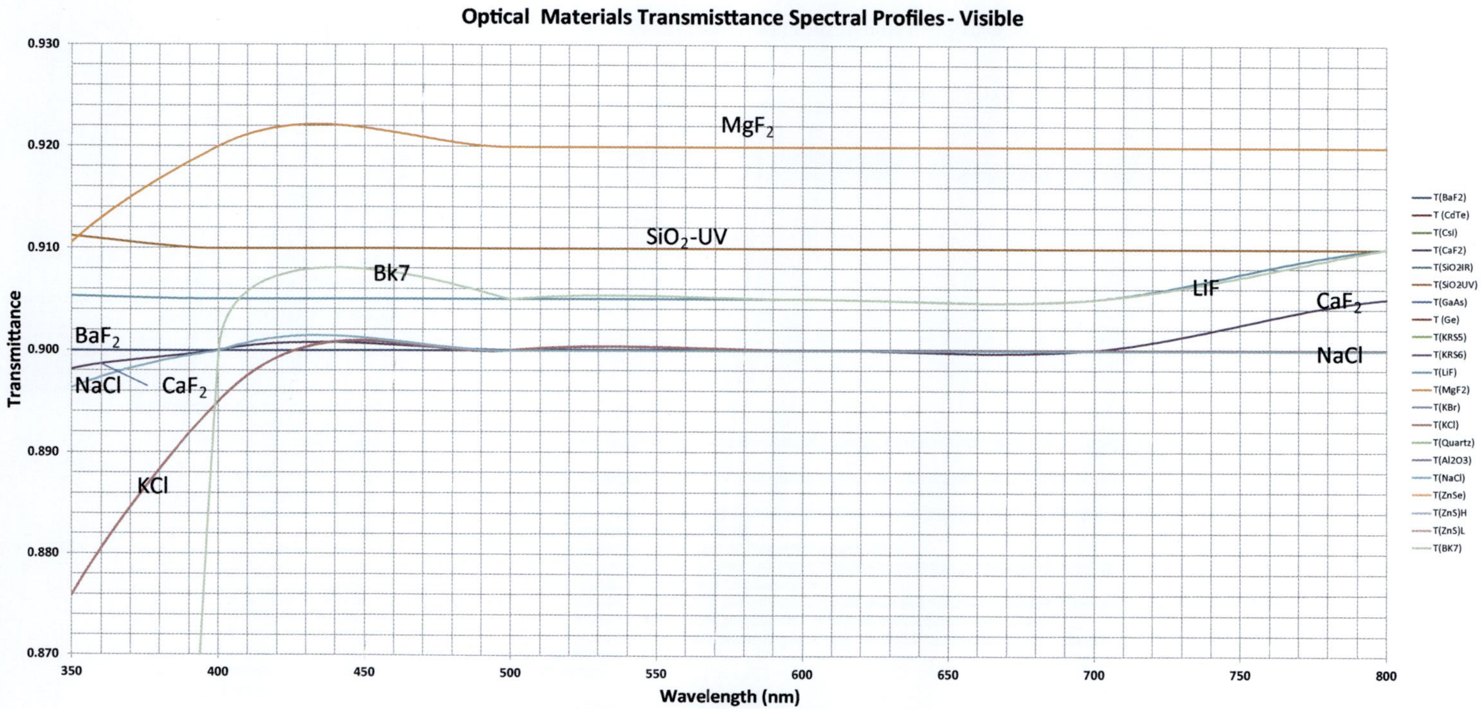

Fig. 8.27 Visible region: Close-up of Figure 8.25 showing optical materials comparison measured in transmittance from 350 nm to 800 nm.

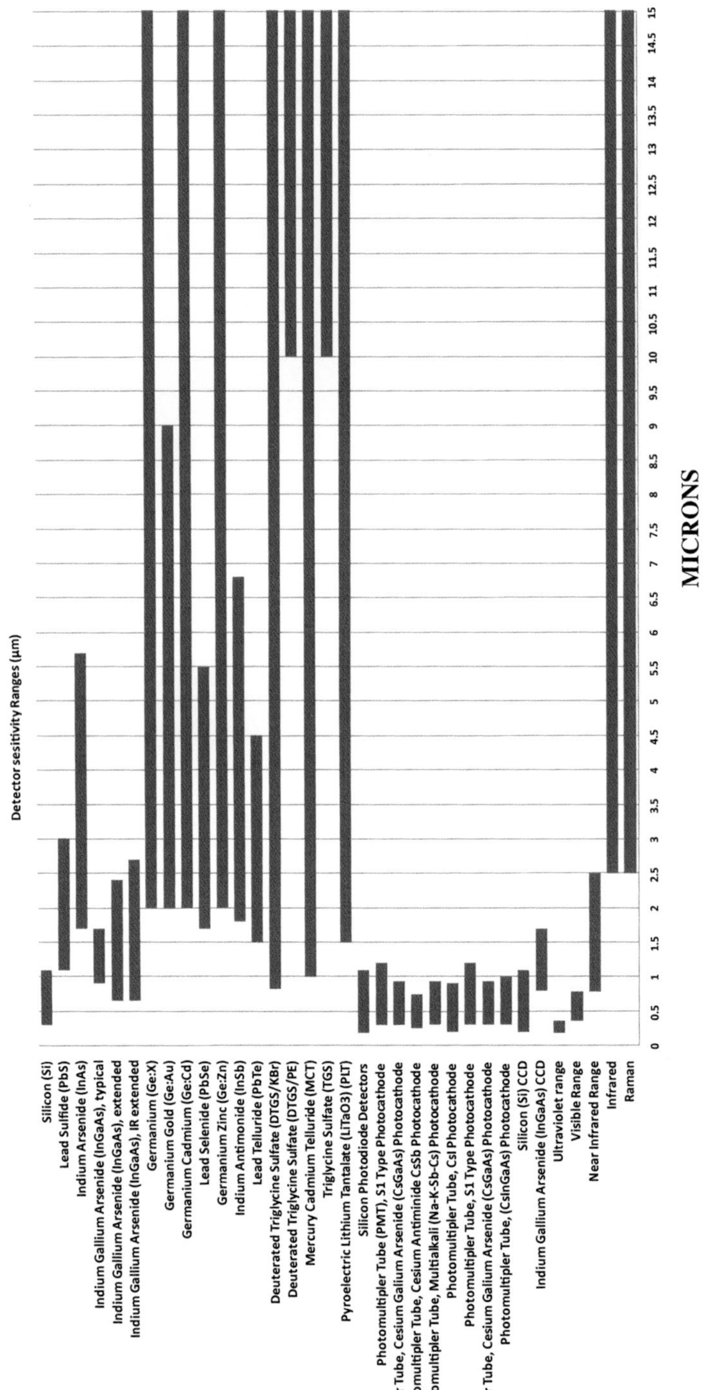

Fig. 8.28 Detector sensitivity ranges from 0 microns (0 nm) to 15 microns (15000 nm).

Table 8.18 Detector sensitivity ranges from 0.13 microns (130 nm) to 15 microns (15000 nm).

Detector sensitivity ranges (in microns)	Start (μm)	End (μm)	Range (μm)
Silicon (Si)	0.3	1.1	0.8000
Silicon Photodiode Detectors	0.19	1.1	0.9100
Photomultipler Tube (PMT), S1 Type Photocathode	0.3	1.2	0.9000
Photomultipler Tube, Cesium Antiminide CsSb Photocathode	0.25	0.75	0.5000
Photomultipler Tube, Multialkali (Na-K-Sb-Cs) Photocathode	0.3	0.93	0.6300
Photomultipler Tube, CsI Photocathode	0.2	0.9	0.7000
Photomultipler Tube, S1 Type Photocathode	0.3	1.2	0.9000
Photomultipler Tube, Cesium Galium Arsenide (CsGaAs) Photocathode	0.3	0.93	0.6300
Photomultipler Tube, (CsInGaAs) Photocathode	0.3	1	0.7000
Silicon (Si) CCD	0.2	1.1	0.9000
Indium Gallium Arsenide (InGaAs) CCD	0.8	1.7	0.9000
Ultraviolet range	0.19	0.36	0.1700
Visible Range	0.36	0.78	0.4200

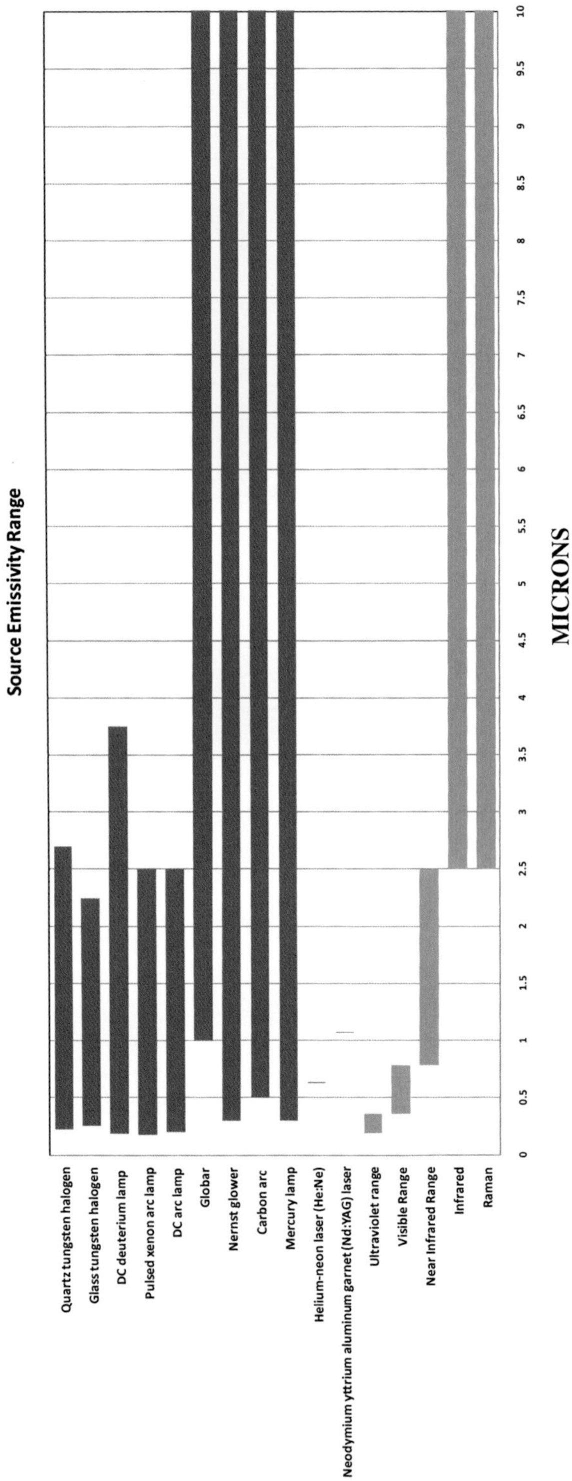

Fig. 8.29 Source emissivity ranges (in microns).

Table 8.19 Source Emissivity Ranges (in microns).

Source Emissivity Ranges	Start (μm)	End (μm)	Range (μm)
Quartz tungsten halogen	0.22	2.7	2
Glass tungsten halogen	0.25	2.25	2
DC deuterium lamp	0.185	3.75	4
Pulsed xenon arc lamp	0.18	2.5	2
DC arc lamp	0.2	2.5	2
Globar	1	100	99
Nernst glower	0.3	35	35
Carbon arc	0.5	100	100
Mercury Lamp	0.3	100	100
Helium-neon laser (He:Ne)	0.6327	0.6328	0.00010
Visible Range	0.36	0.78	0.420

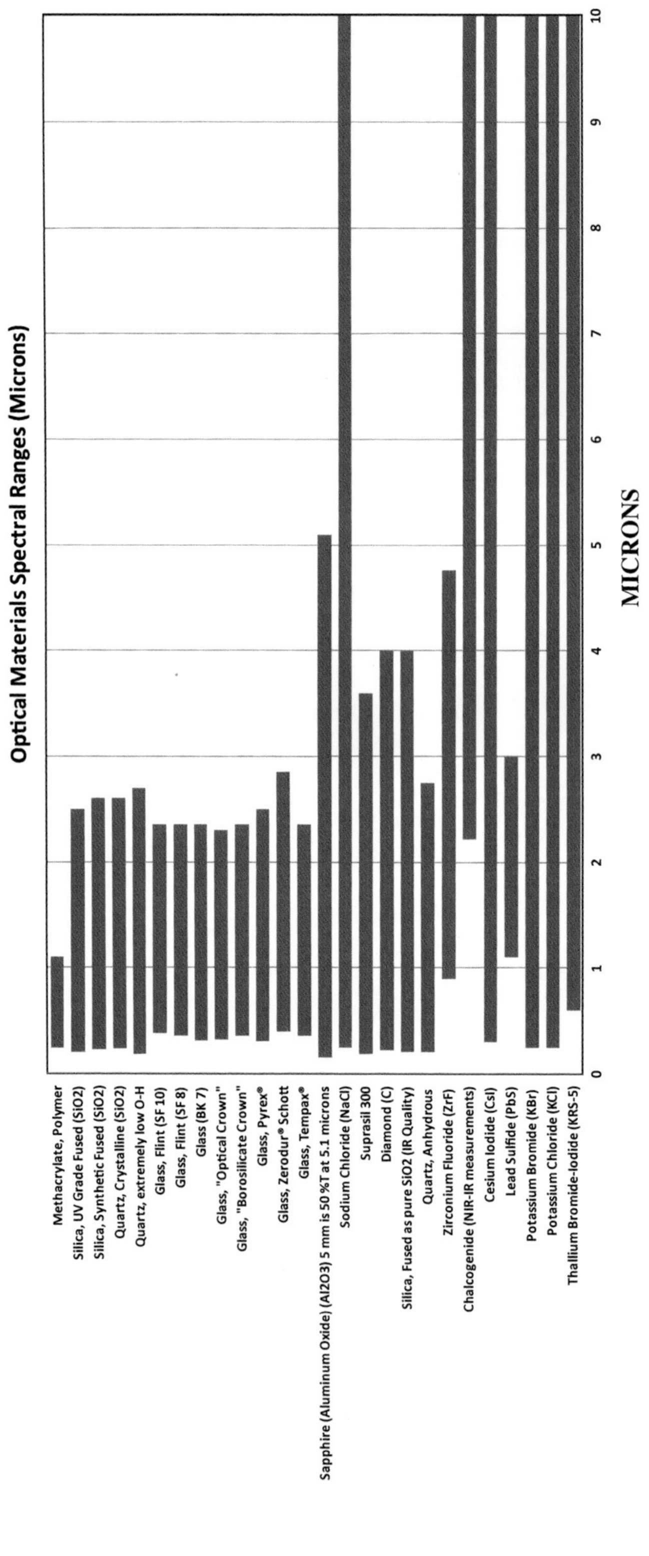

Fig. 8.30a Optical materials transmittance ranges (in microns).

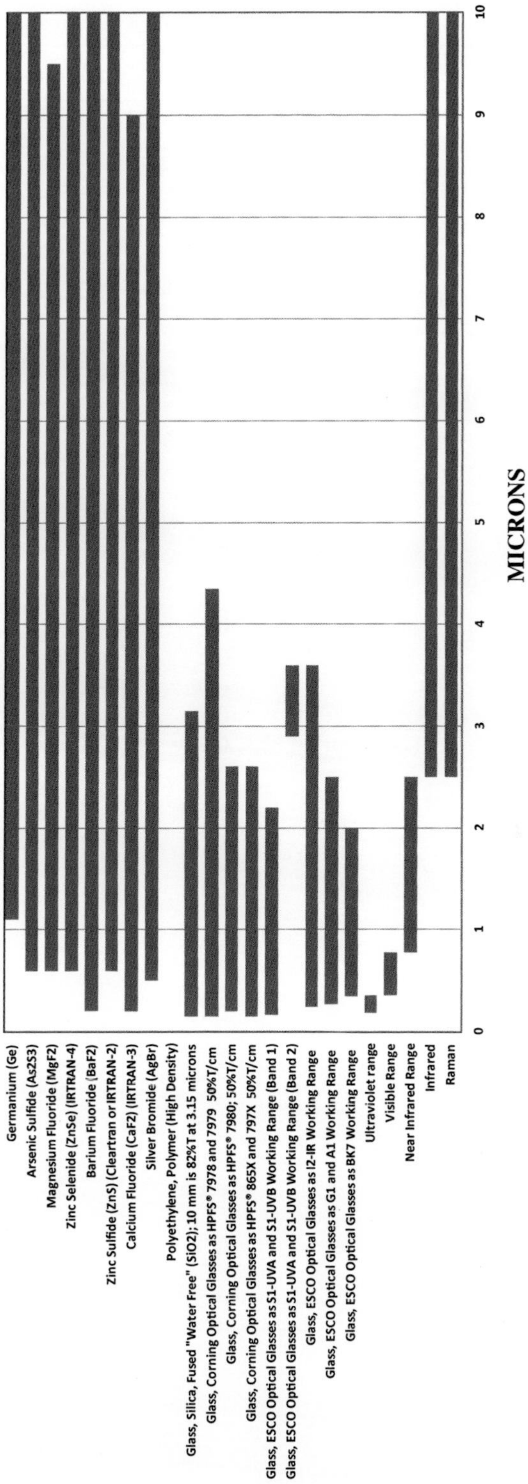

Fig. 8.30b (continued) Optical materials transmittance ranges (in microns).

Table 8.20 Optical materials transmittance ranges (in microns).

Optical material spectral ranges	Start (μm)	End (μm)	Range (μm)
Methacrylate, Polymer	0.25	1.1	1
Silica, UV Grade Fused (SiO_2)	0.2	2.5	2
Silica, Synthetic Fused (SiO_2)	0.23	2.6	2
Quartz, Crystalline (SiO_2)	0.24	2.6	2
Quartz, extremely low O-H	0.19	2.7	3
Glass, Flint (SF 10)	0.38	2.35	2
Glass, Flint (SF 8)	0.355	2.35	2
Glass (BK 7)	0.315	2.35	2
Glass, "Optical Crown"	0.32	2.3	2
Glass, "Borosilicate Crown"	0.36	2.35	2
Glass, Pyrex®	0.31	2.5	2
Glass, Tempax®	0.36	2.35	2
Sapphire (Aluminum Oxide) (Al_2O_3) 5 mm is 50%T at 5.1 microns	0.15	5.1	5
Sodium Chloride (NaCl)	0.25	16	16
Suprasil 300	0.19	3.6	3
Diamond (C)	0.22	4	4
Silica, Fused as pure SiO_2 (IR Quality)	0.2	4	4
Quartz, Anhydrous	0.2	2.75	3
Cesium Iodide (CsI)	0.3	50	50
Potassium Bromide (KBr)	0.25	26	26
Potassium Chloride (KCl)	0.25	20	20
Barium Fluoride (BaF_2)	0.2	13	13
Calcium Fluoride (CaF_2) (IRTRAN-3)	0.2	9	9
Glass, Silica, Fused "Water Free" (SiO_2); 10 mm is 82%T at 3.15 microns	0.15	3.15	3
Glass, Corning Optical Glasses as HPFS® 7978 and 7979 50%T/cm	0.15	4.35	4
Glass, Corning Optical Glasses as HPFS® 7980; 50%T/cm	0.2	2.6	2
Glass, Corning Optical Glasses as HPFS® 865X and 797X 50%T/cm	0.15	2.6	2
Glass, ESCO Optical Glasses as S1-UVA and S1-UVB Working Range (Band 1)	0.17	2.2	2
Glass, ESCO Optical Glasses as I2-IR Working Range	0.25	3.6	3
Glass, ESCO Optical Glasses as G1 and A1 Working Range	0.27	2.5	2
Glass, ESCO Optical Glasses as BK7 Working Range	0.35	2	2
Visible Range	0.36	0.78	0

Table 8.21 Optical materials transmittance data (in T with respect to nm).

Lambda	(Al2O3)	(BaF2)	(BK7)	(C7979)	(CaF2)	(CsI)	(CdTe)	(SiO2-IR)	(SiO2-UV)	(GaAs)	(Ge)
100	0.000	0.100	0.000	0.0000	0.100	0.000	0.000	0.000	0.000	0.000	0.000
200	0.750	0.900	0.000	0.9970	0.840	0.000	0.000	0.890	0.890	0.000	0.000
300	0.800	0.900	0.100	0.9999	0.890	0.620	0.000	0.910	0.910	0.000	0.000
400	0.800	0.900	0.900	1.0000	0.900	0.740	0.000	0.910	0.910	0.000	0.000
500	0.800	0.900	0.905	1.0000	0.900	0.780	0.000	0.910	0.910	0.000	0.000
600	0.810	0.900	0.905	1.0000	0.900	0.810	0.000	0.910	0.910	0.000	0.000
700	0.820	0.900	0.905	1.0000	0.900	0.810	0.000	0.910	0.910	0.000	0.000
800	0.820	0.900	0.910	1.0000	0.905	0.810	0.030	0.910	0.910	0.000	0.000
900	0.825	0.900	0.915	1.0000	0.905	0.815	0.470	0.910	0.910	0.000	0.000
1000	0.835	0.900	0.915	1.0000	0.910	0.815	0.520	0.910	0.910	0.000	0.000
1450	0.850	0.900	0.920	1.0000	0.915	0.818	0.550	0.910	0.850	0.400	0.000
1500	0.855	0.900	0.920	1.0000	0.915	0.818	0.550	0.910	0.910	0.480	0.000
1950	0.870	0.900	0.905	0.9999	0.915	0.818	0.550	0.910	0.600	0.500	0.000
2000	0.875	0.910	0.880	0.9997	0.920	0.820	0.580	0.910	0.810	0.515	0.300

(Continued)

Table 8.21 *(Continued)*

Lambda	(Al2O3)	(BaF2)	(BK7)	(C7979)	(CaF2)	(CsI)	(CdTe)	(SiO2-IR)	(SiO2-UV)	(GaAs)	(Ge)
2350	0.880	0.910	0.500	1.0000	0.920	0.820	0.580	0.910	0.000	0.515	0.415
3000	0.895	0.910	0.080	0.9907	0.921	0.821	0.590	0.880	0.650	0.515	0.415
4000	0.865	0.910	0.000	0.8369	0.923	0.822	0.595	0.300	0.000	0.515	0.415
5000	0.650	0.920	0.000	0.0500	0.925	0.823	0.597	0.000	0.000	0.515	0.415
6000	0.200	0.920	0.000	0.0000	0.905	0.824	0.598	0.000	0.000	0.510	0.415
7000	0.000	0.600	0.000	0.0000	0.825	0.824	0.599	0.000	0.000	0.510	0.415
8000	0.000	0.500	0.000	0.0000	0.740	0.824	0.599	0.000	0.000	0.510	0.415
9000	0.000	0.400	0.000	0.0000	0.400	0.824	0.599	0.000	0.000	0.508	0.415
10000	0.000	0.300	0.000	0.0000	0.100	0.825	0.600	0.000	0.000	0.505	0.405
15000	0.000	0.000	0.000	0.0000	0.000	0.818	0.602	0.000	0.000	0.470	0.365
18000	0.000	0.000	0.000	0.0000	0.000	0.815	0.603	0.000	0.000	0.490	0.340
20000	0.000	0.000	0.000	0.0000	0.000	0.812	0.605	0.000	0.000	0.000	0.210
30000	0.000	0.000	0.000	0.0000	0.000	0.800	0.480	0.000	0.000	0.000	0.000
40000	0.000	0.000	0.000	0.0000	0.000	0.650	0.000	0.000	0.000	0.000	0.000
50000	0.000	0.000	0.000	0.0000	0.000	0.100	0.000	0.000	0.000	0.000	0.000
60000	0.000	0.000	0.000	0.0000	0.000	0.000	0.000	0.000	0.000	0.000	0.000

Table 8.22 Optical materials transmittance data (in T with respect to nm).

Lambda (nm)	(KBr)	(KCl)	(KRS-5)	(KRS-6)	(LiF)	(MgF2)	(NaCl)	(Quartz)	(ZnSe)	(ZnS)	(ZnS-2)
100	0.000	0.000	0.000	0.000	0.000	0.000	0.000	0.000	0.000	0.000	0.000
200	0.650	0.650	0.000	0.000	0.900	0.780	0.100	0.750	0.000	0.000	0.000
300	0.840	0.840	0.000	0.000	0.905	0.890	0.880	0.800	0.000	0.100	0.000
400	0.895	0.895	0.000	0.000	0.905	0.920	0.900	0.810	0.000	0.500	0.000
500	0.900	0.900	0.000	0.175	0.905	0.920	0.900	0.810	0.000	0.640	0.050
600	0.900	0.900	0.000	0.280	0.905	0.920	0.900	0.810	0.650	0.685	0.100
700	0.900	0.900	0.620	0.400	0.905	0.920	0.900	0.810	0.680	0.685	0.150
800	0.900	0.900	0.650	0.480	0.910	0.920	0.900	0.820	0.705	0.686	0.185
900	0.900	0.900	0.660	0.560	0.910	0.920	0.900	0.830	0.710	0.686	0.240
1000	0.900	0.900	0.670	0.620	0.910	0.920	0.900	0.835	0.715	0.687	0.295
1450	0.900	0.900	0.672	0.665	0.911	0.920	0.900	0.845	0.720	0.687	0.370
1500	0.900	0.900	0.673	0.680	0.913	0.920	0.900	0.850	0.722	0.695	0.400
1950	0.900	0.900	0.674	0.695	0.914	0.920	0.900	0.870	0.723	0.695	0.480
2000	0.900	0.900	0.675	0.705	0.915	0.920	0.900	0.875	0.725	0.700	0.500
2350	0.900	0.900	0.677	0.715	0.915	0.920	0.900	0.880	0.725	0.700	0.530
3000	0.900	0.900	0.677	0.730	0.915	0.925	0.900	0.890	0.725	0.705	0.570
4000	0.900	0.900	0.677	0.750	0.905	0.930	0.900	0.860	0.725	0.705	0.640
5000	0.900	0.910	0.677	0.765	0.870	0.910	0.900	0.670	0.725	0.710	0.740
6000	0.900	0.900	0.677	0.780	0.800	0.750	0.905	0.200	0.730	0.710	0.760
7000	0.900	0.900	0.677	0.775	0.560	0.550	0.910	0.000	0.730	0.710	0.700
8000	0.900	0.900	0.678	0.774	0.330	0.300	0.910	0.000	0.730	0.710	0.735
9000	0.900	0.900	0.679	0.772	0.100	0.050	0.910	0.000	0.730	0.710	0.725
10000	0.900	0.900	0.680	0.770	0.000	0.000	0.910	0.000	0.735	0.670	0.710
15000	0.900	0.880	0.677	0.745	0.000	0.000	0.500	0.000	0.750	0.400	0.400
18000	0.900	0.800	0.675	0.720	0.000	0.000	0.100	0.000	0.650	0.000	0.100
20000	0.905	0.625	0.673	0.700	0.000	0.000	0.000	0.000	0.100	0.000	0.000
30000	0.100	0.000	0.670	0.330	0.000	0.000	0.000	0.000	0.000	0.000	0.000
40000	0.000	0.000	0.640	0.000	0.000	0.000	0.000	0.000	0.000	0.000	0.000
50000	0.000	0.000	0.480	0.000	0.000	0.000	0.000	0.000	0.000	0.000	0.000
60000	0.000	0.000	0.000	0.000	0.000	0.000	0.000	0.000	0.000	0.000	0.000

8.5 Standard Measurement Geometry for Reference Materials

Reference materials are measured under specific conditions and measurement geometry configurations. This aspect is critical for repeatable and reproducible measurements of SRMs (Standard Reference Materials) and secondary reference materials. The following figures illustrate the characteristics of standard measurement geometry conditions for measuring reference sample materials. See the index or Chapter 7 of this volume for more information and illustrations of measurement geometry configurations.

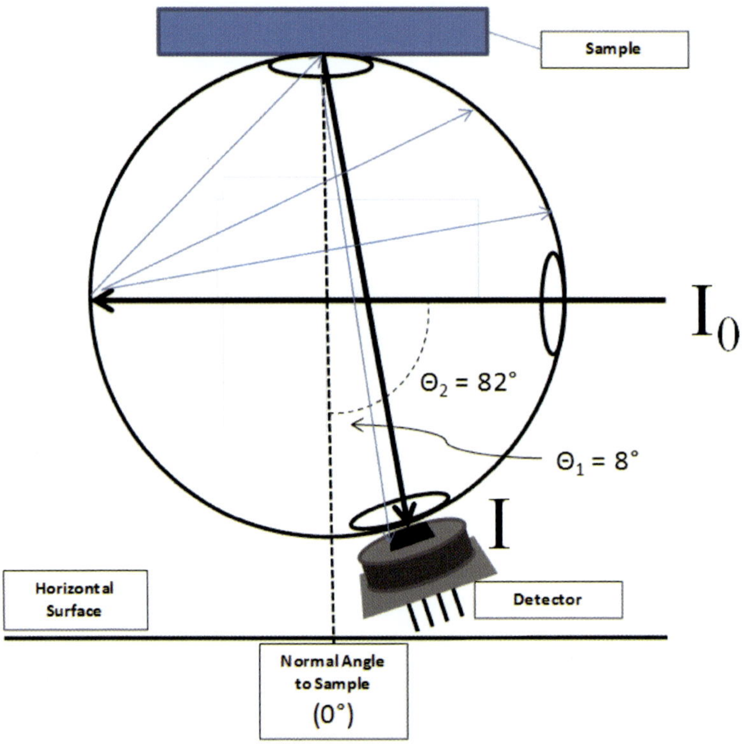

Fig. 8.31 d/8° sample measurement geometry (8°/Hemispherical Spectral Reflectance Factor Geometry). An integrating sphere is used for diffuse illumination and collection of light.

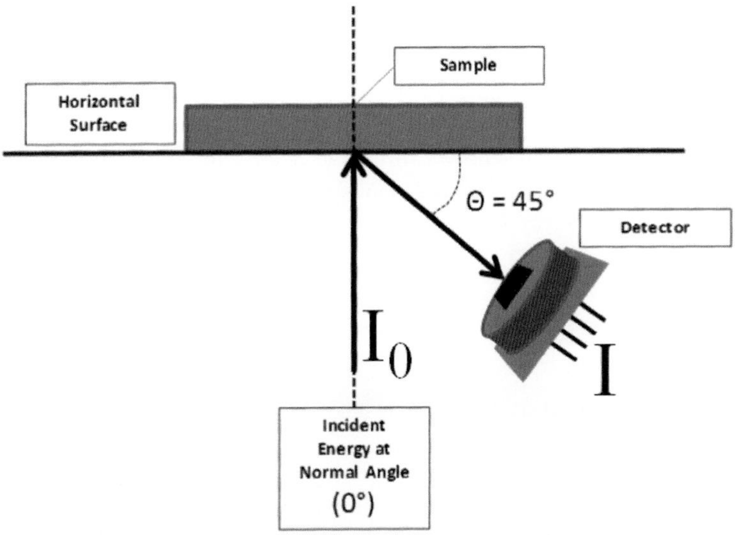

Fig. 8.32 0°/45° sample measurement geometry for reflectance/Reflection Measurements. The Reflectance spectrum may be converted to absorbance using Beer's law as absorbance = $\log_{10}(1/R)$.

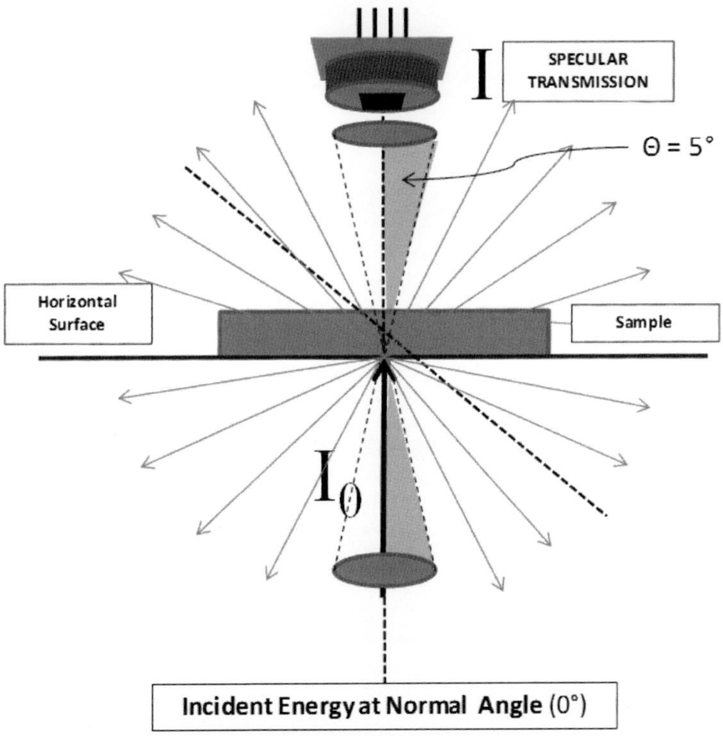

Fig. 8.33 0°/180° specular transmission sample measurement geometry. The measurement may also be made slightly off-axis by 2–5 degrees. The Transmittance/Transmission spectrum may be converted to absorbance using Beer's law as absorbance = $\log_{10}(1/T)$.

References

1. NIST SRM website: URL at http://www.nist.gov/srm/index3column.cfm
2. ASTM Standard Practice for Describing and Measuring Performance of Ultraviolet, Visible, and Near-Infrared Spectrophotometers; American Society for Testing and Materials: ASTM International designation E 275-08(2013), Philadelphia, PA, 2013.
3. ASTM Standard Terminology Relating to Molecular Spectroscopy; American Society for Testing and Materials: ASTM International designation E 131-10, Philadelphia, PA, 2010.

Chapter 9

Glossary of Visible Spectroscopy Terms

Terms are given in alphabetical order.

ABSORBANCE — Measure of concentration of material present: Negative log (base 10) of Transmittance [$-\log_{10}$ T], or the product of extinction coefficient, pathlength, and concentration, written in many forms as $A = abc$, $A = \varepsilon bc$ or $A = \varepsilon lc$ (sometimes also written as the product of the absorptivity, concentration, and pathlength as $A = \varepsilon cl$).

ABSORPTIVITY — Probability of light absorbing at a particular wavelength for a specific analyte under specific conditions, e.g., pH, solvent, and temperature. Thus, a specific amount of material at specified conditions will absorb a specific fraction of the light striking it. Absorptivity is signified by an epsilon (ε) or also a lower case "a".

ANALYTE — The particular material or quality to be determined in an analytical analysis.

BEER'S LAW — Relationship between the amount of light absorbed by an analyte and its concentration (c), pathlength (b), and absorptivity (a), written as $A = abc$. See Section 0.3 in the Front Material of each volume for details, or the index.

CALIBRATION — Determining the spectral response of some analytical method to known amounts of pure analyte.

CALIBRATION CURVE — The results of a calibration when graphed, usually Cartesian coordinates, e.g., concentration (in molarity) versus absorbance.

CONCENTRATION — The amount of analyte in a given volume of solution, e.g., moles per liter.

CUVETTE — Transparent receptacle in which sample solutions are introduced into the light path of spectrometers. Usually, two sides are equal, i.e., 1 cm × 1 cm, while the third dimension is elongated, possibly as long as 15 cm. For UV work, the material is quartz. Visible work permits use of glass or plastic cuvettes.

DETECTOR — Device used to detect the intensity of the radiation from either sample or reference beams. Usually a simple silicon diode or a more sensitive photomultiplier tube.

EXTINCTION/EXTINCTION COEFFICIENT — Words sometimes substituted for absorbance and absorptivity, respectively.

FREQUENCY — The number of times per unit that the magnitude of an electromagnetic wave goes from maximum to minimum then back to maximum amplitude. The unit for the number of waves per second is Hertz (Hz).

GRATING — A reflective surface covered with evenly spaced, microscopic grooves, whose purpose is to separate individual wavelengths from "white" light. The distance between grooves and the angle of the faces are determined by the wavelengths to be separated. The grating (except for diode arrays) is rotated at a set speed and the desired wavelength is emitted through an exit slit onto the sample or standard.

LIMIT OF DETECTION — Lowest amount of analyte that may be seen above the noise level of instrument.

LINEAR — Straight line. In context, this means that for a doubling of the analyte concentration, the signal will double. This allows prediction of unknown concentration from calibration curve.

LINEARITY — An experiment demonstrating that the response of an instrument changes in a predictable and linear fashion with increasing analyte.

NOISE — Any signal generated by the detector not directly responding to the light transmitted at the required wavelength.

PATHLENGTH — The distance the light passes through the sample in its holder. In practical terms, the inside dimension of the cuvette being traversed by the light beam.

REFERENCE — In context, everything that is in the sample light path except the analyte of interest — cuvette, solvent, and any buffer or matrix used to prepare the sample.

REFERENCE STANDARD — Analyte wherein the purity is documented and used to construct a calibration curve.

REFLECTION — The phenomenon of electromagnetic radiation reflecting from the surface of a medium of different refractive index than the incident medium the emr is traversing.

REFLECTANCE — The measurement value of reflected electromagnetic radiation (emr) (I) ratioed to the incident emr (I_0), generally expressed as percent or $I/I_0 \times 100$.

SCANNING — The process where the wavelength range of the system is viewed in order, usually from lowest to highest wavelength. This usually occurs when the grating is rotated about its axis.

SENSITIVITY — See "Limits of Detection".

SIGNAL — The output of the detector due to its response to light emerging from the sample holder or reference cell.

SIGNAL-TO-NOISE RATIO — The numerical ratio of the total signal at 100% *T* to the noise of the instrument.

SLIT WIDTH — Size of opening of slit through which light emerges. Size depends on wavelength range, separation ability of wavelength selector, and desired isolation of specific wavelength. Often fixed or automatically programmed.

SOLVENT — Liquid used to dissolve the sample analyzed. Commonly water or methanol of high purity. Usually designated as specially purified for UV work, e.g., "Spectro-Quality" or "Spectro-Grade".

SOLVENT CUTOFF — The wavelength at which the solvent absorbs a significant portion of the light, causing a loss of signal and inability to perform an analysis. In other words, the solvent becomes opaque to the wavelengths being used. This is common in the ultraviolet, rare in the visible.

SOURCE — Also known as the "lamp". This is the origin of the light used in the spectrometer, an incandescent wire for visible light, a deuterium gas discharge for ultraviolet.

SPECTRUM — Series of wavelengths of radiation, belonging to a specific portion of the electromagnetic continuum, e.g., the visible spectrum, where the "colors" are viewed in increasing wavelength. For the visible portion of the continuum, the colors are red, orange, yellow, green, blue, indigo, and violet.

STRAY LIGHT — Any radiation reaching the detector that is not emitted from the sample at the chosen wavelength.

VISIBLE — The portion of the electromagnetic spectrum detectable by the human eye. The portion of the spectrum from 380 to 780 nm. The visible region is sometimes designated as 350 nm to 770 nm.

WAVELENGTH — The distance from one crest of an electromagnetic wave to the same position on the subsequent wave. Peak-to-peak distance, usually measured in nanometers.

Volume 2 Index

D

N

O

P

Q

R

S